P9-CJV-217

CONCEPTS OF INSANITY

Concepts of Insanity

in the United States, 1789 - 1865

NORMAN DAIN

RUTGERS UNIVERSITY PRESS   ·   *New Brunswick, New Jersey*

TO PHYLLIS

ACKNOWLEDGMENTS

This book is an outgrowth of investigations that I made with Dr. Eric T. Carlson, Clinical Associate Professor of Psychiatry, Cornell University Medical College, New York City, and Associate Attending Psychiatrist, Payne Whitney Psychiatric Clinic, New York Hospital. Dr. Carlson has been conducting a broad study in the history of psychiatric thought in the United States, and for three years I worked as his research assistant. I am deeply indebted to him for his encouragement, advice, and criticism; he has shared his psychiatric insight with me and has been unusually kind in innumerable ways.

Several other staff members at Payne Whitney Psychiatric Clinic-Cornell University Medical College were helpful. Dr. Oskar Diethelm, former Psychiatrist-in-Chief and now Emeritus Professor of Psychiatry, Dr. Ralph Baker, and Mrs. Evelyn Woods Dahlin criticized my work and shared their research findings with me.

Professor Richard Hofstadter of Columbia University guided the book in its early stages (as a doctoral dissertation) and offered valuable criticism and unfailing encouragement throughout. To Professor David Donald of Johns Hopkins University, under whose direction this study was begun, I owe gratitude for rigorous training in the historical art and for kind efforts on my behalf. Professors George Rosen, Robert Cross, William E. Leuchtenburg, Otto Kleinberg, and Morris Zelditch of Columbia University gave me many suggestions to improve the manuscript.

I am grateful to Professor John Higham of the University of Michigan for helpful criticisms and for assisting me in other ways. Professors Donald H. Fleming of Harvard University and Charles E. Rosenberg of the University of Pennsylvania also read the manuscript with care and made useful comments. I am indebted to my sister, Mrs. Marcia D. Travers, for stylistic criticisms of several chapters. My wife and most demanding critic, Phyllis Dain, assisted me materially in all aspects of this study; the entire book has benefited from her knowledge of history and her editorial ability.

Many librarians were helpful, particularly those at the New York Academy of Medicine, Columbia University Libraries, the American Antiquarian Society, and the Massachusetts Historical Society. I am especially grateful to Miss Altagracia Miranda, librarian at the Payne Whitney Psychiatric Clinic, for her willingness to make interlibrary loans for me. The Oskar Diethelm Historical Library at Payne Whitney, the New York Academy of Medicine Library, and the National Library of Medicine are rich in printed source materials in early medicine and psychiatry and were generous in providing access to them. I am indebted to the American Antiquarian Society for the use of its Woodward, Earle, and Chandler manuscripts and for its collection of early accounts of criminal trials, which I used to study popular opinion on insanity.

The following persons and institutions allowed me to consult special manuscript materials: the Houghton Library, Harvard University (which gave me permission to quote from the Dorothea L. Dix and the American Freedmen's Inquiry Commission papers); Dr. Theodore L. Dehne, Superintendent of the Friends Hospital, Philadelphia; Dr. Lauren H. Smith, Physician-in-Chief and Administrator of the Institute of the Pennsylvania Hospital, Philadelphia, and Dr. Clifford B. Farr, Director of the Historical Library and Museum, Institute of the Pennsylvania Hospital; Mr. Clifford K. Shipton, Director and Librarian of the American Antiquarian Society; Dr. George L. Banay, Librarian of the Worcester State Hospital Medical Library, Worcester, Massachusetts; the Library of the College of Physicians, Philadelphia; Ridgway Branch, Library Company of Philadelphia; and Yale University Library.

This book was supported in part by a research grant (M-2146) from the National Institute of Mental Health, U.S. Public Health Service.

Contents

The way society handles its mentally ill has been the subject of scandalized public attack many times. Humane, healing care for the mentally ill . . . remains the great unfinished business of the mental health movement. . . . A large proportion of mental patients at present, as in the past, are not treated in accordance with democratic, humanitarian, scientific, and therapeutic principles. We have substantially failed them on all counts.

Final Report of the Joint Commission
on Mental Illness and Health, 1961.

Society's reaction to the mentally ill has largely determined the way they are treated. All civilized societies have established standards of acceptable behavior and then devised ways of identifying and dealing with persons who deviate from these standards. But the norms have varied.

The line between "sanity" and "insanity," between "normal" and "abnormal," between "neurotic" and "psychotic" has been tenuous and changing. What has not changed much is the rejection of those who are mentally ill.

Few persons have been more consistently feared and mistreated than the insane. Until recently in the Western world, they were often thought to be possessed by the devil and were universally loathed. Men who equated the ability to reason with the essence of the immortal soul, and insanity with loss of reason, considered the insane bereft of man's most desirable powers, perhaps of humanity itself.

Although people slowly have become more enlightened and less superstitious, they have continued to feel repelled by the insane. It still is difficult for most persons to recognize psychological disturbance as illness and to accept the mentally ill as sick and helpless. In contrast to those recognized as physically ill, the mentally ill do not elicit sympathy. Often their disordered psyche and supposedly bizarre and unpredictable behavior disturb normal people. If an insane person commits a crime— and some of them are capable of committing atrocious ones—he is protected from legal punishment because he is not held legally liable for his behavior. Many citizens, regarding crime with a vengeful spirit and insanity as divine retribution for sin, have found this exemption hard to accept. They have demanded that the criteria for legal insanity protect as few offenders as possible. Others have feared that recognizing the irresponsibility of the insane violated the concepts of free will and moral accountability and undermined Judaeo-Christian morality.

The insane always have lived at the mercy of the community. They cannot fight for themselves, and their relatives, shamed by the stigma of mental illness, often do not try to help them. When physicians and laymen have held enlightened views, the insane have been humanely treated and even cured. However, this seldom happened until less than two hundred years ago. For centuries before, almost everyone had considered mental illness as a religious, moral, or legal concern rather than a medical problem and had assumed that the insane were incurable.

This study is concerned with the problems that confronted Americans in their early efforts to discard unscientific and unduly pessimistic attitudes and to place insanity under the aegis of medicine.

The process began in the late eighteenth century, when a few physicians and laymen in Europe and the United States developed a sympathetic, therapeutic approach to the insane that was called moral treatment. In this country, the succeeding years were marked by the rise, decline, and renaissance of a hopeful attitude toward the mentally ill. From the 1780's until the Civil War, psychiatry grew as a medical specialty, and its practitioners were hopeful, at times highly optimistic. General medical practitioners and the lay public followed this trend, their pace varying with their level of education, medical sophistication, and closeness to urban centers. From the 1860's until the middle of the twentieth century, pessimism about the prognosis of insanity and institutional neglect of its victims again predominated. Only since the end of World War II has there been a significant renewal of hope and concern about their fate.

In many respects the attitudes gaining acceptance among today's psychiatrists correspond more closely to those that existed in pre-Civil War days than in pre-World War II days. Many current therapeutic techniques—open hospitals, non-restraint, and individualized care in small institutions—are in effect a re-introduction of the moral treatment of the mid-nineteenth century. At the same time the American public, though no longer grossly misinformed about mental illness,[1] differs little in its attitudes from the public of a century ago.

Why has there been this cyclical development in psychiatry and relatively little change in public attitudes? This book may help contribute to an explanation by dealing with both popular and medical concepts of insanity in the United States at a time when psychiatry stood, in many ways, at much the same point as it does today. The ideas of physicians specializing in the care of the mentally ill during the initial upswing in psychiatry and then its decline form the core of the study. The concepts held by other physicians, reformers, and well-informed laymen, and by the mass of the public are compared with those of the specialists. I have attempted also to describe the diffusion of this thought among the public and the interaction of psychiatric with popular ideas.

This study begins in 1789, when Benjamin Rush demanded reforms in the treatment of the insane at the Pennsylvania Hospital, and ends, for the most part, in 1865. The closing date is a logical stopping place, for afterwards many new problems, such as the development of neurology and of private psychiatric practice, complicate the history of American psychiatry. By the end of the Civil War the state hospitals, which contained the overwhelming majority of the hospitalized insane, had become largely custodial institutions. But all chronological boundaries are compromises, and the story of the decline of optimism actually ends about the turn of the century, when moral treatment virtually disappeared in the corporate mental institutions that had introduced it in the United States. I have therefore extended the account of moral treatment to 1900, for only then can the rise, development, and decline of optimism be properly understood.

The evidence indicates that much of American psychiatric thought had origins outside of medicine. As late as 1865 little was known about mental illness, and the new profession of psychiatry dealt with disorders only recently included within the province of medicine. Many non-medical beliefs greatly influenced the early psychiatrists' approaches to such basic theoretical problems as the definition of insanity and the principles of pathology, etiology, and cure. Consequently, I have sought to show how philosophical, religious, and social ideas, as well as changes in the socio-economic and ethnic structure of American society, helped to shape psychiatric concepts. I have tended to dwell on the unfortunate consequences of this process, especially during the mid-nineteenth century, but the effects were not always negative. Much of the impetus to the development of enlightened psychiatry arose out of an optimistic approach to man's nature that permeated educated and socially conscious circles during the latter part of the eighteenth century. Moreover, the most radical reforms in the care of the insane in England, which was the dominant influence in the United States, originated with laymen.

In a complicated and intricate way psychiatric ideas grew out of current thought, both enlightened and backward, in many different fields. Science uses a much greater freedom in its search for ideas and inspiration than is often assumed. The antiseptic isolation commonly set up as an ideal for achieving advances in science has little resemblance to the usually much richer process through which knowledge is gained. This study reveals something of the limitless complexity that is involved in the pursuit of solutions to nature's problems. Perhaps the observation of Dr. Oliver Wendell Holmes applies to psychiatry more than any other branch of medicine:

> The truth is, that medicine, professedly founded on observation, is as sensitive to outside influences, political, religious, philosophical, imaginative, as is the barometer to the changes of atmospheric density. Theoretically it ought to go on its own straightforward inductive path, without regard to changes of government or fluctuations of public opinion. [Actually there is] a closer relation between the Medical Sciences and the conditions of Society and the general thought of the time, than would at first be suspected.[2]

Part One

Psychological Medicine Comes to America, 1789–1824

A   N E W   M E D I C A L   S C I E N C E

1

A famous painting by Robert Fleury depicts the renowned French alien-
ist Philippe Pinel ordering the chains removed from insane women at
the Salpêtrière during the French Revolution. This scene symbolizes a
change that may be as significant for the history of mental illness as the
Revolution was for the history of the Western world. Before that time
the insane in Europe and the United States, irrespective of class origin
or economic status, could expect little but misery and torture. Even
their nearest relatives feared them and were ashamed of them; they suffered ridicule, neglect, and physical and mental torments. Those who
were poor wandered aimlessly around the countryside or, shackled and
mistreated, languished in jails, almshouses, and, in Europe, asylums
notorious for their terrible conditions. In the United States homeless
deranged persons were often auctioned off to work for those who would

support them at minimal cost to the county. The insane of the wealthy and middle classes usually wasted away at home—ill-fed, ill-clothed, and chained in unheated attics—where they were occasionally bled and purged by a physician.

A large part of the public believed that mental illness was either God's punishment for evil or the result of nefarious relations with the devil. In either case the afflicted was considered a moral outcast who might contaminate others; he was a disgrace to his family, who feared that they might inherit the disease. The Christian churches accepted exorcism as a major method of curing insanity, but many persons resorted to more forceful means. The alleged moral corruption of the insane served as a justification for severe punishment designed to cast out the devil, and the common belief was that insanity, depriving man of his reason, reduced him to something less than human.

By the late eighteenth century the medical profession of Western Europe and the United States no longer thought insanity had a supernatural origin. Enlightened physicians believed it was a natural disease, which, like all others, should be treated by medical means. They assumed that human behavior was influenced by physical laws that were universal in operation, over which individuals had incomplete control. This approach should have led physicians to dispense with their moralistic attitudes,[1] but most of them did so slowly and imperfectly. They still shared the lay public's pessimism and tended to consider insanity incurable. In practice, therapy prescribed by doctors was not much different from the treatment laymen gave to cure the insane confined in jails, almshouses, madhouses, and private homes.[2] The therapeutic methods advocated by the leading medical authorities and teachers of the eighteenth century ranged from physical restraint, cathartics, emetics, and bleeding to, in William Cullen's words, "a very constant impression of fear" and the infliction of bodily pain in difficult cases.[3] Despite occasional admonitions to be gentle, physicians emphasized strong measures of control, so if the layman used violent techniques, his actions were often an extension of conventional medical practice.

By unchaining the insane in 1793, Pinel helped to inaugurate the era of modern psychiatry. With his contemporary, the English Quaker William Tuke, Pinel replaced prevailing medical and lay practices with a psychological and humanitarian approach.[4] The founders of the new point of view, called moral treatment, emphasized psychological factors. They believed that insanity could be cured and based their therapeutics on kindness and the consideration of each patient's physical and emotional needs. The ideal regimen included placing the patient in a mental hospital where he would receive considerate treatment, occupational therapy, entertainment, mild exercise, good food, and comfortable lodgings.

By 1824 many of the new ideas had been accepted by physicians in the United States who were interested in the care of the mentally ill and, to a lesser degree, by prominent general practitioners and lay leaders in various fields. In general, a feeling of optimism about the curability of mental illness appeared among segments of the middle and upper classes, and in Boston and Hartford all classes contributed to the establishment of insane asylums that attempted to practice moral treatment.

This chapter and the one following deals with concepts of insanity and its treatment in the United States from 1789 to 1824, the time the new psychological medicine * was introduced. In 1789 Benjamin Rush began the reform movement with his petition on behalf of mental patients at the Pennsylvania Hospital; in 1824 the first period of construction of corporate institutions † professing to practice moral treatment came to an end.

2

Although the new psychological medicine of the 1780's and 1790's revolutionized thought and practice, not all of its principles were new. Most of them had antecedents in the prevailing medical thought of the

* Hereafter the terms "psychological medicine," "moral treatment," "moral management," and "moral therapy" are used interchangeably to mean the new system introduced by Pinel, Tuke, and others.

† The term "corporate institution" is not entirely correct and is used for want of a better one. It refers to mental hospitals founded and controlled by private citizens—in most cases with financial help from local or state governments—usually but not always chartered by the state, and operated on a non-profit basis. The "corporate" mental hospital (also called "privately endowed" in this study) is distinguished from the wholly government financed and controlled institution (here called "publicly-supported") and the proprietary or private hospital run by private citizens for profit.

eighteenth century, and the new movement might be considered a cul-
mination and extension of certain aspects of accepted medical theories.
Pinel and other pioneers in psychiatry in England, France, Italy, and
Germany developed some existing but relatively minor aspects of the
contemporary medical approach toward insanity—the psychological and
the humanitarian. Numerous physicians who accepted the idea of moral
treatment retained much of the general orientation of pre-Pinel medical
thought in relation to insanity. The following section summarizes the
ideas and practices of eighteenth-century physicians before the advent of
moral treatment, as expressed by the European (primarily English and
Scottish) authorities to whom Americans looked for leadership.

To discover how eighteenth-century physicians categorized pathological mental conditions we must go beyond the superficial definitions
in medical writings of that time. Concepts of insanity were revealed in
descriptions of its characteristic symptoms. The most common opinion
was that insane persons did not think clearly and suffered from delusions or hallucinations. Another trait was inappropriate behavior, the
result of disordered thought. But the standards by which thought and
action were judged are difficult to determine. Physicians assumed that
sane observers would recognize normal, or at least abnormal, behavior.
The author of a widely read medical book expressed prevailing professional opinion when he wrote: *"A delirium without a fever* is the common definition of madness." He admitted that this "was not a very accurate" definition, but explained: "There is no great occasion to be
solicitous about the definition of a disease which every body knows." [5]
An American medical student discussed in his thesis on insanity the difficulty of defining that illness and finally came up with a definition given
by Benjamin Rush: "A false perception of truth; with conversation and
actions contrary to right reason, established maxim, and order." [6]

"Melancholia," and "mania," or "madness," signified stages or degrees
of insanity, rather than different mental illnesses.[7] Mania usually
referred to violent behavior. Many mentally ill persons, who might be
placed in any one of a variety of diagnostic classifications today, were
thought of as "maniacs" or "madmen." When they were calm, these
patients might be placed in another grouping, such as "monomania," if
their characteristic symptom was mental derangement on one or a few

subjects. If they reverted to violence, they were again considered maniacal. Cases in which sadness and depressed feelings predominated would
be classed as "melancholic"; a patient suffering from melancholia might,
if he became active and forceful, be called a maniac. Uncertainty arose
most often about patients suffering from hysteria, hypochondriasis, epilepsy, and senile dementia.* Were they insane? One author asserted that
no one who was not suffering from "a real unequivocal mania," characterized by irrational thought and action, should be considered insane.[8]

Although the eighteenth-century physician was not able to be clear
about what he meant by insanity, he was definite about its etiology. He
accepted the idea that the causes of insanity were natural ones. The naturalistic approach brought the afflicted under the care of the physician
rather than the clergyman and placed the disease within the province of
science, not religion.

Physicians agreed that almost any event or circumstance, other than
supernatural phenomena, might produce mental illness. They divided
the causes into predisposing, or remote, and precipitating, or inciting.
Among the possible predisposing causes were a familial history of insanity, poor upbringing, sedentary life, libidinous excesses, febrile diseases,
an overly pessimistic or optimistic personality, ill-founded dread of
divine vengeance, climate, and even the type of government or economic
system under which a person lived.[9] Poor heredity was an especially
potent cause. Observing that insanity sometimes ran in families, both
the lay public and the medical profession believed the disease could be
inherited. While laymen thought that insanity itself was transmitted

---

* A recent medical dictionary defines these terms as follows: "*Hysteria.* . . . A chronic neu-
rosis, or psychoneurosis, characterized by disorders of the will, perversion of the inhibitory
powers of consciousness, and partial cessation or exaltation of the individual functions of the
brain. It is marked by symptoms of the most varied character, from simple nervous instability
and attacks of emotional excitement, with causeless crying or laughing, to convulsions, muscular contractures, vasomotor, trophic, and psychic disorders." "*Hypochondriasis.* . . . A
morbid concern about the health and exaggerated attention to any unusual bodily or mental
sensations; an unfounded belief that one is suffering from some disease." "*Epilepsy.* . . . A
chronic functional nervous disorder, characterized by attacks of unconsciousness or convulsions or both, and usually associated in the later stages with mental disturbance." "*Senile
d[ementia]*, progressive mental deterioration with loss of memory, especially for recent events,
and occasional intercurrent attacks of excitement, occurring in the aged." (*Stedman's Medical
Dictionary* [19th rev. ed.; Baltimore: Williams & Wilkins Company, 1957], pp. 691, 685, 475,
384.)

through "inheritance," physicians thought only the predisposition was hereditary; a precipitating cause was needed to produce the active disease.

When predisposing conditions existed, the precipitating or inciting causes were the events and activities that preceded and presumably brought on the derangement. Possible inciting causes included bodily disease, brain trauma, immoderate manual labor, excessive mental effort, masturbation, and, most important, strong emotions elicited by disappointment in love, business, or politics, and excessive pride, terror, or joy.[10]

Theoretically the supposed causes of insanity could apply to all socioeconomic groups, but physicians thought that the upper classes were most prone to this illness. English medical authorities believed that nervous disease was increasing at an alarming rate,[11] and some attributed this trend partly to the growth in comfort brought on by commercial success.[12] They also believed that commercial riches were amassed through a process involving sharp fluctuations in fortune that unsettled the emotional life of the merchant.[13] In the United States, Benjamin Rush, a Jeffersonian, described the dangers to mental health in Federalist Alexander Hamilton's financial program: "The funding system, and speculation in bank script, and new lands have been fruitful sources of madness in our country." [14] Medical men thought that the rich were more cultivated and consequently more impressionable than the poor, so they were peculiarly susceptible to emotional disturbances and insanity. As one author explained, "The mind, in proportion as it is expanded, exposes a larger surface to impression." [15]

Medical authorities frequently confused symptoms with causes. Because the thoughts of the insane were unpredictable and often fanciful, physicians assumed that insanity was the result of imagination gone astray. They concluded that occupations that used non-scientific or non-mathematical techniques, such as creative writing, jeopardized mental balance. Those who did such work were urged to pause frequently to divert their energies to less dangerous employments. Well into the nineteenth century, physicians and laymen wrote articles about this, and it was generally believed that geniuses, particularly artists and poets, frequently suffered some degree of insanity.[16]

The emphasis on the harmfulness of unduly strong emotions had various origins. Some medical men, influenced by the associationism of Locke and his successors, stressed the destructive memories and associations that violent emotions could arouse. These feelings could evoke such strong memories that judgment would be obliterated. Strong emotions might also use an undue share of the body's supply of energy and enervate the ability to reason. Other physicians based their approach on the threefold faculty psychology then current. Although differing on some points, they usually agreed that the mind was divided into three main faculties—reason, feeling, and will—and that sanity prevailed when reason remained master over feelings and will. Violent emotions would overthrow the power of reason.

These ideas seemed to correspond with those of leading eighteenth-century thinkers, who supposedly regarded normal man as a creature of reason. However, according to Arthur O. Lovejoy, a modern historian of ideas, the philosophers of the Age of Reason believed that although reason *should* control the other mental faculties, in fact the passions, or emotions, always ruled supreme; reason served primarily to accomplish the aims of the passions.[17] What, then, distinguished sanity from insanity? The philosophers, unconcerned with mental pathology, did not deal with this question, though they could have argued that the insane had lost the ability to use reason as a tool of the passions. Those men who were concerned, the physicians, were generally content to apply what seemed to be the only objective test for insanity, that of irrationality. Only toward the end of the eighteenth century did a few physicians see that insanity might be manifested primarily in morbid or excessive passions rather than deranged reason.

The relationship between general concepts of disease and a partial recognition of the psychological nature of insanity is not altogether clear from the writings of eighteenth-century physicians. Medically, the eighteenth century was one of system-building, and the most famous physicians adhered to one of several all-inclusive theories of disease into which insanity was imperfectly fitted. These systems—solidism and humoralism predominated—attempted to account for all mental and physical illnesses as the results of general morbid bodily conditions. None of the prevailing schools developed a detailed explanation of the way in which physical and psychological factors interacted to cause insanity. A majority of physicians took a basically somatic view of insanity; they believed it was a physical disorder.[18] Even their discussion of psychological factors rested on the assumption that some bodily pathology caused the mental derangement. No matter what the mental condition, no mental illness could occur without this physical malfunctioning. Excessive emotions were thought to cause insanity by upsetting the body's equilibrium, but physicians did not make clear how this process worked.[19]

Another mystery was the way in which the allegedly immaterial mind or soul made contact with the brain, its agent within the body. "How mind acts upon matter, will, in all probability, ever remain a secret," wrote William Buchan. "It is sufficient for us to know, that there is established a reciprocal influence betwixt the mental and corporeal parts, and that whatever disorders the one likewise hurts the other." [20] Physicians believed that brain damage did not affect the mind or that which many conceived to be synonymous with it, the immortal soul. In insanity the injured brain supposedly distorted the mind's instructions, could not execute them, or transmitted incorrect sensory messages to the mind, which in turn ordered actions inappropriate to the situation.

Although many of the remedies prescribed for insanity were pragmatic in origin, some of them evolved from prevalent medical theories. Bleeding and purging, for different reasons, were the major therapeutic means of both solidists and humoralists for practically all diseases, and the insane patient was bled and purged ceaselessly under medical care. The prevailing theory of crisis encouraged the use of these remedies, which supposedly brought on a crisis in the body and forced it to eject the harmful substances—excessive humors or solid matter—that caused the disease. As Emil Kraepelin noted, physicians "were never able to decide whether the course of insanity was determined mainly by the basic pattern of the disorder or by external events," and they hoped that "artificially induced crises would have a decisive influence on the progress of the disease." [21]

They also recognized that psychological factors could play a role in the treatment as well as in the precipitation of mental illness.[22] Besides prescribing violent and often harsh methods of control for maniacs, many doctors recommended mild treatment for hysterics, melancholics, and hypochondriacs. They suggested diverting the patient's unhappy thoughts with work, amusement, and travel with congenial companions; sometimes they proposed good diets and pleasant living conditions.[23] Even the maniac received some sort of psychological treatment in shock therapies designed to subdue and cure him, such as cold shower baths, threats of terrible punishment, and sudden immersion into a pool of water.

On the whole, physicians tended to be pessimistic about the prognosis for insanity. They had many prescriptions; some were so extreme and harsh that they threatened the life of the patient, but few were likely to cure him.

3

At the turn of the century the shift from pessimism to optimism about the curability of insanity and from emphasis on somatic to psychological forms of treatment coincided with the spirit of reform and humanitarianism in Western Europe and the United States.[24] The new attitude toward the insane was reflected in the United States in agitation for prison reform, abolitionism, and the movements for temperance and the extension of the suffrage. The hopeful, perfectionist beliefs expressed in these reform movements received strong support from many Protestant religious groups as well as from individuals influenced by secular ideas associated with the Enlightenment.

To many persons the successes in astronomy and physics, the rapid strides made in technology, and the struggles for political democracy in the United States, France, and England were practical proofs of the Enlightenment's faith that man could control his environment and improve his life on earth. Men justified their growing concern with worldly matters by replacing the concept of man's depravity with one of his perfectibility. In the United States the swiftness with which the country was being settled, the successful outcome of the revolution against England, and the spirit of confidence that prevailed after the "victory" of the War of 1812 reinforced the eighteenth-century notion that man was perfectible. The second great religious awakening, which swept the United States from 1795 to 1835, gave expression and impetus to the idea of perfectibility by rejecting Calvinist theories of predestination.[25]

These trends probably account as much as any medical discoveries for the spread of moral treatment. No doubt medical acceptance of the concept of the natural origins of insanity prepared the ground for psychological medicine, as did advances in physiology which revealed the functions of the nervous system. The influential French medical philosopher Pierre Cabanis, interpreted psychological phenomena in terms of physiology, combining the psychological and somatic points of view to produce a unified concept of man and providing a theoretical explanation of moral treatment. Mind and body were interacting parts of a whole, and if emotions could cause disease, psychotherapy could cure it.[26]

Without recognizing the crucial role played by non-medical thought, it is difficult to explain how a layman such as William Tuke could independently develop a whole system of moral treatment. The psychological medicine of the moral treatment school, although influenced by specific discoveries in the physical sciences as well as by those in psychology and medicine, was also guided by the general trend toward empiricism and the optimism engendered by it.[27]

Moral treatment had no specific national origin in Western Europe; it was developed simultaneously and independently during the last two decades of the eighteenth century by such men as Chiarugi, Pinel, Tuke, and, to a certain extent, Rush. Their ideas about the care of the insane were expressed in the following passage from the inaugural dissertation of Dr. T. Romeyn Beck of New York City, published in 1811:

MORAL MANAGEMENT. This consists in removing patients from their residence to some proper asylum; and for this purpose, a calm retreat in the country is to be preferred: for it is found that continuance at home aggravates the disease, as the improper association of ideas cannot be destroyed. A system of humane vigilance is adopted. Coercion, by blows, stripes, and chains, . . . is . . . laid aside. The rules most proper to be observed are the following: Convince the lunatics that the power of the physician and keeper is absolute; have humane attendants, who shall act as servants to them; never threaten but execute; offer no indignities to them, as they have a high sense of honour; punish disobedience peremptorily, in the presence of the other maniacs: if unruly, forbid them the company of others, use the strait waistcoat, confine them in a dark and quiet room, order spare diet, and . . . tolerate noisy ejaculations; strictly exclude visitors; let their fears and resentments be soothed without unnecessary opposition; adopt a system of regularity; make them rise, take exercise and food at stated times. The diet ought to be light, and easy of digestion, but never too low. When convalescing, allow limited liberty; introduce entertaining books and conversation, exhilarating music, employment of body in agricultural pursuits, . . . and admit friends under proper restrictions. . . . Forbid their returning home too soon. By thus acting, the patient will "minister to himself." [28]

Pinel thought moral treatment appealed to the moral sense through setting an example and teaching the patient to return good for good. Under the new system, cruel punishments and almost all "shock" treatments were forbidden; cold baths and physical restraint, however, were sanctioned when necessary to subdue or punish patients. The administration of purgatives, emetics, and other drugs, and the widespread practice of bleeding insane patients were frowned upon by many of the European founders of moral treatment and had virtually no place in their system.

Moral treatment resembled what is known today as milieu therapy, or the therapeutic community, that is, the creation of a complete therapeutic environment—social, psychological, and physical. "Although much emphasis was placed on the relationship between physician and patient," a twentieth-century psychiatrist comments, "moral treatment embraced a much larger psychological approach than individual psychotherapy. Indeed, perhaps the greatest asset of moral treatment was the attention it gave to the value of physical setting and social influences of hospital life as curative agents." [29]

Although moral treatment did not necessarily involve a new theory of the pathology of insanity, a few of its advocates among physicians, including Pinel, thought that its success, along with pathological evidence, lent support to the supposition that insanity could occur in the absence of brain lesions.[30] But most medical men, especially Americans, who accepted moral treatment adhered to the traditional theory that all cases of insanity involved physical disease. Nevertheless, both groups could accept the new psychological medicine. If the disease was purely mental, the new system followed logically and acted as a cure. If mental illness resulted only from somatic disorder, the removal of the indirect psychological causes of insanity required the application of moral treatment, for American somaticists believed that the mind and body were so closely related that what affected one must affect the other.

The advocates of moral treatment, however, did not always act from theoretical considerations, and there was much confusion among them. Despite the work of Cabanis, few of them espoused or attempted to create a unified theory of pathology to replace the ideas they challenged. Concerned with practical results, they adopted Pinel's approach without fully understanding his theoretical position. In downgrading much of the older medical therapeutics in favor of moral treatment, many doctors and laymen were rejecting ineffective past practices rather than past theories.

This was true of the British merchant William Tuke, who, because of his close contact with American Quakers, had more influence than Pinel in introducing moral treatment in the United States. Tuke, like Pinel, did not consider the insane completely unreasonable or incapable of response; he regarded them as "children who have an excess of force and who make a dangerous employment of it." [31] At the Quaker insane asylum at York, England, which Tuke organized in the 1790's, the care of the patients was dictated by the enlightened principles of the Society of Friends. The inmates were treated as sick persons free from moral guilt, and the healing process was encouraged by working upon their emotions and intellect. The York Retreat provided not only humane care but also a religious atmosphere, recreation, and agricultural employment for mentally ill Friends.[32] Tuke believed that the wealthy as well as the poor would benefit in an institution where "everything is done to make the patients as comfortable as they can be, and to endeavor to impress upon their minds the idea that they will be kindly treated." [33]

4

Although Tuke had the greatest influence in the establishment of the first private and corporate insane asylums in the United States—half of the eight asylums built before 1824 were patterned after the York Retreat—Benjamin Rush probably had more effect on medical thought and practice concerning the insane than any other American. Rush, one of the leading American physicians of his day and often called the father of American psychiatry, petitioned for humanitarian reforms at the Pennsylvania Hospital before Pinel's classic treatise on insanity appeared in print.[34] It is uncertain how far Rush had developed the concepts of moral treatment before he read the works of Pinel and others; some of his later proposals for reform were made after the publication of Pinel's work in 1801 and the opening of the York Retreat in 1796.[35] Rush did not mention the sources of the ideas in his major work on insanity, which came out in 1812.

Rush had developed a humanitarian and social approach to medicine early in his career, during the 1770's and 1780's. He believed that good health depended upon social, political, and economic as well as physical environment and endorsed a stable and ordered society founded upon democratic and republican principles. Rush's endorsement of reform in the treatment of the insane evolved from his medical philosophy, which was derived partly from his liberal social and political outlook.[36]

In his psychiatric work Rush broke with traditional beliefs. He demanded that mental illness be freed from moral stigma, that the insane be treated with kindness, that their care be under the supervision of physicians, and that religious melancholia could best be cured by medicine rather than by preaching and moralizing; [37] even so, his ideas about the specific nature and treatment of insanity were not as advanced as those of European psychiatric pioneers. While he campaigned for humane care, Rush remained firmly committed to most of the remedies commonly used in the eighteenth century. In the insane wards of Pennsylvania Hospital—the first general hospital in the United States and the first to admit mental patients—Rush practiced bloodletting, purging, heavy dosing with emetics and other chemicals, physical restraint and chastisement, and stimulation of terror as shock therapy. He added the humanitarian elements of mild psychological medicine to conventional eighteenth-century medical theories and practices. Rush was, therefore, chiefly a transitional figure in the history of psychiatry.

Despite his readiness to comment upon any medical or philosophical question,[38] Rush was not an original philosopher nor a consistently logical thinker. He shared the confusion, particularly about the mind-body relationship, of other writers on insanity. He revealed the influence of several philosophical schools—deism, Scottish realism, and materialism—and presented theoretical formulations that are often confused and contradictory.[39] At one time he wrote in a materialist vein: "All operations of the mind are the effects of motions previously excited in the brain, and every idea and thought appears to depend upon a motion peculiar to itself." A few pages later, he expressed the idealist position that the mind was distinct from the physical organ, the brain. Mental illness, he asserted, was a bodily affliction; it involved the brain, not the immaterial mind whose seat was somewhere in the brain.[40] Although the ultimate logic of his dualistic position seems, according to one writer, to go in the direction of materialism,[41] and, to another, of Scottish "common sense" or Cartesian dualism,[42] many of Rush's contemporaries interpreted his theories as materialistic,[43] and his medical theories seem to have the latter tendency.

Rush shared the conventional medical view of insanity as a fundamentally somatic disease, that is, a pathological brain condition that produced psychological symptoms; the etiology might be psychological or organic, but the pathology was somatic. Like many eighteenth-century physicians, he formulated an all-inclusive theory of disease. He differed in his monistic rather than dualistic approach. To Rush, almost all ailments represented manifestations of one disorder, fever, and had one remedy, depletion. His theory of pathology was, true to the scientific spirit of the eighteenth century, a mechanistic one. He thought that regularity ruled the universe and that science could discover the laws of health and disease: "Truth is simple upon all subjects, but upon those which are essential to the general happiness of mankind, [the truth] is obvious to the meanest capacities." To assume that it is difficult to learn how to cure illness "is to call in question the goodness of the Supreme Being, and to believe that he acts without unity and system in all his works." [44]

It is not surprising that Rush sought to formulate a medical system that was simple in its theoretical structure and its therapeutic prescriptions, especially since he was eager to discover uncomplicated cures for all diseases. Basically, he converted the influential dualistic theory of pathology of John Brown, his fellow student at Edinburgh, into a monistic system.[45] According to Rush, the prerequisite for ninety-nine out of a hundred illnesses was debility, a condition of insufficient motion which was produced by either too much or too little motion. In the first instance preternatural, or excessive, stimuli acted upon the body's excitability, or its ability to respond to stimuli. This action provoked the excessive discharge of motion, which Rush called excitement. Eventually a portion of the system's excitability was exhausted and the excitement lowered to an unhealthy level. Brown had called this condition of reduced excitement "indirect debility"; Rush renamed it "debility from action." In the second instance debility occurred when normal stimuli were removed and the system fell below a healthy degree of motion or excitement. Brown called this "direct debility"; Rush called it "debility from abstraction." The healthy body was conceived as a sort of storage battery charged by the normal life processes, such as the ingestion of food, and discharged in the form of bodily action in response to stimuli. Any imbalance was dangerous and might lead to fever, which, according to Rush, was the most common form of disease, including insanity. While Brown, following the celebrated Scottish physician William Cullen, saw the two kinds of debility as different morbid bodily conditions or illnesses, Rush reduced debility to a single phenomenon that differed only in origin; he made it the precondition of illness, or fever, rather than the illness itself.

Rush defined fever as an "irregular or a convulsive" action in the blood vessels. This idea contrasted with Cullen's theory that disease involved excessive tension or excessive laxity of the nerves; Rush considered tension in the blood vessels the primary factor. When debility existed, he thought, the introduction of some irritating element, physical or emotional, resulted in fever. Conditions that produced fever when debility from action occurred included: heat, intemperance, unusual labor, violent emotions, stimulating passions of the mind, over-stretching the body, or burning. Conditions that produced fever when debility from abstraction occurred included: cold; famine; fear, grief, and despair; and excessive evacuation. Debility from abstraction especially predisposed the body to fever, for it resulted in the accumulation of unused energy, ready to be discharged into the blood vessels if an irritant was introduced into the system. It was more difficult to explain how the body whose excitability was exhausted from excessive motion (debility from action) had the energy to upset the blood vessels. Rush postulated that excitability from some other part of the body would automatically flow to the debilitated region to provide the energy to convulse the blood vessels—a sort of hydraulic system.

The treatment for fever consisted of reducing the blood pressure. This accounts for Rush's well-known predilection for bloodletting as the primary therapy for all ailments and his reliance on purges, emetics, and low diets. Brown's view that there were two forms of debility, or illness, led him to recommend two kinds of treatment, restoration and depletion; Rush advocated one remedy, depletion.

All of Rush's theory applied to insanity, in which the abnormal condition of the blood vessels was supposedly localized in the brain, rather than in the stomach, as others claimed. According to Rush, madness was "as much an original disease of the blood-vessels, as any other state of fever. . . . The derangement in the operations of the mind is the effect only of a chronic inflamation of the brain, existing without an abstraction of muscular excitement." [46] The application of his general theory of fever to mental illness provided him with a rationale for using strong and painful therapies, including depletion and various mechanical means to draw the blood from the head. For example, he thought depleting the stomach with emetics transferred the morbid excitement of the brain to the stomach and restored sanity. If he produced hunger with a sufficiently low diet, the morbid excitement causing insanity might move from the brain to the stomach, a less vital organ. When hunger debilitated the stomach to a level below that of the brain's blood vessels, the morbid energy would flow from the higher level, the brain, to the lower one, the stomach, and insanity would be cured. During the active stage of insanity, shock therapies, such as cold showers, supposedly slowed down the movement of the blood in the brain or sent the blood elsewhere. Under certain conditions the same thing could be accomplished by measures to calm the mental patient, keep his surroundings cool, quiet, and dark, and avoid irritating him unduly. He invented a special tranquilizer chair which kept the patient upright and immobile, partly in order to "save the head from the impetus of the blood as much as possible." [47] The mechanistic character of his theory is also indicated by his description of specific types of insanity. In schirrus, or hardening, the brain "loses its mobility so as to become incapable of emitting those motions from impressions which produce the operations of the mind." But if the brain is too soft, as in idiocy, it cannot receive and "modify the impressions which excite thought in the mind." [48]

Like his British mentors, Rush believed in the existence of various predisposing and inciting psychological causes of insanity, including imaginative occupations and political and economic environment. This approach fitted into his general theory of fever, for on his list of irritants that could precipitate fever were strong emotions and psychological states. But he believed as the medical profession did, that psychological causes produced insanity indirectly by initiating a physiological process that induced the disease; without this process no emotion, however intense, could lead to insanity. Theoretically, either mental or medical means might be used to lessen tension in the brain's blood vessels when emotions caused the illness, without contradicting somaticism, for psychological methods caused a physical change. Sometimes Rush applied psychological methods so he could control the patient and administer the techniques of depletion that were supposed to cure the disease. He thought that bloodletting was the most effective way to treat insanity, and no doubt believed that experience supported him. When venesection was carried far enough, it calmed the most violent patient.[49]

Rush retained many traditional beliefs, which he often elaborated in light of his own theories. For example, he thought that heredity could predispose one to insanity. He saw this predisposition in somatic terms; it was "a peculiar and hereditary sameness of organization of the nerves, brain, and blood-vessels" which sometimes pervaded "whole families, and render[ed] them liable to [madness]." This type of madness, though more easily aroused than that stemming from "acquired predisposition," was, contrary to common opinion, just as readily cured.[50] Rush also ascribed to the old belief that the violent insane resembled animals and were "for the most part easily terrified, or composed, by the eye of a man who possesses his reason." The will of intractable madmen could be broken by the methods used to subdue elephants: denying them food to deplete their physical strength and their will to resist.[51]

Another common idea was reflected in Rush's observation that in certain forms of violent madness, the "nerves are insensible to cold, heat, and to irritants of all kinds" and thus they resist "all the usual remote causes of fever from the insensible qualities of the atmosphere." [52] Experience seemed to confirm that the insane were immune to the ill effects of heat and cold and free from many other physical ailments as long as they remained mentally ill. Underlying this belief was the widely held view that the body could have only one illness at a time or at least that each system of the body could feel only one impression at a time. This theory justified the painful therapeutic techniques prescribed for insane patients, as well as the widespread neglect of their basic physical needs by the lay population.[53]

What of Rush's contribution to psychological medicine? It is probably an exaggeration to consider him, as some have suggested, a precursor of Freud because he recommended that mental patients write their experiences and recollections or because he discussed the undesirable effects of repressed emotion.[54] These concepts did not form any part of Rush's theoretical system, and in advancing them he appears to have been influenced more by empirical and humanitarian considerations than by an incipient theory of the unconscious.[55] He urged the insane to write their thoughts and secrets on paper in the hope that when they saw what they had written they would be shocked into rejecting their pathological ideas—a technique suggested to him by a patient who found relief in using it himself.[56] Observation also led Rush to recognize the importance of the doctor-patient relationship. He taught that the physician must have complete mastery in his encounters with the mentally ill: He should cultivate a commanding eye, voice, and posture. Dignity, honesty, and, above all, kindness must characterize his relations with the patient; the doctor should be absent when force was employed as a last resort. He should inspire the patient with hope of recovery and try to distract him from morbid and "guilt-ridden preoccupations." Rush realized that many anti-social actions considered sinful, such as suicide, impulse to murder, habitual lying, drunkenness, and compulsive stealing, might be emotional disorders.[57] Despite his traditional medical approach, Rush believed, as Pinel did, that insanity did not always involve disorder of the intellect. In some cases insane persons reasoned well, but their "will [became] the involuntary vehicle of vicious actions, through the instrumentality of the passions." He called this condition "moral derangement," an illness that involved the moral faculty as well as the will.[58]

Although Rush was primarily a system builder who tried to explain his psychological practices and clinical observations in mechanistic terms, he often used analogy and experience to justify worthwhile techniques that had no place in his over-all theory. Because Rush had a physiological approach to mental illness and relied heavily upon venesection, he could not accept moral treatment as the primary means of cure. Even after Pinel's work became available, he considered moral treatment secondary to medical treatment. Nevertheless, he believed that psychological methods were important in treating all diseases, physical as well as mental, and he emphasized psychological therapy more than his American colleagues. He was the first American physician to make a serious study of mental illness,[59] one of the few doctors to recognize "moral derangement," and a leader in the fight to ameliorate the conditions of the insane. With some success he demanded improvements at the Pennsylvania Hospital, such as heating the corridors and baths of the insane wards; improving sanitation; increasing the number of attendants; separating patients by sex and classifying them by type and extent of illness; and abolishing physical violence and painful treatment except for therapeutic purposes. He emphasized kindness and proposed occupational therapy and amusements.[60] These were important elements in moral treatment as developed by Tuke and Pinel. Rush was optimistic about the power of his methods to cure all diseases and much more sanguine in his prognosis for insanity than the cautious Pinel.

5

It is not known how pervasive the new concepts of moral treatment were within the American medical profession from 1789 to 1824. Rush, one of the foremost physicians of his day and a professor for thirty years at the nation's leading medical school at the University of Pennsylvania, had great prestige, even after his death in 1813. Comments of social reformers and physicians indicate that his ideas had a significant influence during his lifetime, and the professor who succeeded him at the University of Pennsylvania continued to use his notes for some years.[61] In addition to approximately three thousand physicians who had studied with him at the University or in his private practice,[62] Rush had followers who read everything he wrote. European medical men called him the "Sydenham of America" or the "American Hippocrates." Rush's theories of psychology and his approach to the insane reached the medical profession through his many articles, his wide correspondence, and, most important, his book, *Medical Inquiries and Observations upon the Diseases of the Mind,* which went through five editions between 1812 and 1835.

Leading physicians of New York, Hartford, Boston, and Philadelphia generally accepted the ideas of Pinel, Tuke, and Rush on the need for reform in the care of the insane. These physicians, together with laymen, waged successful campaigns to establish mental hospitals dedicated to moral treatment.[63] Several of them became heads of the new hospitals, and they in turn influenced the next generation of asylum superintendents.

Most prominent of these early psychiatrists were Rufus Wyman and Eli Todd. Wyman served as first superintendent of McLean Asylum near Boston from 1818 to his retirement in 1835, and Todd was chief of the Connecticut Retreat for the Insane at Hartford (then called the Hartford Retreat and today renamed the Institute of Living), from its opening in 1824 until his death in 1833. Wyman and Todd leaned more toward the concepts of Tuke and Pinel, respectively, than toward those of Rush. They rejected most traditional medical therapy and relied heavily upon moral treatment.[64] They wrote little and paid only slight attention to theory; hospital management and patient care were their chief concerns. Their asylums, together with the Friends' Asylum (officially called the Asylum for the Relief of Persons Deprived of the Use of their Reason) at Frankford, Pennsylvania, served as model institutions for the practice of psychological medicine. Numerous visitors, both lay and medical, came to observe their operations; new mental hospitals imitated their methods; and leading psychiatrists of the mid-nineteenth century received their training there.[65]

The influence of moral treatment upon the medical profession can also be seen in the dissertations accepted by American medical schools as early as the 1790's. Students could obtain extensive and systematic instruction in psychiatry only at the University of Pennsylvania, where Rush lectured. However, the appearance of a number of dissertations dealing with mental disease indicates that the subject was not wholly ignored elsewhere and that students were exposed to the latest ideas.[66] These theses were not original works; they were summaries of the most important medical writings on the chosen topic. Pinel, Rush, and other advocates of moral treatment were extensively paraphrased and quoted, and students showed an understanding and acceptance of the new approach.[67]

Two long reviews of Rush's *Medical Inquiries and Observations upon the Diseases of the Mind* reveal the interest of knowledgeable physicians in the work of the new specialists in mental illness. In 1813 the New York *Medical Repository* published an anonymous review by someone evidently well-informed about the latest developments in psychiatry. He considered Rush's work most significant because it extended physical remedies to disordered intellectual and moral faculties, and even to the confused faculty of the will. The courts, he suggested, would be "better guarded against erroneous and shocking decisions" if they recognized that loss of reason entailed loss of free will and responsibility to the laws of God and man. Although he admired Pinel's concepts of moral treatment, the reviewer complained that his system did not contain enough medical remedies. "Much remained to be done after [Pinel], and it is accomplished by our fellow citizen [Rush]." [68]

The second reviewer was prominent Boston physician George Hayward. Writing in the *New England Journal of Medicine and Surgery* of 1818, he criticized Rush's book. He recognized it as the first original American contribution to psychiatry, but thought it was too confused and crude in its theory to be of much use to physicians and medical students. Hayward valued venesection but, contrary to Rush, considered moral treatment more important than orthodox medical therapy. He did not agree that a consciousness of morality and of God was inborn, but thought that it was the result of education. He also questioned Rush's theory that fullness of the blood vessels in the brain caused insanity; fullness, Hayward asserted, occurred in everyone every day without resulting in insanity or delirium.[69] He was more skeptical than Rush about the amount of knowledge existing in the field of psychiatry, although he acknowledged the great advances made in recent years.

6

In contrast to the few enlightened leaders of the profession, the majority of American medical men were ignorant of developments in the treatment of mental illness. Diffusion of medical knowledge was uneven, and, as far as can be determined, by 1824 the new ideas had not yet reached the average general medical practitioner. The historian of the Philadelphia almshouses noted that in 1808 physicians seldom visited the inmates: "They appeared to think that insanity was incurable, and even the mildest cases were in cages like wild beasts." [70]

A letter written by a Delaware physician to a New York medical journal in 1802 is an example of the kind of communication that was published about mental illness during the first few decades of the nineteenth century. The doctor related that he had found an insane patient at home:

> chained to the floor, with his hands tied across his breast—clothes torn off, except the shirt—his feet and elbows bruised considerably—and his countenance, grimaces, and incoherent language, truly descriptive of his unhappy condition. As he was free from fever, and his pulse not tense or preternaturally full, I deemed this a fair case for the application of cold water . . .[71]

The doctor did not say whether he freed the patient or disapproved of the treatment he had received. Other communications reveal that physicians continued to prescribe purges, emetics, venesection, and opium.[72]

Published letters are one of the few direct sources of information about the attitudes of the average physician. The difficulty of determining what physicians thought about mental illness implies that they did not think about it much; it is far easier to discover their views about other diseases. In the rural and small town environment where the majority of Americans lived and where most physicians practiced, insanity, though prevalent, did not present as great a medical problem as in the crowded cities, and contact with the latest ideas and leading medical men was less frequent. Traditional pessimism about the prognosis of mental illness probably discouraged inquiry and interest, and the poverty of most insane persons did not encourage physicians to be concerned with psychiatric therapy. The few medical journals that were published before 1824 contained little data about mental disease and less about moral treatment, and it is unlikely that the average general practitioner read any of the books that explained the new psychiatric approach.[73] He did not read widely in general medicine and undoubtedly referred primarily to standard general works written before the studies of Pinel, Tuke, and Rush were published.[74]

The majority of physicians lacked adequate medical education. There were only a handful of medical schools in the United States before 1824, and the number of doctors graduating from those at New York and Philadelphia, where they might have learned about moral treatment, plus the few who received a medical education abroad, was small. In Rush's day only about 10 per cent of all practitioners in the United States held a medical degree. In the absence of licensing laws or enforced medical standards almost anyone who wished could and did practice medicine and assume the title of doctor, and there were many quacks who administered medical care without as much as a textbook. Most young men who wanted to become doctors would apprentice themselves to established physicians rather than enroll in a medical school. Often these physicians were not graduates of medical schools either, and at best they usually held the conventional medical views of the eighteenth century.[75]

An equally important reason for the lack of acceptance of moral treatment among small-town physicians was the paucity of local mental institutions. Mental illness could be tolerated in the country more than in the populous cities, so the need to found hospitals and discover cures was less apparent in rural areas.[76] Moreover, the new mental institutions in or near the large cities catered mainly to the upper and middle classes. Rural patients with small incomes could not afford the expense of commitment even when the rates were reduced to less than the cost of maintenance.[77] Rural communities remained largely ignorant of the benefits of the new therapy, which could be practiced only in hospitals.

7

Physicians who accepted moral treatment were generally unwilling to apply it without conventional medical therapeutics,[78] for they believed insanity was a somatic disease that had to be treated medically. This conviction was based on the traditional concept of a mind-body dichotomy, which predicated the existence of an immaterial, immortal, and inviolable soul that could not become diseased. Thus, insanity was a disease of the mind's physical agent, the brain. Although Rush also spoke of the mind and brain as distinct entities, his emphasis upon the physical nature of insanity derived from the medical rather than the philosophical or theological implications of his theory. Attempting to establish that insanity was medicable, he had no great concern about the immortality of the soul. If insanity were a somatic disease, medicine alone had the right to treat it, and theology and philosophy must surrender their prerogatives.

However, there were physicians who reversed Rush's order of importance by giving moral treatment first place and medical means, second. Foremost among these stood Todd and Wyman.[79] Todd, a close adherent to Pinel's system, abandoned bloodletting, purging, and blistering. Under his direction the Hartford Retreat did not employ fear or "unnecessary restraint," and patients were treated with sympathy.[80] Wyman, who was a phenomenologist and believed in the theory of associationism, agreed with Pinel and Rush that the affections and emotions could be deranged while the reason remained intact. The passions, he contended, were the primary source of man's actions and could become powerful enough to overthrow the intellect's control.[81]

Wyman did not believe that insanity always was an organic disease that required medical therapy. If there were signs of inflammation or of a structural or functional disease of the brain, Wyman recommended medical therapeutics. But purging, bleeding, low diets, and other conventional medical means were often prescribed indiscriminately, he declared; they had value only if organic disease necessitated the use of depletive agents and then only when the strength and general health of the patient were good. Depletive remedies were "seldom useful in relieving mental disease," especially among debilitated patients. "They [were] usually injurious, and frequently fatal." In cases of mental disorder "without symptoms of organic disease, a judicious moral management is more successful. . . . Moral treatment is indispensable, even in cases arising from organic disease." [82]

Both Todd and Wyman were attracted more by the moderation of Pinel and Tuke's methods than by theoretical considerations, and, as time went on, their success with moral treatment reinforced their preference for it. Like their European mentors, these two early American psychiatrists tended to avoid questions about the mind-body relationship and emphasized psychological medicine in their therapeutics. As American psychiatry developed into a special profession in the mid-nineteenth century, it was characterized by Todd and Wyman's optimism, practicality, and humanism, but lacked their freedom from ideological and theological commitments.

(2)

L A Y   O P I N I O N   I N   T R A N S I T I O N

1

As the medical world awakened slowly to the needs of the insane and the possibility of their cure, it left the lay public far behind. A general apathy existed, and only the most educated and religiously liberal persons of the urban upper classes followed the progress of physicians. Not until major advances were achieved and publicized did the public begin to orient its opinions to medical rather than philosophic and religious precepts.

In 1822 Wyman complained of the great gulf between the masses in New England and those who advocated moral treatment there. Before that time, he wrote, people considered insanity incurable, and lunatics were doomed to long and severe confinement. "Many, who have adopted a more correct opinion, have been deterred from sending from home [to an asylum] their lunatic friends by a belief that harsh and severe treatment, exciting fear and terror, would be thought most beneficial." Medical men had approved and often advised such treatment, he said, but a revolution of opinion about treatment had occurred. The new approach was becoming known, but the process was slow.[1]

Dr. George Parkman, who had been trained by Pinel, operated a private mental hospital; he described the discouraged attitude of New Englanders toward insanity.[2] The fear that mental institutions would not give kind care to patients is apparent in an announcement of the opening of the Hartford Retreat in 1824. The notice, appearing in the *Christian Spectator,* repeatedly emphasized that patients would be "treated with the utmost humanity, and receive every attention," and would be "visited daily" by Dr. Todd. "Under the immediate care of such a physician and of such [kind] attendants, the friends of the insane may feel assured, that no effort will be spared to affect, in every case a restoration to reason and health. . . . Unnecessary severity will in no instance be sanctioned." [3]

In sharp contrast to a generally ignorant and indifferent public, a small number of educated laymen gave as much impetus as the medical profession to the reform movement. Educated persons of the late eighteenth and early nineteenth centuries were much more likely to be well informed about contemporary medicine than later generations. By 1800 specialization had not advanced substantially in America, and the cultured man still read general medical and scientific works. Benjamin Franklin—a founder of the Pennsylvania Hospital—was probably better versed in the medicine of his day than many who earned their living in the profession.[4] Other men with political and scientific interests, John Adams and Thomas Jefferson, were also relatively sophisticated about medicine.

Lay participation in the movement to reform the care of the insane was not simply a matter of fund raising. Some laymen were also pioneers in spreading the new, optimistic theories about insanity. They initiated two of the earliest American mental institutions, Friends' Asylum and Bloomingdale Asylum [5]—both dedicated to the use of moral treatment— and figured prominently in the founding of the Pennsylvania Hospital and most of the other asylums built before 1824. Initially, laymen administered several of these institutions and applied the new therapy to patients. Although the main concern of these lay reformers was the practical aspect of the care of the mentally ill, they were well acquainted with the theories of Pinel, Tuke, and Rush. Their general outlook was similar to that of the enlightened physicians of their day.

2

Many of the early lay reformers were Quakers or strongly influenced by them. This is not surprising, for the American members of the Society of Friends, like their brethren in England, were conspicuous for their philanthropic activities. In the United States they established some of the first hospitals, dispensaries, and almshouses, as well as asylums for the insane. The Friends' Asylum was a Quaker institution, and a Quaker, Thomas Eddy, was the guiding spirit in the founding of the Bloomingdale Asylum. Both the Friends' Asylum and the Hartford Retreat were patterned after Tuke's Retreat at York, and the establishment of the Pennsylvania Hospital was largely the work of Friends. The Society of Friends in America maintained close connections with their coreligionists in England and were greatly influenced by Tuke and other British reformers. It was assumed that the two national groups would think and act alike on important issues.

Frederick B. Tolles, in his study of Quaker merchants of colonial Philadelphia, suggested that a pervasive pacifism underlay the Friends' acceptance of Tuke's theories and that they opposed the older psychiatric approach because it sanctioned harsh physical treatment.[6] But an examination of the annual reports and diaries written by the successive superintendents of the Friends' Asylum from 1817 to 1824 shows that although moral therapy was emphasized, the application of physical pain, restraint, and strong medical means was not eliminated. The use of the cold bath, strait jackets, bleeding, blistering, emetics, purging, and other means of controlling patients reflected a pragmatic attitude. The Quakers at the Friends' Asylum did not hesitate to use physical restraint and punishment when they thought them necessary.[7] Their disallowance of chains and whippings came from the conviction that these measures were not good therapy as well as from a commitment to humanitarianism.

Perhaps the strongest element in the Quakers' rejection of the older ideas was faith in the perfectibility of man, which prevented them from treating him like a beast to cure his mental illness. They believed that everyone possessed grace, or an "inner light," and in a sense was partly divine and worthy of humane treatment. The rationale for the earlier cruel treatment had been the belief that insanity was a punishment for sins committed by a depraved and unworthy person. The Friends, however, took a naturalistic view of insanity; they thought that all men could be improved and could achieve perfection no matter what their previous status or present condition. Consequently the Quakers had an essentially humanistic and optimistic attitude toward the insane.

The American Quakers did not develop medical or theoretical outlooks that were any different from Tuke's theories. They employed religious worship as an adjunct to therapy and rejected the demonological concept of insanity. The superintendent of the Friends' Asylum rarely permitted Friends to come to the institution to conduct religious services.[8] He thought that "religious good [might] be communicated . . . in lucid intervals"[9] and lucid patients who might benefit from religious instruction could obtain it at regular religious meetings in Frankford rather than at the asylum. The other patients had contacts only with persons who knew their cases thoroughly and were trained to handle them. The Quakers stressed occupational therapy, principally farming, as their special contribution to the cure of mental patients and thought this was the most beneficial element of moral treatment.[10] Occasionally they used force to make patients work.[11] The Friends' Asylum superintendent commented approvingly on the rich soil upon which Bloomingdale Asylum was built: It was good for farming.[12]

There was some conflict between lay Quakers and physicians about the proper emphasis upon moral treatment. The first superintendent of the Friends' Asylum, a layman, protested that the frequent use of medicine by the resident physician hindered a fair test of the value of moral treatment.[13] Despite the conviction of the Quaker trustee and founder Thomas Eddy that treatment should be confined to moral means at Bloomingdale,[14] physicians continued to bleed, purge, and dose patients. This disagreement about medical and moral means was related to the problem of who should administer therapy. When moral treatment was first introduced, lay hospital administrators, with the consent of physicians, often supervised its application. Probably this occurred because Tuke was not a physician [15] and also because of the common opinion that his system, which largely rejected the use of drugs, was non-medical, basically administrative, and therefore the province of laymen.

The problem was similar to the current controversy about who should practice psychotherapy. In the early nineteenth century it was even less clear than today why one had to be a physician to do so. It seemed to many that the only requirements were human sympathy and common sense, attributes not confined to the medical profession. The issue of lay versus medical control of moral treatment, however, was not serious at first. Later physicians demanded the right to direct moral treatment when it became plain that the new therapy would play an increasingly greater role in psychiatry and that without such control their position in asylums would be subordinate to laymen.

While individual Quakers were successful in introducing moral treatment and founding mental hospitals, as a group they were not as influential as they might have been in disseminating the new ideas. Although the asylum at Frankford attracted the attention of physicians and others interested in the care of the insane, it was too small and sectarian to have any great impact in its early years. Before the 1830's the Friends' Asylum operated at half its capacity of forty patients. Until 1834 only Quakers were admitted and even the relatively low rates were prohibitive for poor patients.[16] Since their asylum—non-profit but private and sectarian —received no public money, its sponsors did not need to popularize their accomplishments in order to obtain financial aid from the state legislature. They discussed the activities of the asylum largely with other Quakers, so the public probably knew comparatively little about their work.

The Quakers who were active in the moral treatment movement belonged to the wing of the Society of Friends concerned with social reform rather than politics. They were closely associated with physicians in advocating an optimistic view of mental illness and in founding mental hospitals, and they, more than other laymen, shared the progressive views of the medical profession. The Quakers were not originators, but they followed the innovators and took a more advanced position than many physicians in the United States at that time.

3

Members of the Society of Friends were not the only laymen familiar with progressive medical thought. Equally up-to-date, if more skeptical, were some of the nation's leading intellectuals and statesmen. Most of them had close personal as well as intellectual and political relations with Benjamin Rush and were interested in medical questions. Rush belonged to the aristocracy of talent among American politicians, scientists, religious leaders, and intellectuals during the late eighteenth and early nineteenth centuries and knew intimately many of the famous men of his time. He was a close friend of Jefferson and Adams and was well acquainted with Benjamin Rittenhouse, Benjamin Franklin, Benjamin Waterhouse, John Witherspoon, and Joseph Priestley. They regarded Rush as one of the great physicians of the day, knew of his interest in mental illness, and discussed his ideas with him and among themselves. But because they were skeptical of theories and empirical in approach, they did not accept his medical theories without qualifications. Less optimistic than Rush and somewhat fatalistic, they were inclined to discount his and other physicians' claims of having discovered the key to all illness.[17] For example, Jefferson told Rush that he found consolation in looking for the good effects that came from great evils. He suggested that yellow fever, then a seasonal occurrence in many parts of the United States, might benefit humanity by inhibiting the growth of great cities, which were "pestilential to the morals, the health and the liberties of man." [18]

Although Jefferson did not believe that all diseases would eventually be conquered, he may have considered insanity curable. One cannot be certain because of the unusual circumstances in which he expressed his opinion. John Rush, son of Benjamin, killed a close friend in a duel, went insane, and in 1810 was committed to the Pennsylvania Hospital for the rest of his life.[19] In a letter of condolence, Jefferson told Rush that he knew of many persons who recovered from insanity and that he had always believed it was one of those diseases for which a cure was highly probable; he related the history of one of his relatives who was restored to sanity and became a successful teacher.[20] Whatever his real beliefs about the curability of insanity, Jefferson clearly approved of Rush's humanitarian tendencies.[21]

Jefferson tended to distrust physicians' knowledge of disease and believed that nature's healing power was man's best hope. In much the same vein as Pinel, Jefferson said the physician would prove himself wise if he were "a watchful, but quiet spectator of the operations of nature." [22] Jefferson's great regard for the work of Cabanis, who gave a theoretical foundation to moral treatment, and his generally skeptical medical views seem to place him closer in spirit to the new French school of medicine than to Rush, whom he nevertheless respected.[23]

John Adams, another close friend of Rush, commented on the latter's *Medical Inquiries and Observations upon the Diseases of the Mind* to Benjamin Waterhouse:

> Rush is so near my heart, that I must return to his very interesting Volume. It seems to me, that every excess of Passion, Prejudice, Appetite; of Love, Fear, Jealousy, Envy, Revenge, Avarice, Ambition; every Revery and Vagary of Imagination, the Fairy Tales, the Arabian Nights, in short, almost all Poetry and all Oratory; every écart, every deviation from pure, logical mathematical Reason; may in Some Sense be called a disease of the mind.[24]

Adams drew the logical conclusion from Rush's theories, which in this respect conformed to conventional medical thought of his day. This emphasis on literal truthfulness was also typical of Puritanism, which sanctioned scientific interests, but mistrusted symbolism, poetry, and imaginative thought of a non-mathematical nature.[25]

The support given to the hospitals that were built to practice moral treatment indicated the approval of American intellectual, business, political, and social leaders. Prominent citizens of Massachusetts, New York, and Pennsylvania responded to the appeals of physicians and lay reformers by contributing funds for the new asylums. They also served on fund-raising committees and hospital boards and signed petitions to the state legislatures for hospital charters and financial grants.

In Boston virtually everyone of any prominence participated in the campaign for a hospital that would admit insane patients.[26] In an appeal for funds before the Boston Humane Society, William Tudor, Jr., a prominent author, businessman, and philanthropist, explained to the wealthy members that although all classes were subject to insanity it was more frequent among the upper classes. No one was safe from derangement, but the disease struck those of superior intellectual talents most often.[27] In Connecticut the State Assembly set up a joint committee to hear eminent physicians who spoke in favor of an appropriation to establish an insane asylum. Their testimony convinced the committee that the insane could be cured by the new European methods.[28] In New York the governors of the New York Hospital apparently persuaded the state legislature that Bloomingdale Asylum should be operated on the principles of moral treatment.[29] Widespread interest in the insanity of King George III, articles in the English quarterly reviews devoted to the parliamentary investigations of British mental asylums in 1814–15, and descriptions of moral treatment in British and American journals likely to be read by upper-class laymen probably helped to educate the leaders of American society and enlist their support for new mental hospitals.[30]

4

The founders of the new asylums were assisted by the local Protestant clergy, who contributed and campaigned for funds. Several ministers, impressed by the possibility of curing the mentally ill, were especially active in raising funds for the Hartford Retreat and McLean Asylum. It is uncertain whether they continued to believe in demonological possession as a cause of insanity. After expressing his optimism about curing mental illness by hospital care, one minister concluded his appeal for funds with this contention:

> No charitable act of his [Christ's] is so often mentioned as casting out demons. Whatever was the nature of demonic possession, it is well known that writers of great note suppose it to have been no more than different species of insanity. At least the case of many maniacs and lunatics now is very similar to that of the possessed and the lunatics described in the gospels.[31]

He apparently equated demoniac possession with insanity of natural causation.

The Rev. Thomas Robbins, of East Windsor, Connecticut, speaking at dedication ceremonies of the Hartford Retreat, alluded to Jesus' healing of those *"possessed with devils, and those which were lunatic."* At that time, he said, the demoniacs were exorcised, the lunatics were restored, and the insane found a safe retreat in Christ. But this power to cure insanity through miraculous means "is now withdrawn," and the insane could be restored only by natural means. Robbins did not make clear, however, whether he believed that demoniac possession still occurred.[32]

John Wesley—the founder of Methodism and author of a medical best seller—believed in witchcraft and credited all human disease to Adam's fall and original sin. Since the fall, nature had conspired to punish man for his revolt against the Creator, he declared. Yet he followed the teachings of secular minded British physicians in proposing practical cures for insanity that had nothing to do with God or the devil.[33]

In at least one instance a clergyman explicitly reconciled his religious beliefs with advanced medical views on mental processes and insanity. During a funeral sermon, the Rev. Clark Brown quoted from Cullen's *Physiology* approvingly and took a sensationist position similar to Locke's. " 'Sense and intuition reach but little way'; the greatest part of our knowledge is received either through the medium of certain organick parts of the body, or from deductions and intermediate ideas." The brain is the material organ of the immaterial mind, he said. Since knowledge comes through the medium of the senses, damage to either the brain or the senses could lead to insanity.[34] His approach ignored demonological possession or divine action. At the same time he proclaimed the immateriality of the mind, which was seen as God's creation. The body might be diseased and disorder the mind. Thus a person could become insane if physical derangement of the senses or brain suspended the "immaterial and intellectual existence." Brown's position is at variance with that of many clergymen and physicians throughout the nineteenth century, for it acknowledged that the immaterial mind itself could be deranged.

Like many physicians and laymen, clergymen probably conceived of moral treatment as essentially a humanitarian reform and missed or overlooked its broader philosophical and medical implications. The emphasis by non-Calvinist denominations on the benevolence of God and on man's perfectibility must also have influenced church leaders to sponsor efforts for more humane care of the mentally ill. It is possible, too, that the successes claimed by the new hospitals gave ministers as well as devout laymen the idea that moral treatment was a means of saving souls lost to God. More mundane considerations, such as competition between churchmen of Protestant sects to do good works, encouraged them to overlook contradictions between the theory of moral treatment and Biblical explanations of the cause of insanity.[35] Churchmen as a group, however, did not greatly concern themselves with reforms in the care of the insane before 1824.

5

The masses were certainly not much concerned with insanity. When asked, the public might support the establishment of a mental hospital, but unless affected directly by the mental illness of a friend or relative, most people gave little thought to the matter. Relatives of insane persons were reluctant to talk or write freely about it; to them insanity was the mark of the devil or a deplorable strain in their heredity. This general indifference or avoidance of an uncomfortable subject makes the task of ascertaining popular opinion particularly difficult. Some impression may be obtained from popular medical books and fiction, comments of physicians in charge of mental hospitals, statements of relatives committing patients to asylums, testimony during criminal trials involving insanity, and press accounts of these proceedings.

During the late eighteenth and early nineteenth centuries the layman could not read many books or articles in English that approached insanity from a moral-treatment point of view. The new psychological medicine first became known by word of mouth and later by descriptive articles in journals read only by physicians and well-educated laymen. Between 1789 and 1796 Rush called for reforms in the insane wards of Pennsylvania Hospital, Tuke planned the York Retreat, and Pinel unshackled insane patients at Bicêtre. Not until 1806, however, when Pinel's classic work appeared in translation, did physician and layman have access to a systematic account of moral treatment in the English language. Rush's *Medical Inquiries and Observations upon the Diseases of the Mind* came out in 1812, and the first detailed description of the methods used at the York Retreat was published in 1813.

The average layman did not read these works or the journals that discussed the new psychiatric ideas. If he read anything about medicine, it was usually a popularly written medical handbook or encyclopedia that served him as a physician when he was ill. These handbooks—there were a number of them in circulation—contained both traditional folk remedies and the theories, sometimes quite ancient, of physicians.

One of the most popular books was William Buchan's *Domestic Medicine,* which appeared in numerous American printings from the mid-eighteenth to the mid-nineteenth centuries and which allegedly had more influence "than any other similar work ever published." [36] Buchan, like most physicians writing for the general public, took a naturalistic view of mental illness; he also emphasized psychological factors in both the cause and cure of insanity.[37] He shared his colleagues' belief that melancholia and "madness" were only different degrees of the same disease. Although stressing irrationality as an essential criterion of insanity,[38] he did not, like so many other physicians, equate insanity with violence.[39]

According to Buchan, melancholy and mania were caused by: hereditary predisposition; intense thinking, especially about one subject; violent passions or affections such as love, fear, joy, and "over-weening pride"; excessive venery; "narcotic or stupifactive poisons"; a sedentary life; solitude; suppression of evacuations; and acute fevers or other diseases. Whatever weakened the body and disturbed the emotions could produce nervous disease. "Violent anger will change melancholy into madness; and excessive cold, especially in the lower extremities, will force the blood into the brain, and produce symptoms of madness." Insanity might also be brought on by eating food that was difficult to digest, by dryness of the brain, and by "gloomy or mistaken notions of religion." He advised against strong liquors, tea, coffee, salted and smoked animal food, shellfish, garlic, and onions, among other things, and recommended exercise and a strict vegetable diet for mental patients, as well as traditional medicines.[40]

Buchan, like many mid-eighteenth-century medical men, was generally pessimistic about the prognosis of nervous ailments.[41] Some cases had better prospects than others. Insanity resulting from physical trauma was more amenable to cure, and "madness attended with mirth [was] not so dangerous as that which is accompanied with sadness." The appearance of other illness, such as nosebleed, "violent looseness," "scabby eruptions," or "bleeding piles," sometimes cured mental disease.[42]

Although Buchan wrote before the systematic development of moral management, he and most of his colleagues were aware that psychological factors played a role in curing insanity. In cases of depression, he recommended paying great attention to the state of the patient's mind, which should be soothed and diverted with amusements, entertaining stories, games, music, and congenial company. But he thought the highly excited madman should be treated by evacuants, bleeding, purges, and medicines.[43] In contrast to many other physicians, Buchan strongly opposed institutional care and condemned confinement in asylums as the worst form of treatment. He endorsed freedom of movement and farm work or a long journey with agreeable companions to a warmer climate. He wrote of Bedlam and other asylums: "These institutions, as they are generally managed, are far more likely to make a wise man mad than to restore a madman to his senses." [44] He advocated exercise, amusements, and a vegetable diet at home.[45]

Buchan's ideas have been summarized in some detail because his book was so popular. One can only speculate about how he influenced his readers. His approach contradicted traditional lay theories about demoniac possession or divine punishment causing insanity. However, it confirmed popular distrust of mental institutions and corroborated the belief that insanity was often a sign of bad heredity and usually incurable. Although his basic attitude was sympathetic and non-moralistic, Buchan sanctioned harsh and terroristic treatment of maniacs. In many respects his views were far from those of the moral-treatment school.

Other general medical books discussed insanity, but few came close to Buchan's in popularity and good sense. They agreed that insanity was a natural disease, which usually could be cured only by medicine. Even in cases of hypochondriasis and hysteria, regarded chiefly as disorders of the imagination, medical therapies were often the prescribed remedies. Few medical works written for the layman stressed the psychological element either in medicine generally or in insanity in particular.[46]

Approaching Buchan's book in popularity was Wesley's compilation of inexpensive, common-sense cures, *Primitive Physic*. In the relatively short publishing span between 1747 and 1829, it went through thirty-two London editions and at least seven American editions.[47] Wesley was unimpressed by the theories of system-building physicians or by their prescriptions, although he cited the eminent Sydenham, Dover, and Cheyne as exemplary medical men. He thought that the only general preventive of pain and ill health was exercise, which also had great restorative powers, especially when combined with temperance and proper eating habits. He advised placing a violently mad patient directly under a powerful waterfall for as long as he could bear it; he also prescribed the application of cold compresses to the head, the use of various cheap medications, and the consumption of nothing but apples for a month.[48] These cures compare favorably with the much more harsh ones usually recommended by the medical profession.

Wesley did not discuss psychological methods, perhaps because he was concerned only with remedies that the average man could apply. He had two mottoes: every man his own physician and all cures simple ones. Considering the conventional medical practices and knowledge of the mid-eighteenth century, this was not bad advice. How sound it was some years later when advances were being made in the care of mental patients is another question.

The treatment of insanity in popular medical literature, which was still widely read before 1824, predated and ran counter to many of those principles of moral management that were revolutionizing the care of the insane in Europe and the United States: hospitalization of all cases; application of gentle moral or psychological means even to maniacs; reduction in the use of medical therapy; minimization of harsh and frightening measures; recognition of other criteria of insanity than irrationality and violent behavior; and strong faith in curability.

6

Popular fiction of the late eighteenth and early nineteenth centuries tended to reflect the attitudes in medical books.[49] By that time the Puritan strictures against fiction had lost much of their effect and, despite medical warnings that reading novels could cause insanity, English novels found a ready market in the United States.[50] Until the second quarter of the nineteenth century the only serious American novels dealing with mental illness were *Wieland* and *Edgar Huntly* by Charles Brockden Brown.[51] The other few works of fiction that depicted mental disorder at length were written by British authors. They probably tended to reinforce their readers' commonly held concepts rather than to create new ones.

These books were Gothic novels, which in style and content emphasized the unusual, the spectacular, and almost always the shocking and violent. In *Melmoth, the Wanderer,* by Charles R. Maturin, a sane man was confined in a horrible insane asylum. The religiously deranged protagonist of James Hogg's *Private Memoirs and Confessions of a Justified Sinner* killed his brother, mother, and sweetheart. In *Wieland,* an insane husband murdered his wife and children; Scott's crazed *Bride of Lammermoor* stabbed her unloved bridegroom.[52]

The fictional maniac characteristically had a furious, troubled look; he groaned and produced frightening sounds and was a "hurricane of human passions." [53] "The depth and malignity of his eye is hideous. His breath is like the airs from a charnel house, and his flesh seems fading from his bones, as if the worm that never dies were gnawing it away already." [54] In *Melmoth,* the "devil" tells the hero, who is in an insane asylum: "There can be no crime into which madmen would not, and do not, precipitate themselves; mischief is their occupation, malice their habit, murder their sport, and blasphemy their delight." [55] Despite the extravagant language and sometimes stereotyped characterizations, the descriptions of insane persons in violent conditions were often conceived with skill and realism. One story was based on a newspaper account and conformed to the latest medical theories of insanity.[56] Even though the authors knew that not all insane persons were criminals or raving maniacs or prone to give flamboyant demonstrations, they portrayed them in this way, doubtless for dramatic purposes.

The attitude of novelists toward the possibility of recovery was pessimistic. Maturin's asylum might have been modeled after the notorious Bedlam in England. He described it as a terrible prison—bleak, dirty, run by bestial guards who whipped the chained inmates mercilessly and fed them the worst kind of food. No mention was made of cure; on the contrary, once committed to an asylum even a sane man had no hope of being released.[57] In all of the novels except *Fleetwood,* by William Godwin, the events led the insane characters to death and destruction. The concept of insanity as a disease amenable to treatment and cure was seldom explicitly expressed.[58]

The apparently supernatural manifestations presented as playing an important role in causing mental derangement are shown in the denouements of these novels to have natural explanations, and in two cases the writers present disquisitions on the falseness of the supernatural approach.[59] Only the *Bride of Lammermoor* leaves the reader in doubt about the role of supernatural forces in causing insanity, but Scott explains on a largely rational basis the process by which derangement occurred.[60]

Conforming with prevailing medical theory, the novelists endowed deranged characters with predisposition to insanity or what today might be termed pre-psychotic personalities. They were overly passionate and impatient of opposition, were inherently evil, had previous mental breakdowns, or had a family history of insanity or mental defects. Invariably, the writer exaggerated a peculiar trait until it became an abnormality and served as the weak link in the character's sanity, which collapsed under stress.[61]

To what extent these non-supernatural explanations of mental disorder succeeded in impressing readers is impossible to say. Great emphasis upon seemingly supernatural phenomena possibly overshadowed the "scientific" rationalizations for them at the conclusion of the novels. Still, considering the prevalence of other-worldly elements in the Gothic novels of the time, readers might have been exceptionally aware of any attempt to show that unnatural behavior could have a natural cause. However, the exclusive depiction of insane persons as irrational and violent probably supported popular views that madness was always unmanageable.

7

Many people read little more than the Bible, and the Biblical concept of insanity as demonological possession, to be treated by exorcism and often more drastic means, undoubtedly persisted among the uneducated until well into the nineteenth century, if not longer. For example, the father of the first patient admitted to the McLean Hospital in 1818 told the hospital board that he thought his son was, as the Bible phrased it, "possessed with a devil," and that he had sought to cure him by regular whippings.[62] In another case, the trustees of the Worcester asylum reported that the mother of a deranged boy refused treatment for him because "an evil spirit . . . troubled him, and until the Lord was pleased to take it off, she was quite sure, that nothing any man could do, would be useful to him." [63] As late as 1841, the first report of the new Department of the Insane at the Pennsylvania Hospital complained about "popular errors respecting insanity" and asserted that the hospital opposed "the doctrine that insanity was a visitation of wrath and vengeance, or a reproach." [64]

In 1796 a magazine writer disclosed an obvious and not uncommon conflict between a natural and a supernatural approach to insanity. He commented upon a man who had murdered his wife and four children:

> The cause for his wonderfully cruel proceedings is beyond the conception of human beings—the deed so unpremeditated, so unprovoked, that we do not hesitate to pronounce it the effect of insanity—yet . . . when we reflect on the equinimity [*sic*] of [the murderer's] temper, and the comfortable situation in which he was, and no visible circumstance operating to render him frantic, we are apt to conclude, that he was under a strong delusion of Satan. But what avail our conjectures, perhaps it is best that some things are concealed from us, and the only use we can now make of our knowledge of this affair, is to be humble under a scene of human frailty to renew our petition, "Lead us not into temptation." [65]

Another writer attributed a murder by an insane person to original sin. Such crimes indicated the "depravity of the human heart, and the imbecility of the human mind," and left no doubt that without God's aid man "becomes his own destroyer," who practices inhuman and awful murder.[66]

A more secular approach is revealed in a newspaper account of a "shocking murder" in Nashville, Tennessee. In a nearby county a man had brutally killed his wife while their children looked on. A "hellish grin" on his face, he accused her of having a lover and then axed her; "when the fury of the monster was glutted," he ran away, returned, and ran away again. When caught, he confessed "the whole of his turpitude." He came from a "respectable family" and was considered a "worthy man, when free from the baneful effects of ardent spirits; which on several occasions, have entirely destroyed the sanity of his mind for weeks together." The writer did not think that the murderer's lawyer could "plead with truth his insanity," although no doubt that plea would be attempted. However, he had a right to a fair trial, and the paper "would be the last to excite the public sympathy for or against him"—a somewhat hypocritical statement, considering the sensational and condemnatory report it gave of the murder.[67]

Newspapers and trial recorders frequently dwelled on the so-called bestial character of the criminally insane. This attitude differed significantly from Rush's. If he occasionally treated violent patients like wild animals, it was for therapeutic reasons; he never believed that they were inhuman. To him they were sick persons who might need rough handling to be cured. Laymen, however, did not always have this approach. Newspaper reporters and witnesses in criminal trials frequently expressed the opinion that the insane were beasts who deserved their fate and warranted no sympathy. One newspaper characterized an insane murderer as a "monster in human form . . . callous to the feelings and inaccessible to the last cries of humanity." The implication is that he was responsible for his acts and morally guilty of ignoring pleas for mercy.[68]

This attitude probably stemmed in part from the prevailing moralistic approach to insanity and from the common assumption that man was superior to the animals because he possessed a soul, whose distinctive feature was the power of thought. Loss of reason was seen as the loss of the soul and of humanity and God's grace.[69] Various factors seemed to give support to this view: the difficulty of curing insane persons; the uncontrolled, unpredictable, brutish violence of maniacs; and the apparent ability of mentally ill persons to withstand extremes of heat, cold, hunger, and sleeplessness.

Study of newspaper comment about trials involving criminal insanity and of verbatim reports of these trials reveals the criteria used by observers, witnesses, counsel, and judges to determine insanity. There seem to have been three major tests: The defendant had to be irrational at all times; he had to be unable to distinguish right from wrong and to lack a sense of guilt for his crime; he had to demonstrate a violent temperament before committing the criminal act. Then as now there was no clear definition of insanity in American jurisprudence, and legal decisions on the subject were confused and contradictory. Nevertheless, loss of reason and inability to tell right from wrong at the time of the crime were and still are the criteria most commonly used by the courts in cases of criminal insanity.[70] These standards were not applied in cases of the defendant's obvious idiocy or imbecility, conditions that both physicians and laymen often confused with insanity. Evidence of great intellectual deficiency seemed to be enough proof of irresponsibility and thus insanity.[71]

One reporter analyzed a man who had senselessly murdered his wife and five children. The writer believed that the murderer could reason because he took his own son from among three sleeping children and killed him. He must therefore have known right from wrong and be judged sane. He ran away, which seemed to corroborate this opinion, for it was generally assumed that the insane, who allegedly felt no guilt, did not flee from the scene of their crimes. Flight was also supposed to be evidence of remorse, or at least recognition that an immoral act had been committed; thus, a fleeing murderer was presumed to know right from wrong and to be legally sane.[72]

Witnesses thought that violent behavior was an important consideration. Except in cases of idiocy or advanced dementia, * if a person

* Dementia: "Insanity characterized by more or less complete abolition of the mental faculties or reason, memory, etc." (*Stedman's Medical Dictionary*, p. 384).

pleaded insanity in a court of law, he was expected to be a raving maniac; anything less would raise serious doubts about his insanity. This position was not simply an exaggeration of the one held by medical men, who at that time tended to perceive only the more obvious cases of mental derangement. Though they regarded loss of reason and violent action as the most reliable tests, a few went beyond these criteria. Rush spoke of forms of insanity characterized only by lack of a sense of guilt for anti-social and illegal acts, and other leading physicians recognized non-violent forms of mental illness.

The proceedings of trials involving insanity represent one of the few primary sources of information about prevailing attitudes. Relevant facts are available about seven trials that took place between 1789 and 1824. The following analysis of five of them must, however, be qualified. It is probable that to protect society against crimes by sane persons, prosecuting lawyers, juries, and judges often balked at terming border-line or even obviously deranged defendants legally insane. The authorities, like society in general, wanted vengeance; when murder was involved, they considered committing an insane person to an asylum or prison as neither adequate punishment nor sufficient deterrent to potential criminals. Nevertheless, these court records furnish valuable information that is for the most part corroborated by other sources. Although physicians experienced in caring for the insane lived in large cities where most of these trials took place, they did not appear as expert witnesses. Apparently jurists at that time believed that neither they nor the juries needed assistance from the medical profession in determining the sanity of a defendant.

In 1801 the lawyer for a young man accused of brutally killing his sweetheart failed to plead insanity despite many indications that the defendant was mentally ill. The boy had no motive and showed no remorse. He allegedly killed the girl, whom he loved and who returned his love, in daylight within sight of her father's farmhouse. She was murdered by several dozen stabs from a penknife, and, although the defendant claimed that she committed suicide, her body had wounds that could not have been self-inflicted. Yet neither counsel for the defense, the prosecution, nor any witness seemed to doubt the defendant's sanity. The defense lawyer, however, objected that one of the prosecution witnesses was deranged because he was confused, wild, and incoherent.[73]

The compilers of the proceedings of this trial sought to reassure those who had misgivings about the sanity of the defendant, who was convicted and sentenced to death. They wondered at his leisurely escape from prison after his conviction and his surprise at being pursued. They thought his indifference during the trial and failure to show remorse or to make a confession on the scaffold was strange. They could not explain the murderer's lack of motive, and recognized that some people might contend that he had been temporarily insane. But they argued that motiveless crimes were not the consequence of excusable insanity but rather the offspring of uncontrolled passions. Their position seemed to deny insanity as a valid defense against criminal prosecution.[74]

In another case a former Negro slave who unaccountably poisoned her own child, who lived, and another woman's, who died, did plead insanity. But neither the police nor her employers thought that she was insane, for she seemed rational at all times, despite the testimony of a former owner that she tended to be restless, unsteady, and flighty. These characteristics induced the owner to free her. The prisoner herself believed that she had been possessed by the devil. To the judge, the use of poison indicated forethought, which showed that the poisoner must be rational and hence sane. The plea of insanity, he told the jury, was often used only as a last resort and must be considered cautiously, especially if poisoning were involved. The fact that no motive could be found was no reason to attribute the crime to insanity. The jury convicted her, and she received the death penalty.[75]

A sixty-year-old man was convicted of arson in New York even though it was brought out at the trial that he had become unaccountably brutal, violent, and vindictive in recent years; often was drunk; so abused his wife that she obtained a separation; and, as a result of a quarrel with a neighbor, set fire to his own home, crawled under his bed, and cut his throat. This incontrovertible evidence did not convince the jury that he was insane. Several persons testified that he had been more sober than usual on the day of the crime and that he was not subject to insanity. The judge told the jury that no matter how horrible and unnatural the act, the defendant could not be found insane if he was capable of distinguishing "good from evil" when he committed it.[76]

The fourth case is interesting mainly because of the defense arguments and the fact that they were considered valid by witnesses. Counsel for an alleged murderer pleaded insanity on the grounds that the defendant's forebears had been deranged and that the defendant himself had been absent-minded and eccentric from infancy. If he had been sane, he would have fled farther from the scene of the crime, "beyond the reach of justice." One witness based his belief in the insanity of the defendant on knowledge of his parentage rather than on his actions.[77]

In the fifth case, a New York man was convicted of biting off his unfaithful wife's nose. Several defense witnesses supported his plea of insanity. One testified that before the crime the defendant had "frequently beat his head against a wall during the night and exhibited every other symptom of derangement," and that immediately after the crime he showed "wildness, indicative of phrensy." Several other witnesses also believed the defendant to be deranged, and one said that he had always thought that the accused was in some degree insane "but . . . at all times harmless." Nevertheless, the prosecution rejected the plea of insanity, for the prisoner allegedly had indicated that he knew right from wrong at the time of the crime; he had closed the windows so his wife's cries would not be heard and had escaped from the house. "When a man, through the influence of passions, has been hurried into a state of temporary phrensy, and under that excitement, commits a crime, he never can allege insanity as an excuse." The prosecution did not explain the difference between a "state of temporary phrensy" and temporary insanity. He concluded that the plea of insanity was generally used in desperate cases and should be "strictly scrutinized." [78]

The judge, Cadwallader D. Colden, mayor of New York City and a founder of Bloomingdale Asylum, told the jury that whatever the reason for the excitement, "a man should never suffer himself to be hurried into a state of temporary insanity by any of the violent passions." Colden evidently accepted Locke's "faculty" psychology, which assumed that a person could suspend the satisfaction of his desires by first rationally deciding not to become emotionally committed to an act, if it were wrong. Then his will could not force him to act.[79] A legally insane person, the judge believed, would not be rational or have a sense of guilt and would almost always show loss of memory. Tuke, Pinel, and Rush would have challenged these criteria as unfailing signs of mental illness; they were not moralistic about insanity. They recognized the possibility that a type of insanity might exist that warped the sense of moral obligation supposedly necessary to prevent crime and that will and passion might not be controllable by reason. If this control were lost, a person's reason might not be able to reject a criminal action before his will became committed to it. He became the victim of "irresistible impulse." [80]

The idea that the personality was divided into isolated compartments acting independently and that the moral faculty itself could be alienated by external causes presented a serious challenge to the courts as well as to popular beliefs. To lawyers and judges searching for clear standards by which to restrict the scope of legal insanity, the concept of a compartmentalized personality was anathema. It made the determination of responsibility for criminal acts difficult and thus undermined one of the chief functions of the courts. The courts assumed that the moral faculty was almost always intact; unless totally insane, a person knew right from wrong. The criminal, as a rule, was therefore guilty of consciously choosing to violate the dictates of this faculty. Physicians like Rush, who acknowledged the possibility that the moral faculty could be deranged while the reason remained unaffected, appeared to leave the courts without any moral basis for punishing crime.[81] As the plea of insanity became more common, this problem increasingly plagued the criminal courts, for they were designed essentially as institutions for punishment and revenge, not as agencies for determining psychological health.

8

In many important respects early nineteenth-century lay thought on insanity resembled the views of conventional eighteenth-century physicians. This conclusion applies mainly to persons with some education who were likely to read books and magazines and who consulted physicians. The poor and ignorant probably retained many of the prejudices and superstitions of the past. One cannot even assume that the more enlightened views of the literate resulted from agreement with the medical profession's attitudes. No doubt some medical ideas—that insanity was a natural disease, for example—were accepted by many laymen. It seems undeniable, however, that much medical and lay opinion pre-dated the eighteenth century and originated in age-old folk experience, fears, and imagination as well as in religious beliefs.

For example, the commonly held conviction among laymen and phy-sicians that insanity was hereditary was based most likely on observation and not explained until later by physicians. The widespread hopeless-ness about the prognosis of the disease doubtless had a similar origin. Medical opinion also probably did not foster the belief—almost uni-versal in Rush's day—that maniacs were impervious to pain, hunger, and cold; a more likely source was superficial observation and interpretation of behavior.

Because many attitudes toward insanity were based on a cultural heritage independent of medical knowledge and because medical beliefs, particularly about a repugnant subject, were slow to spread among the general population, physicians could change their outlook drastically without making much impression, except on a few educated laymen. Over a quarter of a century after the pioneering work of Pinel and Rush, the great majority of the American people apparently were imper-vious to the revolution in psychiatric thought.

It is likely that the upper middle and especially the upper classes tended to change their ideas less slowly than the lower classes, particu-larly the poorly educated small farmers who made up the bulk of the population until the late nineteenth century. This resulted in a greater difference in class attitudes during the 1820's than before the introduc-tion of moral treatment. As a practical matter, the masses could be expected to accept the new ideas only if they were convinced of their validity by education and experience, both of which they had little chance to obtain. Only then could a *modus vivendi* develop between their religious and superstitious beliefs and medical progress. The uned-ucated tended to distrust the scientific or medical approach not only because it lacked elements that they could comprehend, such as magic, the supernatural, and an appeal to the emotions, but also because reason and education were the property of the upper classes. Members of the latter group, especially if they lived in cities, had the general education and the access to news of scientific and medical advances that enabled them to understand and accept the new ideas on an intellectual basis.

They were inclined to frequent the more liberal, less fundamentalist churches, and had some personal experience with the operation and effectiveness of the new asylums as trustees, contributors, or friends of patients.

In a few urban communities the public at large, without knowing very much about the principles upon which the new mental hospitals were established, actively welcomed them. The Boston and Hartford asylums, though initiated and built by a few wealthy, educated, and prominent citizens, received donations from the poorer sections of the population, in response to general appeals for funds. When founders of the Massachusetts General Hospital asked donors whether they wanted their money to go toward the construction of a general hospital or an insane asylum, or both, those from the poorer areas of Boston were more anxious for an asylum than those from prosperous neighborhoods.[82] This lower-class support probably reflected the obvious need of city-dwellers for institutions to care for their mentally ill rather than an understanding and acceptance of moral treatment. No doubt some of them found that homemade attempts to drive the devil out of the insane did not work and hoped that mental hospitals would resolve their problem. Then, too, as people gradually came to view insanity as a natural disease, they presumably became less ashamed to reveal its presence in their families. Some devout persons were anxious to cure insanity in loved ones in order to save their souls, for persons bereft of their reason could not receive Christian dispensation.[83] This does not mean that the majority of people were freed from the attitudes that predominated from 1789 to 1824. Crowds still flocked to the Pennsylvania Hospital on Sundays, for example, to amuse themselves by teasing the inmates and watching their antics. There was a small fee for this questionable pleasure.[84]

The first insane asylums practicing moral treatment in the United States were an expression of enlightened medical and lay opinion, but they tended to perpetuate class differences by restricting their services mainly to the wealthy. Small businessmen, artisans, farmers, and wage earners could not pay for long-term hospital care. The new asylums were not public institutions and could choose their patients; they did not have the capacity to care for more than a very small fraction of the insane and could afford to take in an even smaller proportion of poor patients. Not only did they need paying patients, but they had to cater to the reluctance of many of them to associate with the lower classes. Even when the poor were admitted, they received inferior care or did not benefit from moral treatment because of the nature of their illness. Usually they had been ill and untreated for a longer time than other patients; some were criminally insane, incurable "maniacs" sent to the hospitals from prisons. Before 1825 there were only two mental institutions that were fully supported by the state and open to all citizens; they were largely custodial.[85] Not until 1833 was a state hospital for the insane established as a therapeutic institution.

The upper and middle classes accepted the concepts of moral treatment more readily than the poor or uneducated, but the progress was slow even among them.[86] Only the emotional appeal of Dorothea Dix's national crusade for state mental hospitals in the 1840's aroused an appreciable number of people about the fate of the mentally ill.

Part Two

Changing Psychiatric Views, 1825–1865

PROBLEMS OF DEFINITION

1

The three decades before 1825 were a time of experimentation in the care of the insane in a few exclusive corporate asylums. The development of psychiatry on a large scale came afterwards, when the success of the reform movement enabled physicians to apply some of their experience in the early hospitals to more than a tiny proportion of the mentally ill. From 1825 to 1865 the number of non-proprietary asylums in the United States grew from nine to sixty-two, most of them state supported.[1] Although the terms "psychiatry" and "psychiatrist" did not come into general use until the twentieth century, the branch of medicine concerned with mental illness had developed into a recognized specialty by the 1840's. Its practitioners exercised a virtual monopoly over the therapeutic care of the insane.[2] These early psychiatrists—so designated for convenience—usually served in mental hospitals as superintendents, assistant superintendents, and visiting physicians. At most, their number probably never exceeded two hundred, and for much of the time before 1865 it fell short of half that sum. The leaders of the profession, the asylum superintendents, constituted a small, select group whose medical education and public and professional standing were superior to other medical practitioners.[3]

The majority of these superintendents were not concerned with systematizing their convictions and experiences in print and rarely conducted scientific research. Some of their ideas are recorded in the annual reports of their institutions. With the possible exception of Dr. Isaac Ray, head of Butler Hospital, Providence, Rhode Island, and an expert on medical jurisprudence, no intellectual contribution made by American psychiatric leaders was comparable to that of their counterparts in Europe or of their American predecessor, Benjamin Rush. American psychiatrists were deeply indebted to European thinkers for their basic theories, and most of their more significant medical beliefs were of foreign origin. The Americans owed their reputation mainly to their ability as organizers and administrators of hospitals that practiced the latest techniques of treatment.

In 1844 they organized the Association of Medical Superintendents of American Institutions for the Insane (later the American Medico-Psychological Association and now the American Psychiatric Association). A few months before it was founded, the head of the New York State Lunatic Asylum at Utica, Dr. Amariah Brigham, published the first American psychiatric journal, the *American Journal of Insanity* (superseded by the *American Journal of Psychiatry*), which later became the unofficial and then the official organ of the Association. The articles and editorials in the *Journal,* along with asylum reports, books, and personal papers of psychiatrists, form the basic sources for the study of psychiatric opinion before the Civil War. The *Journal,* however, was not always representative of American psychiatric thought, especially after 1855, when Dr. John P. Gray, superintendent of the Utica Asylum, assumed the editorship. He held this position for thirty years. * Because he seldom gave a hearing to those who disagreed with him, several leading psychi-

---

* Strictly speaking, the *Journal* was edited by the "Medical Officers of the New York State Lunatic Asylum" at Utica, but the superintendent controlled its editorial policy.

atrists stopped contributing to the *Journal*.[4] Nevertheless, it, together with the Association, reflected and influenced the growth of psychiatry as a medical specialty on a national basis and fostered a common psychiatric outlook that John Galt, superintendent of the Williamsburg Asylum in Virginia, characterized in 1846 as "striking agreement, at least as regards essential points." [5]

This accord resulted from a number of other factors as well. First, there was the practice of appointing men with previous asylum experience to head new mental institutions.[6] The older mental hospitals in the East served as training grounds for psychiatrists who became superintendents of many of the new Western and, in a few cases, Southern institutions. The chiefs of the new asylums regarded the superintendents of older establishments as respected authorities and asked them for help in building, outfitting, and running their asylums.[7] A second reason was the desire of superintendents to present a common front on important issues in order to strengthen their recommendations to various legislative bodies. The third unifying influence was a commonly accepted philosophic, religious, and class outlook. Generally of middle-class origin themselves, psychiatrists were most often able to agree on broad theoretical issues whose assumptions involved conventional attitudes of the middle and upper classes. The differences of opinion that did arise concerned practical questions and in part grew out of different experiences in managing patients.

Although American psychiatrists' views on mental disease were generally similar to those of their British and French colleagues, divergent historical, political, and socio-economic forces led Americans either to take different approaches to subjects of interest to both Europeans and Americans or to be interested in different problems. European psychiatrists, for example, had little concern about the comparative susceptibility to insanity of Negroes and whites, a question of significance to Americans.

An important characteristic of American psychiatric thought in the mid-nineteenth century was the influence of religion. As a rule, psychiatrists tried to make their scientific theories conform to established religious beliefs. Those men who did not agree might be charged with being atheistic materialists. This conflict occurred primarily within the medical profession and only incidentally involved organized religion.[8] The line of argument generally adopted by American psychiatrists was determined in large part by their desire to convince the public and the general medical practitioner that insanity could be cured. Without rejecting the conventional philosophical and religious outlook of the middle class, psychiatrists sought to place insanity entirely within the domain of medicine and remove it from the sway of theology and super-stition. The success of the new psychological therapy seemed to chal-lenge conventional beliefs about the somatic nature of mental illness and slowly led psychiatrists to incorporate psychology into a largely somatic psychiatry. Experience with patients, as well as the influence of European thinkers, also encouraged many leading psychiatrists to broaden the scope of mental illness to include "moral insanity," a step that abounded in social, legal, and moral implications.

Psychiatrists found the inherent contradictions between the somatic approach to insanity and the psychological elements of moral treatment difficult to resolve, and after the 1840's they also were hindered by hav-ing to apply the new therapy under radically changing circumstances. The attempts to provide institutional care for the mentally ill of the lower classes, including masses of European immigrants, created addi-tional hardships for asylum superintendents and forced them to re-evalu-ate previously accepted ideas. In their new theories about national and class propensities to insanity, many psychiatrists revealed their social, religious, and national prejudices. These prejudices combined with social conditions and unresolved medical problems to produce an increasing emphasis on heredity as a cause of insanity. Along with this trend, discernible by the 1850's, came a gradual shift away from optimism about curability.

Prior to the Civil War, however, the prevailing mood in American psychiatry was optimistic. The well-known psychiatrist Pliny Earle expressed this attitude in the early 1840's when he insisted that a careful study of the past and present forced one to "acknowledge that, notwith-standing all the crime and wickedness of our day, the human race is never the less [sic] better—more virtuous, more benevolent, more philan-thropic, than at any former time." [9] By giving serious and sympathetic attention to the mentally ill, psychiatrists were part of the humanitarian reform movement of their day. Some of them had liberal ideas about religion, child-rearing, and education and supported causes such as temperance, prison reform, abolitionism, and training the feeble-minded.[10] They frequently took care of their patients seven days a week, lived in hospitals with them, entertained them at their homes, and were willing to sacrifice personal comfort and welfare for their benefit. Yet despite their faith in mankind, psychiatrists generally were not naïve or impractical; they were worldly, capable, and intelligent. Dr. Samuel B. Woodward, first superintendent of the State Lunatic Hospital at Worcester, Massachusetts, expressed the combination of humanitarianism and empiricism that characterized himself and his colleagues:

> Irritation, brutal force and punishment by severe penalties is [*sic*] not calculated to reform men! Insanity was rarely cured by whips and dungeons and chains! There is an obstinacy in the human character that is increased and rendered desperate by the injudicious attempts to effect reform, and especially if injustice be added to cruelty. This remark is not less true in application to the sane and insane mind.[11]

2

Basically practical men with difficult jobs, American psychiatrists from 1825 to 1865 were not primarily interested in theory, particularly not in the field of psychology. They did not adopt a systematic psychological theory; they did not discuss psychology in a systematic way. The majority of them had an essentially Lockian approach, although they also took elements from other theories of psychology—which was the province of philosophers until the nineteenth century. Locke's influence is seen in psychiatric acceptance of sensationism and associationism. According to Locke, the mind was filled with sensory experiences, not innate ideas; an association of ideas was formed in order of their reception in the mind.[12]

The common practice of placing a furious maniac in solitary confinement in a dark room was related to the theory of sensationism. By reducing or eliminating light and sound, as well as human contact, the patient supposedly would be subdued, for the body was conceived of as a mechanism that acted in response to external excitement. The removal of these stimuli also meant that the patient would have no basis for association with previous unbalancing experiences. Associationism justified sending patients to asylums where they would be prohibited from seeing friends, who might be connected with disturbing memories.[13] Asylum superintendents did not endorse all of Locke's ideas. They disagreed, for example, with his conception of insanity as a state in which the patient reasoned well from the wrong premises.

Although Rush had valued the theories of David Hartley,[14] who is considered the founder of associationism as a doctrine,[15] few medical men in the United States seemed to be familiar with Hartley's work. To remedy this situation, Dr. Thomas Cooper, the South Carolina medical professor, appended to his translation of F. J. V. Broussais' *De l'irritation et de la folie* an essay called "Outline of the Association of Ideas." According to Cooper, Hartley taught that the defective intellect of the idiot and the insane arose from "the irregular associations that take place in the encephalic apparatus, owing to the irritated and morbid state of that portion of the nervous system." [16]

Many American asylum superintendents began to think that the immediate cause of insanity often was morbid irritation of the nervous system rather than inflammation of the blood vessels, as Rush's followers had assumed.[17] This change owed little, if anything, to Hartley's associationism. Instead it reflected the influence of general medical theories of irritation that were popular in the early nineteenth century. It also reflected the need for a new theory to justify psychiatric emphasis on sedatives and techniques that strengthened the body rather than the old depletive methods. The origin of these ideas, however, are not clarified in the writings of psychiatrists, who were no more successful than their eighteenth-century precedessors in describing the actual physiological process that produced mental derangement.

Some American psychiatrists, most notably Gray, accepted the Scottish "common sense" or realist school of faculty psychology, which influenced many physicians and academicians in the United States and Great Britain until late into the nineteenth century. It was developed by Thomas Reid and Dugald Stewart to counter Locke's theory that knowledge depended ultimately upon sensory experience and Hume's conclusion that no necessary correspondence between sensations and external objects could be established. In Reid and Stewart's view, Locke's theory of sensationism and associationism was analytical and atomistic; it seemed to contradict the traditional belief in the unity of the soul and denied the existence of innate faculties.[18] In addition, Hume's skepticism weakened faith in the existence of an external world and thereby all religious teachings. The Scottish philosophers contended that there was an objective reality; proof was the experience of history and the opinion of educated people. Man was endowed at his birth with various faculties, such as self-interest, duty, self-preservation, perception, memory, and moral taste, that gave him "instinctive" knowledge of proper ethical and religious behavior. He had freedom of choice between good and evil and was responsible for his acts as long as his reason remained intact. Scottish faculty psychology appealed to psychiatrists who were concerned with maintaining conventional moral and religious principles in their psychiatric approach.[19]

Others leaned toward phrenology, a faculty psychology that was influential in both its "scientific" and popular forms during the three decades before the Civil War. This theory of brain localization, developed by Gall and Spurzheim in Europe, was endorsed by such prominent American asylum superintendents as Amariah Brigham, Pliny Earle, Isaac Ray, and Samuel B. Woodward.[20] Phrenologists divided the physical brain into many areas, each responsible for a different behavioral, cognitive, or emotional trait. Any one of these regions might be improperly developed in relation to the others, or, like muscles, might be strengthened through "exercise" or atrophied through disuse. Insanity was one result of an imbalance of faculties. Although phrenology was condemned by the Scottish school as materialistic and as undermining the unity of the soul, its list of faculties resembled that devised by Reid and Stewart.[21] American psychiatrists of phrenological persuasion denied the charge of materialism. They insisted that phrenology did not reject the concept that the mind was distinct from the physical brain. They maintained that mind and brain were intimately connected but separate; the nature of their relationship was a mystery.

Brigham accepted both Scottish faculty psychology and phrenology without explicitly attempting to resolve the contradiction between them. A reconciliation can be constructed from his writings, however.

He agreed with Reid and Stewart that man had innate faculties that gave him knowledge of God and moral behavior.[22] But he went further and contended that God gave man enough faculties to contain all his knowledge, learned as well as innate. To Brigham, these faculties had a double aspect: They existed in an immaterial mind but could operate only through specific local regions of the brain, each region representing a particular faculty. God was the ultimate source of the faculties, but He functioned through natural laws, which, in the case of the brain, were phrenological. Thus, the metaphysical faculty psychology of Reid and Stewart was converted into a materialistic psychology that also gave a place to God.

To Isaac Ray, phrenology presented an alternative to Locke's sensationist psychology by establishing a correspondence of spirit and matter. He wrote:

> . . . Since Locke's attack on the doctrine of innate ideas, people have become so accustomed to attribute the phenomena of mind to the influence of habit, association, &c., that the *mind itself* seems to be entirely lost sight of, and practically, if not theoretically, believed to be what Hume would make it, a mere bundle of perceptions. From such a philosophy, which makes the most wonderful phenomena of our nature the mere creature of the material world, Phrenology delivers us, and presents in its place a rational and intelligible exposition of the mental powers, and shows their relations to the moral, organic, and physical laws.[23]

Belief in phrenology did not, however, necessarily rule out an associationist approach. Edward Jarvis, statistician, physician, and psychiatrist, discussed the faculties in phrenological terms, and then explained his theory of association: The imagination influenced the "associative faculty" and governed the entrance of ideas into the mind. This process could cause mental errors. Imagination needed the aid of the "perceptive faculty to correct it, and of the reason to control it. The *law of association* is a manifestation of [imagination's] power; circumstances, things and ideas are suggested according to their natural or artificial connections. The habit of associating them together gives them an affinity, so that they may rise up in the mind in the same series of thoughts." The associative and memory faculties, which reinforced old patterns of thought and action, were stronger than the perceptive faculties, which

were concerned with new thoughts and actions. There was, then, a conflict between the perceptive faculties, seeking to introduce new material
in terms of present circumstances, and the associative faculties, continuing to present old and often inappropriate images. The result was often
a "compound idea," made up of old experience similar enough to the
new to be suggested by it.[24]

Mixtures of the various approaches were not unusual. Practically no
American psychiatrist had a clear-cut theory of psychology; an adherence
to a conglomeration of Lockian psychology, common-sense philosophy,
and phrenology was common. Psychiatrists tended to distrust the theoretical systems of philosophers and to value clinical experience and
observation more than theoretical speculation. For knowledge about
insanity, Ray declared, Shakespeare and Molière were much more useful
than mental philosophers like Locke and Stewart, who confined themselves to sane minds and little else; observation was better than reading
books. Woodward wrote: "The results of the observation and experience of such men [as the Drs. Ferriar, Fothergill, Heberden, Tardieu,
and Cullen] . . . who have no theory to maintain, no prejudice to lead
astray . . . are the safest guide for the student or young practitioner
. . . while the speculations of the ingenious theorists may be read as
curiosities. . . ." [25]

Nevertheless, before the Civil War American psychiatrists, although
generally pragmatic in outlook, did not altogether succeed in fulfilling
Rush's command that physicians "assert their prerogative, and . . .
rescue mental science from the usurpations of schoolmen and divines." [26]
To the extent that they were interested in theory, if only as a way of
organizing and explaining observed phenomena, they were not intellectually independent of philosophers and theologians. Their ideas
about the nature of insanity were greatly affected by their philosophical
and religious convictions, which tended to hamper psychiatric progress
on both theoretical and practical levels. The changes that did occur in
American psychiatrists' thought resulted from their experience in treating patients and from the influence of European psychiatry, rather than
from systematic critical investigations of their own.[27]

3

American psychiatrists continued to share Rush's commitment to a somatic pathology. Despite lack of conclusive anatomical evidence, they all agreed that insanity was a physical disorder, usually a morbid irritation of the brain—rather than the stomach, as many French physicians still maintained. Opinion on the etiology of this condition was divided: Some believed it was largely psychological; others thought it was somatic; still others viewed it as a combination of both. Psychological factors could irritate the brain and cause physical disorder, which in turn produced the intellectual and emotional derangement that symptomized insanity.[28]

Psychiatrists often spoke as if insanity were merely a group of psychological symptoms. Sometimes this was just a convenient or shorthand form of expression, but not always. They had to deal mainly with psychological phenomena and frequently relied upon psychological therapy, so that, try as they might, they found it difficult to remain consistent somaticists.

Their attachment to somaticism led to a curious mixture of idealism and materialism. They shared the conventional belief in the existence of a non-material, eternal soul, which was equated with the mind and was thought to be separate from its physical agent, the brain. The immaterialist conception of the mind, a major tenet of Christianity, seemed to require a strictly materialist concept of mental pathology to free the immortal soul from the possibility of disease. If the mind was endowed with eternal existence, it had to be independent of a material brain, which could become diseased and die. Consequently, mental illness had to be essentially a material or anatomical phenomenon.[29]

Earle, in one of his lectures to physicians, declared:

> Were the arguments for the hypothesis that in insanity the mind itself is diseased tenfold more numerous than they are, and more weighty, I could not accept them. My ideas of the human mind are such that I cannot hold for a moment that it can be diseased, as we understand disease. That implies death as its final consequence, but Mind is eternal. In its very essence

and structure (to use the terms we apply to matter), in its elemental composition and its organization, it was created for immortality. Consequently, it is superior to the bodily structure, and beyond the scope of the wear and tear and disorganization and final destruction of the mortal part of our being.[30]

Brigham, who took a similar position,[31] believed that the impossibility of reasoning the insane out of their illusions and misconceptions was evidence of the somatic nature of the disease. If the mind functioned independently of the brain, "it would be natural to expect that mere mental derangement might be cured by reasoning, and by appeals to the understanding." Since this was not the case, it was fortunate that mental patients were "assigned to the physician, and treated for corporeal disease." [32]

Psychiatrists who were sympathetic to a psychological pathology could be charged by a fundamentalist like Gray with believing that the mind, by being susceptible to disease, was both material and mortal. In that case, Gray declared, mind and brain were synonymous and religion a fraud, a conclusion he could not accept.[33] An anonymous British reviewer, in the *Boston Medical Intelligencer,* indicated the strong prejudices against those who questioned the mind-body dualism, the spirituality of the soul, and presumably religion:

> The fashionable modification of this doctrine which lately made so much noise on both sides of the channel—namely, that the sum total of the organic functions *was* the soul, though couched under the term *life,* is now on its wane, even in France; but, whether from the fear of the priests, the eagle eyes of the press censors, or the prevalence of a more enlightened philosophy, we are unable to determine.[34]

Although conformity with religious principles demanded acceptance of a somatic pathology, there were other important reasons why American psychiatrists clung so tenaciously to this position. During the first half of the nineteenth century, scientists made great progress in establishing cause and effect relationships between organic pathology and disease symptoms. These correlations enabled more accurate and objective delineation, diagnosis, and treatment of specific diseases. The whole movement of modern medicine inclined toward somaticism in the narrow sense—a sort of mechanical materialism. The growing emphasis upon local pathology in medicine in general discouraged interest in psychological causes, pathology, and therapy. Psychiatrists, too, hoped to discover a relationship between bodily lesions and symptoms; then they could abandon their symptomological approach and treat the cause of mental disease.[35] To Pliny Earle, "the advocates of the doctrine of mental disease unaccompanied by physical lesion, either organic or functional," were "the metaphysicians *par excellence* of insanity." [36]

The subordination of psychological pathology to somatic pathology was crucial to the struggle against demonological and superstitious views of insanity. A consistently "immaterialist" pathology that did not envisage some sort of brain damage as the final cause of mental illness seemed to perpetuate supernatural explanations of insanity and to discourage progressive treatment. Again and again asylum superintendents, trying to convince the public of the value of mental hospitals, pointed out that insanity was subject to medical treatment and cure because it was a physical disease of the brain. The remarks of the superintendent of the Friends' Asylum were typical:

> Insanity, in its various forms and degrees, has its origin in some disturbance of the brain, either structural or functional—which disturbance may spring from either a moral or physical source. Let it arise, however, from which it may, the proximate cause producing the deranged manifestation of mind, is always located in the brain—and the disease should be viewed in the same light as any other malady to which the human system is obnoxious. This view of the subject, besides being in accordance with sound philosophy, and rendering the practical application of just principles of treatment comparatively certain, destroys the groundwork of that vulgar prejudice, which shrouding insanity in the mysticism of metaphysics, cuts off the hope of medical relief, and too often excludes the unhappy sufferer from that consideration and tenderness by which comfort is ensured, and commits him to the care of those, alike ignorant of his disease, and uninterested in his welfare or recovery.[37]

The only American psychiatrist who seemed to be seriously troubled by the mind-body dichotomy was Isaac Ray. His book, *Mental Hygiene*, touches briefly on the problem; he recognized that its importance arose from its theological implications. The fear of materialism, he declared, had prevented the new physiological and pathological findings from being fully accepted and fairly represented. Ray was probably referring to a discovery such as the fact that a time interval was involved in the transmission of nervous impulses. This seemed to refute the religio-philosophic tradition that the mind, being immaterial, sent messages to the body instantaneously, that is, independently of the physiological limitations to which material functions were subject. He thought both a materialist and an immaterialist concept of the mind presented difficulties. There was no observable mind without a brain, yet mental action appeared to be something more than a product of brain function. "It may be doubted if it is quite correct to consider the individual as composed of two things essentially distinct [mind and brain] both in origin and nature, instead of regarding him as a being endowed with various powers which, though serving each a special purpose, form an harmonious whole—a single, individual man." Ray could not explain this idea of the unity of man in any detail, but he felt that applying its logic to mental hygiene led to the principle that what "improves the physical qualities of the brain also improves, in some way or other, the qualities of the mind." [38]

European psychiatric specialists were not nearly so uniformly devoted to preserving the mind-body dualism as their American colleagues. Pinel and several other eighteenth-century European rationalists had been unconcerned about metaphysics and the immortal soul and viewed the disorders of the mind more scientifically.[39] They thought the mind, which was the mortal brain functioning, could be diseased. Later psychiatrists such as Cox, Crichton, and Arnold in Britain and Leuret in France rejected the idea, which was accepted in the United States, that insanity involved brain lesions. Observing that hardening and other signs of damage were found almost exclusively in the brains of persons who had been insane for a long time, they concluded that brain lesions were a result rather than a cause of irrationality.

A more extreme view, abandoned by "enlightened" physicians in England by the 1830's,[40] but popularized in Germany by Heinroth for another decade, disregarded somatic pathology; illness was seen only as a disorder of the immaterial mind. Heinroth, noticing that no lesions or disorganization were found in the brains of many persons who died insane, insisted that moral depravity alone—sin, guilt, and evil conscience—produced insanity. When sinful indulgence and want of mental discipline gave the evil tendencies in man's nature dominance and destroyed all powers of restraint, insanity was the result.[41] Although this position in itself did not necessarily involve a theological viewpoint, Heinroth, a mystic, believed that God inflicted insanity as punishment for a sinful life. Many American, British, and German psychiatrists thought this approach was retrogressive and could result in renewed pessimism and cruelty toward mental patients. They feared Heinroth had gone too far. His theory seemed to buttress the moralistic attitudes that physicians had been trying to counteract among the public since the time of Rush and Pinel.

4

Divergence from the somatic approach in the United States was tentative at most and lagged behind European thought; some of the polemics in the *American Journal of Insanity* against the psychological or nonsomatic approach was probably directed against unconventional European psychiatric theories. Without abandoning their theoretical commitment to somaticism, many Americans moved toward accepting a psychological pathology. This trend was manifested in their observations that insanity could be cured by moral or psychological means alone. Brigham wrote: "Many cases recover without any medical treatment." [42] Dr. H. A. Buttolph, though placing moral means second to medical means, noted that in many cases moral therapy was either superior to medical therapy "or all that is required for the recovery of the patient." [43] Dr. Luther V. Bell, superintendent of McLean Asylum, agreed with the British psychiatrist John Conolly that a course of therapy that cured insanity without the use of medicine hurt "the pride of medical science." But, Bell wrote, if moral methods were that effective, they must be considered as "general medicines." He told Dorothea Dix that experience had convinced him that although "medical agents were of use in assisting nature to restore the mind by regulating the body," moral treatment was the essential treatment for insanity. No specific medical therapy for it existed: "The corporeal derangements, of which mental disease was one of the symptoms, were too numerous." [44]

This acknowledgment that patients might be restored to mental health through moral means alone conflicted with the view that the pathology of insanity was invariably somatic. If a somatic pathology was insisted upon, how could it be admitted that psychological means alone could cure insanity? One could, as Bell did, argue that there was not an inevitable contradiction. Just as psychological factors might cause, in some undefined way, a morbid condition in the brain, psychological therapy might affect, in a similar way, a cure. Bell wrote: "A state of mind capable of reacting favorably on the physical cause [of insanity] was attained mainly by moral influence." [45] Generally, American psychiatrists did not reason this way despite their belief in psychosomatic illness.[46] Their commitment to somatic treatment was too strong.

They tried to reconcile the inconsistency of their position by utilizing the concept of functional disorder. Pinel and his protégé and successor Jean E. D. Esquirol had used it to explain insanity in which lesions did not form. Pinel had quickly recognized that "the successful application of moral regimen exclusively, gives great weight to the supposition, that, in the majority of instances, there is no organic lesion of the brain nor of the cranium." [47] The absence of gross lesions or the inconclusive character of those discovered in autopsies led French physicians to conclude that a functional rather than an organic disorder had produced mental disturbance in those persons and that the brain could be acted on directly by psychological means.[48]

A leading British physician, John Charles Bucknill, objected that this theory had theological or metaphysical rather than scientific implications. If functional disorder, in contrast to organic disorder, entailed no changes in the brain, then functional disease was a metaphysical concept. All mental diseases had to be "organic," for all changes, or "dynamic modifications of vital functions" could not take place "without alterations of material organization." "Not a flashing thought or a passing feeling" could occur without accompanying changes in the living organism, even if no one could detect them. The simple difference between what had been called functional and organic disease was that in the latter, gross damage could be observed; in the former, scientific observation was not keen enough to discover alterations.[49] In effect, Bucknill claimed that the so-called functional disorders, although not visible or established by evidence and therefore a theoretical postulate, were no less somatic than lesions.

Bucknill's theory conformed to the current outlook in medicine, physiology, and neurology, all of which were then strongly anti-metaphysical. A standard text on physiology maintained, for example: ". . . mania or delirium probably never occurs, without the physical condition of the brain having undergone some change, directly or indirectly," although powers of observation were limited and pathological anatomy offered little data with which to form opinions. The same was true of apoplexy or paralysis, yet there was no doubt that the "cause is seated in the encephalon." [50] Similarly, adherents of phrenology also believed that all mental activity involved some material change in the brain. One phrenologically inclined physician noted that "a certain connection must necessarily exist between [the brain's] functional derangement and change in physical structure, according to all the known laws, which govern organic matter." [51]

Like Bucknill, American psychiatrists conceived of functional disorder almost invariably as a pathological condition of brain matter,[52] but in a way that enabled them to explain the efficacy of psychological treatment. By "functional" they did not mean "non-somatic," but "non-organic," a stage of disease that had not yet visibly changed the structure of the brain and still could be cured. Organic disease appeared when the chronic irritation of functional disorder was not treated and produced permanent modifications—inflammation, thickening, induration, or softening.[53] After this happened, mental patients seldom recovered.[54] This interpretation of functional disorder did not necessarily imply that it could be cured by psychological treatment alone, but psychiatrists inferred that this was so.[55] Dr. Charles H. Nichols, then superintendent of Bloomingdale Asylum, declared that medical means, though used predominantly during the first stages of mania, did not often produce cures. After a certain point the "resources of physic" were no longer effective, "partly because the brain [was] still weak from the shock of the acute stage of the disease," partly because some little irregularity of brain function was too "subtle" to be relieved by physical agents, and "partly

from habit, some obliquity of thought, feeling, or action [remained.]"
Medicine should be abandoned wholly or in part and replaced by moral
treatment.[56] If brain derangement were only functional, moral treatment could cure the condition by removing emotional irritants and per-
mitting—perhaps even assisting—the brain's natural restorative powers
to operate. Here, in effect, psychological methods could reverse somatic
changes of a minor order, before lesions had time to form.[57] This position allowed psychiatrists to preserve the essential somatic concept of
mental illness and to keep intact their belief in an immortal soul.

There was no clear, systematic discussion of these ideas in American
psychiatric literature. Psychiatric theory about pathology was generally
vague and ill-defined, mainly because of the pragmatic approach of American psychiatrists, the limitations of medical knowledge, and the difficulty
of reconciling somaticism with psychologism. Experience probably was
the primary factor in the use of moral treatment as a major and sometimes sole therapeutic technique. American psychiatrists were following
the latest fashion in European psychiatry, which was gradually discarding
the heroic medical therapeutics of the eighteenth century for milder
medicines and psychological methods. This trend paralleled the general
movement in medicine against the theoretical systems and depletive
remedies that were popular for hundreds of years. In psychiatry, unlike
other medical specialties, progress in treatment during the first half of
the nineteenth century surpassed knowledge. Psychiatrists had hoped to
arrive at an integrated explanation of insanity by relating brain lesions
to symptoms. But despite their success in studying delirium tremens and
general paralysis, they were disappointed by the difficulty of establishing, through pathological examination, the way insanity affected the
body. In most cases they really could not know the somatic changes
occurring in the brains of insane patients, so they were obliged to rely
upon psychological symptoms in describing the illness as well as in
treating it.

5

Symptomological description was not without its own problems. The
symptoms of mental illness were so numerous and varied that psychi-

atrists found it hard to define insanity, or—more specifically—to delineate the configuration of symptoms that indicated insanity. Earle asserted that defining insanity was an "impossibility." [58] This difficulty resulted in part from an increasing recognition of the complexity of mental disturbances. Psychiatrists agreed that insanity could not be described by only one symptom, and some even extended their concept to encompass hypochondriasis and hysteria.[59] European psychiatrists' delineation of new mental illnesses—such as general paralysis and "moral insanity"—helped to broaden the outlook of psychiatric specialists everywhere.

Dr. R. J. Patterson, chief of the Indiana Hospital for the Insane, noted that it was "difficult, if not impossible" to give an exact definition, but cited Brigham's attempt as being as good as any available: *"Insanity is a chronic disease of the brain, producing either derangement of the intellectual faculties, or, prolonged change of the feelings, affections, and habits of an individual."* [60] Similarly, Ray asserted: "Madness is not indicated so much by any particular extravagance of thought or feeling, as by a well-marked change of character, or departure from the ordinary habits of thinking, feeling and acting, without any adequate external cause." [61] Even psychiatrists who had insisted that intellectual disorganization must occur in all cases of mental illness and had rejected the idea that the emotions alone could become deranged admitted that emotional disorders might, in some cases, be the primary sign of mental disease.

Problems seldom arose about diagnosing irrational, violent, demented, or hallucinating patients. The raving maniac, the cringing paranoid, the town fool were recognized by psychiatrists as insane or mentally defective. The condition that Esquirol called monomania, or irrationality upon one or a few subjects, was widely accepted as a mental illness. Enlightened psychiatrists examined the total personality, not only the intellect: Did the patient show a sharp or gradual change of personality? Was the once kind man now suspicious or selfish? Did the happy person become morose; the gentle, violent; the cautious, extravagant? Did the old man undertake projects more appropriate for a younger person? Did the patient sleep well or fitfully; did he lose weight; did he fit and start, stare vacantly, forget easily, grin foolishly, or exhibit that undefinable expression common to the insane?

The most difficult cases to diagnose were those in which no observable intellectual impairment occurred and no obvious character changes appeared, but in which the actions of the patient were illogical, such as viciousness without any ostensible reason, murder with no discernible motive, or senseless crime involving no gain. To some psychiatrists such acts signified mental disease; to others, a vicious or criminal character.

Pinel, to his surprise, discovered some asylum inmates who acted like other mentally ill patients but seemed to suffer no derangement of the intellect or reasoning power; he called their affliction *manie sans délire.* Well-known physicians interested in mental illness—Esquirol, Georget, Gall, Rush, and especially the Englishman James C. Prichard, also a noted anthropologist—recognized the existence of such an illness. Prichard's classic discussion of the subject appeared in his *Treatise on Insanity and Other Disorders Affecting the Mind,* published in 1835. He gave the disease its English name, "moral insanity," as well as its most precise definition:

> The intellectual faculties appear to have sustained little or no injury, while the disorder is manifested principally or alone, in the state of the feelings, temper, or habits. In cases of this description the moral and active principles of the mind are strangely perverted and depraved; the power of self-government is lost or greatly impaired; and the individual is found to be incapable, not of talking or reasoning upon any subject proposed to him, for this he will often do with great shrewdness and volubility, but of conducting himself with decency and propriety. . . . His wishes and inclinations, his attachments, his likings and dislikings have all undergone a morbid change, and this change appears to be the originating cause, or to lie at the foundation of any disturbance which the understanding itself may seem to have sustained, and even in some instances to form throughout the sole manifestation of the disease.[62]

The concept that Prichard called "moral insanity" served as a catchall for many forms of mental illness in which intellectual powers seemed to remain partially or completely intact. Thus a patient suffering from monomania was rational on almost all subjects, but he often was considered morally insane. In this sense it implied that insanity and the ability to reason correctly might coexist in the same person. There was also an implication about moral or ethical behavior that attracted increasing attention from American psychiatrists by the mid-nineteenth century. Moral insanity was seen as an individual's emotional inability to accept society's judgments about anti-social acts. The morally insane might know that society condemned certain actions, but they themselves did not condemn them. In short, they displayed a warped sense of morality, despite their intellectual awareness of acceptable moral behavior.

The concept of moral insanity proved of great significance in psychiatric history, for it led to the concepts of neurotic character, psychopathic personality, and affective disorders; in medical jurisprudence it is still disputed. The significance here, however, is what it reveals about the basic beliefs of American psychiatrists during the mid-nineteenth century.

Before the 1830's this concept had encountered relatively little opposition, and in the United States, not much attention. Leading European and American physicians who were interested in the care of the insane had accepted Pinel's theory of moral insanity. A writer recently suggested that this happened because the cases cited by Pinel in support of his theory seemed to preserve the belief that all men possessed a capacity for moral action. If an insane person succumbed to an irresistible impulse, he still was thought to have an intact moral faculty, for he supposedly understood the immorality of his act although he was powerless to control himself.[63] However one interprets Pinel there can be no doubt that his successors extended the meaning of *manie sans délire* beyond an "irresistible impulse" or "ruling passion" that forced a person to act immorally against his better judgment. They thought that the morally insane person often possessed a deranged moral sense; he did not know right from wrong in the conventional way. Many of Pinel's contemporaries and successors—Rush, Esquirol, Georget, Prichard, Heinroth, and Hoffbauer, to name a few—apparently did not worry about the possibility that man's moral faculty might be diseased; in fact their writings and case studies indicated that they thought this could indeed happen.

In the decade following the appearance of Prichard's work, moral insanity became an important and controversial issue in American psychiatry. In the 1840's and especially the 1850's, many young men with a more thoroughgoing somatic orientation entered psychiatry and challenged its psychological elements. At the same time, the courts, feeling the effects of more enlightened public opinion, heard a growing number of cases in which the defense pleaded insanity, sometimes moral insanity. Psychiatrists were called upon as expert witnesses. When moral insanity became a public issue, they were forced to endorse it or reject it. An examination of their arguments reveals the extent to which theological, philosophical, and legal considerations influenced their attitudes. It also indicates the confusion among them about the definition of moral insanity. Some made it synonymous with "irresistible impulse"; others stressed the lack of a moral sense; yet others believed that both these and other elements were involved. A few could not surrender the criteria of irrationality and insisted that moral insanity, while predominantly a non-intellectual disorder, had to be accompanied by some intellectual disorganization at the outset or at a later stage.

Isaac Ray, one of the leading figures in nineteenth-century American psychiatry, staunchly defended the theory of moral insanity in his classic *Treatise on the Medical Jurisprudence of Insanity,* published in 1838. Ray agreed with Prichard that the emotions as well as the intellectual faculties were subject to derangement. In a later discussion he pointed out that before the 1830's the medical profession, like the general public, had believed that insanity took only two forms. In one, the patient was incoherent, noisy, violent; in the other, the patient's delusions were less severe, and he was calm and somewhat rational. But, he noted, psychiatrists had begun to recognize forms of mental derangement, such as moral insanity, that did not fit into the oversimplified definitions of the past.[64]

Two leading authorities on psychiatric history, Henry M. Hurd and Gregory Zilboorg, implied that Ray found virtually no support among his colleagues.[65] Actually, the contrary was true. The majority of the most original and outstanding pre-Civil War psychiatrists—Luther V. Bell, Amariah Brigham, John S. Butler, Pliny Earle, and Samuel B. Woodward—accepted the concept as confirmation of their clinical experience.[66] Even before Ray's book appeared, the resident and visiting physicians at the Friends' Asylum reported cases of moral insanity.[67] In general, the concept was embraced by physicians who were most committed to the practice of moral treatment, especially its psychotherapeutic aspects.

In giving a prominent place to the role of emotions in determining human activity, the theory especially interested psychiatrists who, partly because of their experience with moral treatment, were becoming more aware of the importance of emotions in human behavior and personality. Brigham wrote in 1844:

> We do not wish to undervalue the intellect . . . but we wish that all might realise the superiority of our moral nature over intellect itself.
>
> The intellectual faculties are but a part of our mental powers, and contribute but little in fact towards forming what we call the *character* of an individual. . . .
>
> Without these propensities or moral faculties, the intellectual powers would not be exerted at all, or but feebly. The stimulus or agency of the impulse of our moral nature, of benevolence, love, avarice, &c., impel men to action—to gratify these the human race have forever toiled.[68]

The brain, Brigham continued, could be diseased in such a way that the moral faculties become deranged, and the character and conduct of an individual might change markedly. In such cases the intellect remained helpless to resist impulses of an anti-social nature.[69] Here Brigham defined moral insanity as an irresistible impulse that the intellect knows to be wrong.

Dr. A. V. Williams, assistant physician at Bloomingdale Asylum, described a case in which the patient's illness resulted from a childhood disease that made him unfit for "self-government" or living at home. "It is one of those troublesome cases known as moral insanity in which the real condition of the patient might not be recognized at first unless under some special excitement." Williams thought that this patient—who was highly educated, spoke French and German, had studied medicine, was a sort of walking medical and surgical dictionary, and could "talk down a steam boat"—would probably spend his entire life in an asylum.[70]

Moral insanity did not necessarily result from disease or cause a marked change in character and conduct. Phrenologists could explain its appearance as the consequence of an inherited, insufficiently developed moral faculty,[71] and Woodward noted that moral idiocy might be manifested at birth.[72]

Dr. G. C. S. Choate, superintendent of the State Lunatic Hospital at Taunton, Massachusetts, indirectly indicated that many American psychiatrists at first accepted the concept. In 1859 he wrote:

> That the term [moral insanity] should never be applied to cases of mere vicious tendencies and habits, . . . unless accompanied by evident disturbance of the intellectual faculties, is a conclusion to which the opinions of most men who have made mental disease the study of their lives, are gradually, but surely, tending.[73]

More direct evidence of the popularity of the idea was given by Dr. Willard Parker, professor at the College of Physicians and Surgeons in New York City, at a forgery trial in which the defense pleaded moral insanity. In answer to a question about the prevalence of physicians' belief in moral insanity, he replied: "I have not the means of stating how general that opinion is; but my own opinion is that the mass of well-educated physicians entertain that view." [74]

6

During the 1850's, serious opposition arose within the psychiatric profession. Several leading asylum superintendents vigorously denied that a person could reveal insanity in immoral or anti-social acts while his intellect functioned almost perfectly. The younger generation tended to be more consistent somaticists and less fervent believers in moral treatment than the older generation of psychiatrists.

Among psychiatrists, the most influential and implacable foe was John P. Gray, who wrote:

> The general tendency of the doctrine of moral insanity is bad, whatever show or real feeling of humanity there may be in it. It is bad, in a religious view, because it tempts men to indulge their strongest passions, under the false impression that God has so constituted them that their passions or impulses are not generally governable by their will or their reason, and that, therefore, there is no punishable guilt in indulging them. This is fatalism. It is bad in a legal view, because it protects from due punishment

offenses which, with the self-denial and self-control that men rightly trained and rightly disposed are quite capable of exercising, might be avoided. It tends to give to bad education, loose habits, vicious indulgence, neglected parental control, and disobedience to God, an immunity from the prescribed penalties of crime, that is not warranted by the Scriptures, the law of reason, or any codes of human law that assume to be founded on the law of reason or the law of God.[75]

Gray insisted that the Bible did not look upon moral insanity as a disease. Cain, who killed Abel without good reason, might be adjudged morally insane by some, but God knew better and called the act murder, for which Cain was punished. Discussing a case of forgery in which the defense pleaded moral insanity, Gray called the plea a dubious apology for misconduct. He warned that if this kind of appeal could succeed, the time was not far off when every form of insanity, real or simulated, would be presented to ward off punishment.[76]

In Gray's opinion, shared by some of his colleagues, the excuse of moral insanity could be used in court only if the defendant were shown to be suffering from impaired reason.[77] On this basis Gray could preserve the sanctity of the law, for if a man were bereft of his reason, the issue of whether he was also morally insane would be of no significance in the courts, which at that time did not generally recognize moral insanity.

More secular-minded psychiatrists were also concerned with the social and legal consequences of accepting moral insanity as a legitimate mental illness. Dr. Thomas S. Kirkbride, superintendent of the Pennsylvania Hospital for the Insane and an authority on asylum construction and organization, did not believe that "gigantic frauds and startling crimes" were manifestations of insanity. He warned against "every attempt . . . to put crime on a footing with disease, or to confound [insanity] with recklessness, extravagance, and depravity of our race." [78]

Choate believed that licentiousness should not be confused with insanity. His asylum housed a few patients who were not insane, but who were accepted for safekeeping because their addiction to bad habits made them uncontrollable. Some of them appeared to have lost "in a measure their self control," and voluntarily committed themselves in order to be removed from temptation. Choate contended, however, that intemperance, unbridled licentiousness, or propensity to vice were not synonymous with mental illness.[79]

Although not fully accepting the concept, some psychiatrists did not wholly reject it either. For example, Dr. William M. Awl, superintendent of the Lunatic Asylum of Ohio at Columbus, commented that a patient who had attempted to kill an asylum superintendent belonged to a troublesome and mischievous class, "part mad—part knave and rather more than two-thirds downright old fashionedly wicked in heart and head." They also had this type of patient in his asylum, and it was doubtful "if an insane hospital is exactly the right place for them." [80]

Woodward, a firm believer in moral insanity, anticipated these arguments by asserting that, unlike mere depravity, it was always preceded or accompanied by "some diseased function of organs, more or less intimately connected with the brain and nerves." This could be detected by a physician acquainted with insanity, but not by a court or jury. The disease "is one of deep interest, and should not be dismissed hastily in the examination of those arraigned for crime or suspected of insanity." [81]

An extensive discussion of the subject took place at the 1863 meeting of the Association of Medical Superintendents of American Institutions for the Insane. Of the thirteen superintendents who ventured an opinion, five supported moral insanity and eight rejected it. Objections were made mainly on the basis of its legal and social implications. In fact, much of the disagreement so clearly involved non-medical problems that the validity of moral insanity as a medical entity was hardly debated. The real issue was whether psychiatrists should support it as a defense in court.[82] Dr. John E. Tyler of McLean Asylum maintained: "However much we might seem to differ with regard to giving an answer to a direct question as to whether we believe in this thing or that, if a given case were presented to us, there would not be a moment's hesitation . . . in declaring that the case was either insanity or not insanity." Superintendent Andrew McFarland, of the Illinois State Hospital for the Insane, said: "We are not differing so much in regard to the facts, as . . . to the propriety of using a certain term," which would give the public grounds for believing that psychiatrists were "contending that cases of enormous and extraordinary turpitude are kindred to disease." [83]

Insecure about their sociological role and afraid to flout public opinion and legal tradition, these men sought acceptance by supporting existing laws and prejudices; some of them even were willing to grant the courts the right to determine the valid criteria for medical insanity.[84] At the 1863 meeting Ray noted this tendency and admonished his colleagues:

> I am sorry to have seen here, as I have elsewhere, so much apprehension manifested as to the effect which our teachings, our doctrines, and our opinions, are going to have upon the popular voice. Now, gentlemen, it strikes me that this is hardly maintaining the dignity of our office. Before we can adopt any conclusion to which the facts lead us, are we to inquire how it is going to suit the jury, or the court; what the lawyers are going to make of it, or how it is going to strike them? [85]

Although the basic objections to the concept were moral and legal, some psychiatrists also raised theoretical criticisms, to which Ray replied in the *American Journal of Insanity*.[86] He expressed surprise that some of his opponents believed that the theory undermined the concept of the essential unity of the mind. It seemed to him that his strongest critics based their metaphysics on the Scottish common-sense school of Reid and Stewart, who recognized "sentiments and emotions as active powers coexistent with pure reason." Ray did not believe that approach precluded the possibility of moral insanity; if the mind had different faculties, emotion and will could become diseased as well as reason. He also denied the charge that the theory depended upon phrenology for its validity; on the contrary, he insisted, "we rely solely on the results of observation." [87] Nor could he agree that the concept was not a valid one because it might be difficult to determine when a person was afflicted.[88]

Ray correctly assumed that the popular Scottish common-sense philosophy influenced some of his critics. He did not give much attention, however, to the religious and ethical aims of this philosophy or to the threat that the theory of moral insanity presented to it. Like the Puritans, the Scottish school believed that with Adam's fall, man lost his ability for wholly rational thinking. In a sense, then, man was partially insane to begin with. The moral faculty guided him in ethical matters with a surer hand than reason, and it did not depend upon the intellect or learning. As American psychiatrists interpreted Scottish philosophy, man knew right from wrong independently of reason or experience. The Scottish philosophers wanted to establish moral precepts upon an infallible and never-changing principle independent of the vicissitudes of varying sensory experiences. The moral faculty became corrupted through the voluntary action of perverse persons. To admit that this faculty could become deranged involuntarily was to deny, in effect, that it was an absolute guide to action and that free will existed.

At the same time, according to the Scottish philosophers, if a person's intellect became diseased and he committed an anti-social act, he was free from moral responsibility and punishment because no one could tell whether he was morally corrupt or pure in heart. A sick brain might lead a person to go against his mind's desires or to act immorally even if he had morally good motives. This was the logic behind the acquittal of a defendant if he could prove that he had acted for morally pure reasons, even when his deranged intellect led him to break the law. For example, if murder were committed in obedience to the supposed command of God, some judges said the murderer should not be punished. But if the murder was done for gain, an insane defendant might receive the death penalty. As a recent student of common-sense philosophy has written of its moral outlook: "The disposition expressed in an action gives it its moral significance." [89]

The sometimes vehement nature of the opposition to Ray reflected the fear that the new concept might threaten social and religious stability, especially because it appeared to deny man's moral accountability for his actions. To an orthodox thinker like Gray, acceptance led directly to skepticism and uncertainty in religion and ethics, if not to atheism and anarchy.[90]

By 1866 Dr. W. S. Chipley, superintendent of the Eastern Lunatic Asylum at Lexington, Kentucky, estimated that the theory of moral insanity, though still "advocated by many honest, capable and faithful observers," was "repudiated, as a false doctrine, fraught with great evil to society, by a majority of the practical psychologists, known to us to be gentlemen of fidelity, integrity and experience." [91]

Rejection also implied the denial of other non-intellectual disorders as mental illnesses. Some psychiatrists, for example, objected to the idea that alcoholism might be a mental disease. Besides fearing to encourage the drunkard to commit outrages because he would be immune from punishment, they shared the lay public's contempt and loathing for alcoholics and would not admit the possibility that some of them were emotionally ill and needed treatment.[92] Psychiatrists sometimes opposed the establishment of special institutions to treat alcoholics because they believed that alcoholism was self-imposed and could be self-cured if the inebriate was made to feel society's contempt. They did not think that he would be reformed in this way, but they hoped that at least others might be discouraged from turning to drink.

Since a moralistic attitude toward alcoholics has prevailed among both laymen and physicians through the middle of the twentieth century,[93] it is perhaps more significant that several mid-nineteenth-century psychiatrists did recognize that some forms of intemperance stemmed from mental disorder.[94] Woodward even worked to establish "asylums for inebriates." [95] It was probably easier to have a more clinical approach to alcoholism than to moral insanity because of the difficulty of distinguishing moral insanity from viciousness. The alcoholic was a more sympathetic figure than the morally insane patient and had sometimes led an exemplary life until some tragedy or crisis drove him to drink. Excess drinking seemed to involve anti-social actions less often than moral insanity did. Besides, the morally insane person usually showed no remorse or repentance for his misdeeds, while the alcoholic could be most contrite and even energetic in his efforts to overcome his affliction.

7

Although American psychiatrists increasingly recognized the importance of the emotions in personality and behavior and for a time accepted the idea of deranged emotions as exemplified by moral insanity, they did not adhere to a "romantic" or "mystical" concept of human life. Their kind of mysticism involved belief in God and a mind-body dualism; it did not carry over to the nature of man as a whole. Most of them agreed with Earle, who wrote: "Wherever and whenever the rational and the irrational are brought into antagonism, the former, if it have time to accumulate its forces, and direct them to the best advantage, invariably obtains the victory. It is mind that governs." [96] This approach ran counter to the new trend among American intellectuals that stressed the non-intellectual if not the irrational aspects of life. In this regard psychiatrists remained closer to what has generally been considered the scientific tradition of the Enlightenment than the romanticism that won so many artistic and medical converts in Germany before the 1840's and that was expressed most fully in the United States in transcendentalism. Psychiatrists gained some insight into the non-rational nature of human behavior, but they did not look upon this discovery as an indication of man's incomprehensibility. They thought emotions could be trained to serve socially desirable ends and remain under the domination of the intellect. The way to understand man was by analyzing his behavior.

Yet, much as they tried to let their ideas evolve from their clinical experience, American psychiatrists were troubled if their conclusions contradicted established opinion, especially as opposition to unconventional theories grew both within the profession and outside of it. Actually, they had never been wholeheartedly committed to the efforts of continental thinkers like Condorcet and Cabanis to remove religion from the study of man. When psychiatric theories impinged significantly upon society's dominant moral and religious beliefs, they modified them. After the spurt of psychological therapy in the first half of the nineteenth century, strict somaticism gained more and more supporters as an approach to etiology, to treatment, and to pathology. The concept of moral insanity declined in influence with the passing of the pre-Civil War generation of psychiatrists. The succeeding group was in many respects even less adventurous and original, and step by step abandoned its predecessors' practices and ideas. As the next two chapters show, the optimistic spirit that was stimulated by the eighteenth-century rationalists reached its peak by the 1840's and then, under various pressures, slowly gave way to doubt and pessimism.

C A U S E S

1

Nineteenth-century American psychiatrists were certain—in theory, at least—that insanity was a physical disorder of the brain that manifested itself in psychological symptoms. They were neither sure nor unanimous about what caused this disorder, and their ideas changed with time. In their efforts to understand insanity and to treat and prevent it, they spent years searching for and analyzing its causes. Until the 1850's they thought that almost any imbalance or stress—mental or physical—could produce insanity, that is, act injuriously upon the part of the brain concerned with mental processes. The causes they described were mainly psychological and environmental; theoretically, most of them could be eliminated by manipulating the environment or by proper education. Although psychiatrists worked with a long list of causes, they gradually recognized that many of them were really symptoms. Partly because they found it increasingly difficult to classify causes, they slowly modified their belief that mental derangement depended upon the conjunction of predisposing with precipitating causes. In one patient what appeared to be predisposing seemed in another to be precipitating.[1] They also observed that similar factors did not always produce insanity, and they concluded that the disease depended on the peculiar structure of the individual brain as much as, or possibly even more than, outside forces impinging on the brain. Cause, then, could be conceived as a given set of internal conditions or a structural pattern. By the 1860's, this type of cause—seen mainly as hereditary predisposition—assumed great importance in American psychiatry. It was thought possible that persons with such a predisposition would succumb to insanity as the result of the ordinary process of maturation. In more sophisticated form, these theories of causation are found today in the literature of psychology. One author writes that in behavior there are "predisposing conditions and elicitating stimuli, the former having dispositional consequences over some period of time, the latter having immediate and observable consequences." Another has presented the thesis that "input is never into a quiescent static system, but always into a system which is already actively excited and organized." [2]

For most of the pre-1865 period the viewpoint expressed by Dr. Worthington of the Friends' Asylum was more or less typical. Basing his opinions on his clinical experience as resident physician and superintendent, Worthington doubted that the healthy person suddenly became insane; it seemed more likely to him that the disease had underlying or predisposing causes that had been generating for years. The source of the illness was lack of education in religion, morality, and self-control, "which are the surest safeguards against the evils of life." If a man did not have adequate training in an occupation, he might become concerned about making a living; this anxiety could lead to mental instability. Successful men, on the other hand, who were driven by a desire for wealth or "preeminence" and excited by business fluctuations, overtaxed their brains to the point of incurable or fatal disease. Reading works of fiction, "often of a positively immoral tendency," was also bad, for it stirred the imagination at the expense of reason and judgment. Passions were stimulated to overactivity, which could distort ideas of people and objects; this loss of contact with reality engendered a suspicious, misanthropic, and perhaps insane mind. Mental illness also could arise from lack of proper exercise or relaxation and from inadequate, irregular, and hastily eaten meals.[3] Worthington and his colleagues in other asylums placed considerable emphasis upon training children in self-control and self-denial in order to prevent mental disease.[4]

Not all American psychiatrists shared Worthington's stress on the "moral" or psychological causes of insanity. Gray, the chief spokesman for a rigid somaticism, maintained that when he could obtain the relevant facts, he found that only physical conditions produced insanity. He distrusted a psychological approach to etiology because it might undermine the theory of somatic pathology and imply the necessity of psychological therapy, which he considered metaphysical and non-medical. Besides, it was much easier to control physical forces. The subtlety of reasoning and the knowledge required to manage fifty patients suffering from religious insanity, for example, would be beyond the capabilities of physicians. "To discover, then, under such supposed moral causes, that the true source of disease lies in physical disorders, is equivalent to substituting rest, sleep, food and medication for moral reasonings and difficult and vexed theological problems, and thus to bring the case within the range of medical skill." [5] In his distaste for the complications inherent in psychological therapy, Gray no doubt expressed a powerful consideration in favor of a psychiatry without psychology.

In a survey of American psychiatric literature of the past hundred years, Henry Alden Bunker confuses etiology with pathology in nineteenth-century psychiatric thought and states that Gray's views on etiology were predominant in American psychiatry from its earliest years until the 1890's.[6] Actually, however, the first asylum superintendents sought to expand the psychological element in psychiatry. The scientific study of local pathology in medicine emerged as a weapon in the hands of those opposed to psychological psychiatry in the 1850's, but it was not until after 1865 that a more rigidly somatic approach to etiology became common. Before then most psychiatrists believed that insanity could be a psychosomatic disease; in their etiological theories they did not duplicate their strictly anatomical view of pathology.[7] At times they seemed even to forget the somatic pathology. Just as they might refer to insanity as if it were only a psychological phenomenon, they might speak as if psychological factors could directly produce mental derangement without first somehow affecting the brain.

The phrenological conception of the brain provided for psychological as well as physical factors in the development of inborn faculties. The congenital or acquired weaknesses in the structure of the brain might predispose some persons to insanity; in turn, these strengths and weaknesses could also be influenced by the external environment—both physical and psychological—to produce or to prevent mental illness. Woodward, Ray, Brigham, and other phrenologically inclined psychiatrists thought this was the key not only to a correct understanding of mental processes, but also to a means of preventing and treating mental disease. Congenital brain deficiencies and the consequent possibility of insanity might be avoided by eugenic procedures—the mating only of mentally healthy persons. If this proved impossible, one could strengthen congenitally weak faculties by education, for example, so that they would not succumb to derangement. Re-education could be used to cure insanity by encouraging the patient "to understand his own character organization and to participate in suppressing the overactive organs." [8]

Phrenology also countered moralistic attitudes toward human weaknesses. The individual could not be condemned for being the product of natural laws over which he had no control.[9] The criminal and the mental defective—synonymous terms to some phrenologists—were the products of inheritance and environment, not of sin, moral corruption, or vicious character. Many phrenologists with advanced views about social questions shared Woodward's attitude toward crime:

> The views of society on this subject, in my opinion, are wrong. Crime is often the effect of circumstances, but little under the control of the culprit, so much the consequence of strong propensities which early education has not subdued or regulated, but which in innumerable instances have been fostered and encouraged [by poor education or the example of parents' behavior]. . . . I ask, are not the circumstances which have brought him [the criminal] where he is, and which have made him what he is, in any degree extenuating? [10]

Those who rejected phrenology found this viewpoint difficult to accept, but in general all psychiatrists agreed, especially during the 1830's and 1840's, on the crucial role of environment in mental illness. They particularly stressed the effect of socio-economic forces on the emotional and physical condition of the individual. The growth of industry and rise in business speculation, the influx of immigrants, the struggle over Negro slavery, and the attempts to care for the mentally ill of the lower classes brought socio-economic conditions to greater prominence in psychiatric thought.

2

Psychiatrists believed that the advance of civilization harmed the psyche by complicating man's life and multiplying the demands made upon him, an idea common in both the United States and Europe. Progress heightened mental, emotional, and physical stress, thereby increasing insanity. Societies that were economically and politically competitive—and unpredictable—seemed to be fraught with new dangers to mental health. A few psychiatrists attributed the rise in asylum populations during the first half of the nineteenth century to a growing public awareness of the curability of insanity,[11] but the majority of them believed that civilization was a basic cause.[12] Their interpretation of civilization, however, is not always clear. To some, perhaps most psychiatrists, it signified a highly developed intellectual and cultural life in an atmosphere of political freedom. At times, however, many of them stressed the appearance of industry, the rise of an impoverished working class, and the growth of cities as the main characteristics of civilization.[13]

In a long article in the *American Journal of Insanity* Edward Jarvis presented a detailed discussion of the relation of civilization to insanity. He declared that civilization gave rise to new causes. Throughout history certain factors such as suppression of secretions, convulsions, hydrocephalus, old age, rheumatism, and hemorrhoids had led to mental illness. But industrialization, a product of advancing civilization, increased the incidence of mental disease by raising the number of occupational accidents and by exposing human beings to noxious minerals, acids, gases, and paints.[14] The psychological conditions that generated insanity in advanced societies were even more important. According to Jarvis and other psychiatrists, the varied economic and intellectual opportunities in democratic, competitive societies like that of the United States produced uncertainty, anxiety, instability, and mental disorder, in contrast to static despotic societies, which engendered mental stability. They believed that insanity usually occurred when frustrations were greatest, and in a fluid society those who failed to achieve their highest ambitions were subject to keen disappointments and possibly mental illness. Education might mitigate the effects of economic and political democracy, but for the most part the freer a society, the greater the forces leading to insanity.[15] This was not a new idea; Rush and other physicians of his time wrote about it.

Lacking positive statistical proof that insanity in civilized nations tended to increase out of proportion to population growth, psychiatrists pointed to the alleged infrequency of mental illness among primitive peoples. Jarvis, who analyzed the available statistics of insanity and found them inconclusive, referred to the statements of Esquirol and Humboldt and the "general opinion of writers, travellers, and physicians," that insanity "is seldom found in the savage state, while it is known to be more frequent in the civilized state." Brigham reported that two physicians working among the Cherokee Indians had never seen a case of insanity in a Cherokee; "an intelligent Chief, a man now 80 years old," said the same. Africans also rarely suffered from mental illness, Brigham wrote. "Cinques, and other of the *Amistad* Negroes, when in this country a few years since, visited the Retreat for the Insane at Hartford, Ct., and . . . informed [Brigham] that insanity was very rare in their native country." [16]

Despite the lack of reliable statistical evidence,[17] psychiatrists claimed not only that mental disease was on the rise in the United States, particularly in the northeast,[18] but that this country, the world's most advanced nation, had the highest rate of increase. Some European colleagues agreed.[19] A few superintendents questioned these claims. Kirkbride attributed the apparent rise in insanity to increased efforts in seeking out, diagnosing, and institutionalizing the insane, especially the poor.[20] He did not mention that probably many cases that were previously considered borderline were more likely to be sent to hospitals in the 1840's and 1850's. In 1856 Gray commented that the ostensibly alarming increase was the consequence of the inadequate system of caring for the insane poor. According to New York State almshouse superintendents, only one-third of the insane poor in New York State were admitted to asylums in the thirteen years before 1854 and *"during the year 1854 but one in every seven received any further treatment than mere confinement."* [21] The implication is that lack of proper care resulted in an increase in the number of insane who would have recovered if they had received active therapy.

The widespread belief in the alleged concentration of mental disease in the northeastern states, which were the most urbanized, probably stemmed in part from the greater interest in insanity in that region. No extensive investigation was made of the conditions of the insane in the southern states, and both census reports and physicians' estimates listed relatively low numbers of mental cases there. Nevertheless, most New England psychiatrists did not question the supposed high rate of insanity in their section. They attributed it to various causes, such as urbanization, cultivation of the arts, luxurious living, political democracy, climate, and heavy immigration. Dr. James Athon of the Indiana Hospital for the Insane thought that perhaps New England had a higher proportion of mental disease than the newer states because the insane "rarely emigrate, and consequently the number accumulates in those States which have been settled the longest time." [22] He did not explain the reports that there were more insane in the North than in the South.

Southern physicians took satisfaction in the alleged greater incidence of insanity in the industrialized and urbanized North and pointed out the virtues of the southern way of life. Dr. Stanford Chaillé, a prominent New Orleans physician, commented in 1858:

> It is not strange that the medical writers of Northern climates should have endeavored to prove, that the greater number of insane in their respective countries, is attributable to the greater degree of refinement and mental culture prevailing therein; and to establish the law that insanity increases *pari passu* with civilization. We [in the South] entertain the hope and belief that those means which are admitted, even at the North, to be so conducive to the restoration of the insane to health, may have something to do with protecting those who constantly enjoy these blessings from

this terrible affliction. These blessings are, abundance of exercise in the open air at all seasons of the year, a mild and equable temperature, an agricultural life, and the absence of all those exciting *"isms,"* so highly appreciated by *educated ignorance.*[23]

Even in the North the misery, crime, and ignorance associated with early industrialism led some physicians to condemn cities as centers of corruption and breeding places for insanity. The editors of the *American Journal of Insanity* asserted that insanity was "most general among the subjects of vice, frailty, and want," and that this fact was related to the high rate of incurability among urban dwellers.[24]

American psychiatrists shared the old Jeffersonian prejudice that rural life was healthier than urban life. This conviction was associated with the idea that everything man-made, complicated, and not of nature was corrupt. "The farther we depart from the simple habits and customs of our ancestors," wrote the superintendent of the Vermont Asylum for the Insane, "the more shall we prepare for the introduction [of insanity]." [25] This approach, though predating Puritanism, conformed to the Puritan suspicion of easy living. Psychiatrists thought practically everything that enhanced life was injurious to mental stability. Drinking, sex, smoking, snuff, novels, poetry, drama, imaginative thoughts, study, financial speculation, and luxurious living in general were either positively harmful or became so if indulged beyond "moderation." [26]

The role of sex in producing mental illness was given little attention, especially in comparison with its predominance in psychiatric thinking after the appearance of Freud's work late in the nineteenth century. The influence of repressed or insufficiently satisfied sexual urges on mental illness was seldom examined, with the significant exception of hysteria in young girls, for whom psychiatrists often prescribed marriage. If sexual factors were considered in more serious mental disorders, it was usually in the context of overindulgence. The hidden "vice" of masturbation was most frequently singled out as an important cause of insanity. It supposedly debilitated the patient's physical and mental capacities so that he would easily succumb to grave physical and mental illness. The evidence offered for this belief included the observation that many mental patients had practiced onanism before becoming ill and that excessive indulgence in sexual intercourse, as in nymphomania, often led to insanity. When physicians could find no other cause of insanity they frequently attributed it to masturbation. Almost everyone thought this practice so harmful and sinful that numerous popular tracts were written warning young men and women of its perils.[27]

At least one psychiatrist wrote of the danger of repressing normal human impulses. McFarland declared that "exuberant nature" revolted against "the error of the age," which suppressed, discouraged, and dwarfed healthy desires for enjoyment. There was nothing wrong with Germans drinking beer on the Sabbath, nor with the Englishman's liking for the race course, the regatta, the cricket ground, and the boxing club; it restricted the population of the lunatic asylums. In contrast, the sedentary British artisan, forced by his poverty to celibacy and denied the costlier amusements of the wealthy, suffered from "secret vices that gnaw . . . in the hidden recesses of the soul" and caused mental illness. McFarland believed that "so long as we have no national amusements whatever, so long as mirth and sport are considered exclusively as puerilities, so long as the college is without its gymnasium, and its traditional sports, and the school-house has no well-trodden play-ground, so long as man is an iron-bound and close-riveted [sic] dollar-grinding automaton, which bends every movement at some false shrine of morality or respectability, just so long will the wards of American institutions" be full of such mental cases.[28]

3

Advancing civilization supposedly induced greater intellectual activity, another commonly cited danger to mental health. The old idea that excessive use of the mind could produce insanity was still widely held in the nineteenth century. For example, Jarvis believed that civilized societies bred mental illness by greatly rewarding those who quickened their pace of life, and particularly those who expended mental effort or became proficient in special subjects.[29] "In countries where there is the most intelligence and freedom," wrote Brigham, "there will be found the greatest mental activity, and the most cases of insanity." [30]

The editors of the *American Journal of Insanity* agreed with Herbert

Spencer that the body's vital energy was limited and should be distributed between physical and mental activities. They quoted, approvingly, from Spencer: "Everyone knows, too, that excess of bodily exercise diminishes the power of thought" and vice versa.[31] The farmer's life was assumed to be more wholesome than the city dweller's because the farmer's activities and physical labor insured a better balance of nerves and muscles.[32] Even in the nineteenth century most psychiatrists also continued to believe that persons of great talent or genius—who presumably used their intellect or artistic sensibilities to excess—succumbed to insanity more often than others.[33]

It was also thought that in some ways insanity developed mental power. A slight attack sometimes stimulated mental activity, which exercised and strengthened the brain. Earle believed that insanity heightened the faculty of poetical composition, and he cited poems written by patients who had shown little or no poetic inclination before they became ill. The fantastic delusions of the insane indicated how greatly insanity intensified the imagination, an essential ingredient of poetry. Cowper wrote his best poems after his first attack of insanity. The only difference between a poet and a maniac was that the poet knows that his world of images is imaginary and can annihilate them at will, while the maniac is convinced that they are real and is incapable of destroying them.[34]

Some psychiatrists had reservations about the idea of occupational susceptibility to insanity. Although agreeing that sedentary occupations could cause disease, Woodward suggested that intemperance brought on mental illness in outdoor workers and that the search for wealth was the true villain in many other cases. In general, he thought, insanity depended upon temperament and early training rather than occupation.[35] Choate reported on a statistical study of the occupations of approximately six hundred patients at the State Lunatic Hospital at Taunton, Massachusetts. The results indicated that the proportion of persons who had been in occupations supposed to be relatively free from mental strain was about the same as those engaged in work usually considered hazardous to mental health.[36]

Ray believed that progress brought tensions that produced insanity, but he did not agree that increased mental activity—unless immoderately prolonged—caused it.[37] Nor did he think that excess excitement necessarily resulted in mental illness. For example, many psychiatrists maintained that exciting political elections often multiplied cases.[38] But Ray observed that there were few mental patients whose illness could be attributed to the emotional political campaign of 1856 and concluded that excitement had to be of a personal nature, combined with other factors, to produce insanity. These other factors included irregular eating habits, improper clothing, and loss of sleep.[39]

The same conditions supposedly were implicated in religious insanity. On this point most psychiatrists agreed with Ray that this illness could be attributed as much to neglect of food, sleep, exercise, and mental relaxation as to the passion aroused by concentrated religious thought.[40] The religious maniacs, Ray maintained, became mentally ill mainly because of a hereditary predisposition to insanity; their religious passion was the expression rather than the cause of illness. The prevalence of religious insanity was more apparent than real. Since most people, even the non-religious, received some religious training, they often exhibited insanity in a religious guise: ". . . the delusions of the insane do not spring out of the ground, but originate more or less remotely in their own mental experience; and this is the reason why the delusions of our patients are so frequently of a religious character." [41] Discussing this subject, McFarland wrote: "There appear to be two reasons why mental manifestations of the insane have so frequently a religious tinge. One is, that preceding every attack of insanity from constitutional causes, there seems to be a period when most individuals have an indistinct consciousness that something unusual is about to happen." The person searches for religious support, and when the disease takes hold, religion remains prominent in all that follows. "Another reason seems to be, that the insane mind has a natural affinity for the unseen and the mysterious." There was no evidence that the Christian religion produced insanity.[42] Nevertheless, most psychiatrists, including Ray, stressed the contributing role that religious excitement played in the production of insanity and suggested moderation in religious observance.[43]

Ray shared the common psychiatric belief that men could control the forces in society producing insanity. This ability, he thought, derived from man's imitative nature, his tendency to copy the mental and physi-

cal acts of other people. The most important influences in the formation
of character were not the moral teachings of the schools and churches
but the "thoughts, emotions, and impulses, awakened by the mental
movements around them [which] are often the efficient forces that determine the great events of life." [44] Horrible crimes did not always fill sane
people with loathing but sometimes excited "the same class of emotions
in which these very examples originated; and thus is accomplished the
first step towards a repetition of similar acts." The weak-minded in all
communities were most likely to be harmed by such examples.[45] Ray's
solution lay not in blaming those who controlled public communication
or in reflecting philosophically on the workings of the mind, but in
refining public taste by improving methods of education. He also believed that since the social environment contained many of the causes
of insanity, society must be reformed.[46] Brigham hoped that education
would make women and children, who were largely "without the vortex
of speculation and political strife," immune to these causes. Bell, fearing
that vice and misery were becoming rife in America as well as in the rest
of the world, had the same solution as Ray but did not know how it could
be achieved. He believed that Americans had much more will than intelligence and that while individual reforms were good and necessary, no
over-all principle existed to prevent misery in society. He called upon
Dorothea Dix to spend a year thinking and writing about her experiences, to help men learn how to eliminate social vice and misery.[47]

to much work 4

Psychiatrists also took account of the role of family life in mental illness.
Dr. John S. Butler, superintendent of the Hartford Retreat, said some
of his women patients were ill because of their husbands. Refusing to
provide hired help, these men had made the workload of their wives
unbearable by taking in boarders from nearby factories. At the same
time, Butler thought the heavy home responsibilities fostered the recovery of his patients because their families' need for them gave them strong
motivation to become well. No other contemporary psychiatrist discussed the relationship between motivation and recovery in such concrete terms. Butler was also unusual in attributing most mental disease

to unhappy childhood; he thought a happy home life was crucial to mental health.[48]

Dr. George Cook, superintendent of Brigham Hall, a private mental hospital in Canandaigua, New York, noted that children should feel that "there is a place for them in the home-circle, ever vacant in their absence, and which they are expected to fill; thus will be developed a love of home, the chief corner-stone of health and safety to the young." He accused fathers of being strangers to their children, of breeding distrust instead of confidence, and of neglecting their duty to guide children morally and intellectually. Without this direction children were shaped by the evil influences of their neighborhood. The religious hypocrisy of parents also had damaging effects; it fostered distrust of parents, religious skepticism, and weak character. The confused and misled child might eventually plunge "into the abyss of madness." [49]

Woodward was also interested in child rearing and wrote papers on the education and management of the young. He condemned corporal punishment and stressed that kindness and compassion were more effective in dealing with children—as well as criminals and mental patients—than severity and punishment. He believed that parents should teach young children self-control and high moral principles. Lack of this training could lead to crime, nervous diseases, and insanity.[50]

Other phrenologically disposed psychiatrists were concerned with child rearing because they thought that emotional health depended upon a "dynamic balance of motivational forces" that was responsive to education and environment.[51] It was commonly believed that early life could contain the seeds of a mental illness that emerged in adulthood; forcing very young children to study was particularly dangerous because it overworked a still delicate brain and upset its balance. In a book dealing with the influence of mental activity upon health, Brigham devoted much space to this topic—with strong warnings to parents [52]—and asylum superintendents' reports abound in similar discussions.[53] They chastised parents and teachers for their efforts to overeducate the young. Teachers appeared to think that in exciting the minds of students "they are exercising something totally independent of the body,—some mysterious entity, whose operations do not require any corporeal assistance," Brigham wrote.[54]

Their middle-class orientation led psychiatrists to suggest that over-emphasis upon intellectual attainments by the very young was a serious problem in the spread of insanity. Only a small number of children from the upper and middle classes could have suffered such abuse in the mid-nineteenth century. Impoverished city children—especially those of immigrant background—and children in rural areas often received no formal education, and many had only the most elementary kind. These children were not troubled by parents who wanted to turn them into prodigies; they were more likely forced to work in the fields or factories at an early age. Few psychiatrists expressed awareness of this difficulty or showed much interest in educating the children of the poor, despite the emphasis on education in preventive psychiatry.[55]

5

The concern with rearing upper-class children did not originate, as it might have a century earlier, in the theory that insanity afflicted mainly the upper classes. After Rush's time, it was believed that the poor had particular susceptibility. This reversal did not mean that asylum super-intendents thought the upper classes were no longer subject to insan-ity, but that the lower classes had a special propensity. The new idea quickly became so widespread among the well-to-do that psychiatrists had to warn them that the disease respected no persons and that in their own interests they should continue to support mental hospitals.[56]

Before the 1840's, psychiatrists treated few lower-class patients. Their practice was confined to the middle- and upper-class inmates to whom the few non-custodial mental hospitals usually catered. In the days before the founding of mental institutions, only the upper classes could afford doc-tors to care for them privately. In the late 1830's and afterwards the rapid crowding of the new state hospitals with impoverished patients shocked physicians into the realization that large numbers of the poor suffered from mental illness. They revised their theory that the upper classes, with their alleged sensibilities, ambitious drives, intellectual pur-suits, and luxurious living habits, were more prone to mental disease than other groups, who supposedly were too busy earning a living to engage in mentally disturbing activities.

A factor more difficult to evaluate in this change, but one of increasing significance as industrialization progressed and eighteenth-century rationalism declined, was the growing popularity among American psychiatrists of a belief that insanity was often the consequence of vice and moral frailty; both seemed endemic to the urban, immigrant poor.[57] The famous 1854 *Report on Insanity and Idiocy in Massachusetts,* compiled and written by Edward Jarvis and signed by an official commission composed of Levi Lincoln, Increase Summer, and Jarvis,[58] observed a close connection between pauperism and insanity. The commission believed the poor had unbalanced and undisciplined minds, which resulted in "loose habits of thought" that led to instability, failures, disappointments, then to poverty and insanity. They also thought that physical causes of insanity, such as alcohol intoxication, occurred more frequently among the impoverished. "Insanity is, then, a part and parcel of poverty; and wherever that involves any considerable number of persons, this disease is manifested." [59]

In 1859, Chipley advanced a theory that supported this approach: Although man was born with the will power to control his mind, this power seldom developed sufficiently without education and training. An educated person could recognize illusions for what they were and resist their harmful effects, but the ignorant poor became confused in similar situations and often succumbed to mental illness. "This internal power to control the action of the brain" was the key to modern psychiatric treatment according to Chipley. The effectiveness of moral treatment lay in large part in its practitioners' efforts to teach patients to resist illusions by the use of the will.[60] This argument presumably could support the idea that the growth of civilization, insofar as it resulted in educating the lower classes, lessened the incidence of mental illness; it also seemed that prevention lay in more widespread education.

Dr. W. Fisher of the Maryland Hospital for the Insane declared that recoveries in asylums occurred most often among upper-class patients. After moral and medical treatment, they seemed to recover their rational capacities "spontaneously" and gradually regained self-control. In contrast, the "poor and ignorant" usually became permanent asylum residents. The *Report on Insanity and Idiocy in Massachusetts* concurred that the poor seldom recovered.[61]

This pessimistic view did not necessarily exclude sympathy for the poor, especially if they were native Americans with some education and if immorality was not thought to be responsible for their illness. The closer the poor came to the standards of propriety set by the middle classes, the more sympathetically psychiatrists looked upon them. Ray and Brigham were among the few who discussed factors such as over-work and lack of exercise and amusements, and Choate thought that the constant struggle of the lower classes to raise their social and economic status produced mental illness.[62] An article in the *New Hampshire Patriot*—probably written by a physician, possibly by Bell—declared that the New England poor, in contrast to the poor in Europe, were worth restoring to sanity because they generally had some education as well as moral and religious training. New Englanders, however degraded, had "a foundation of moral and intellectual character" that encouraged attempts to cure them. The poor who were cured in Europe were "found hardly worth the labor and cost expended upon them." [63]

Woodward believed that human beings were the product of their edu-cation and circumstances as well as heredity; some of the most respecta-ble members of society might not have resisted the bad environment and temptations to which the poor sometimes succumbed. The rich and the poor should not be judged equally responsible for their behavior. The former were more culpable when they committed anti-social acts because they had less reason for doing so; the latter deserved special commendation when they did not become criminals.[64] Brigham, review-ing a book about "lunatics," remarked unfavorably on the author's mor-alistic attitude toward the insane. Sometimes the disease resulted from a vicious life, Brigham wrote, but most of the afflicted were worthwhile people.[65]

Other psychiatrists did not have such advanced views; they continued to believe that the poor became insane, in part at least, as a consequence of their vicious habits and corrupt morals. National and religious antipa-thies aroused by the emigration of masses of poverty-stricken Irish Cath-olics who crowded into the eastern cities and began to fill the state insane asylums strengthened these prejudices. Asylum superintendents and trustees were not exempt from the nativism of the pre-Civil War years. The 1854 report of the State Lunatic Hospital at Worcester noted that foreigners were so numerous that they practically excluded native Americans from the hospital. The latter were the "intelligent yeomanry of Massachusetts, who can afford to pay the cost of their board, and will not ask for charity." [66] In 1858 the report claimed that the Irish immigrant patients could not adapt to life in America. They looked for the most menial sort of work, gathered in hovels, lived in filth, and preferred "the excitement or solace of rum or tobacco to the quiet, intelligent influences of well-ordered houses." In prosperous times they received high wages and were "able at the cheapest rates to gratify vicious indulgences." Association with them was detrimental to mental health, and "it would be no wonder if the insanity of a highly educated and intelligent and refined person should be increased rather than cured" if brought into close contact with such "coarse," "filthy," and "rough" individuals.[67]

German patients, who made up the other large immigrant group, were usually discussed sympathetically. McFarland characterized them in positive terms: They were physically healthy, docile and affectionate under treatment, and grateful when they recovered. He assumed that the Irish in his institution, the Illinois State Hospital for the Insane, gave little cause for complaint because the troublesome Irish who filled the eastern asylums were too weak physically to go as far west as Illinois.[68]

The anonymous writer in the *New Hampshire Patriot* thought the small proportion of foreign born among the insane in New Hampshire was a point in favor of establishing an asylum there. Its citizens would "have the satisfaction of knowing that whatever sacrifices and expenditures are made for this object will be for the benefit of our own fellow-citizens almost exclusively." Other asylums "are overrun with paupers, for whom no sympathy or fellow feeling can be experienced other than which common humanity dictates; no conviction that in restoring them to reason we benefit ourselves, our posterity, or our country." [69]

Many psychiatrists felt like Choate, who was happy to report a reduction in the proportion of Irish patients in the Taunton Hospital and expressed a wish to send all Irish inmates to state almshouses. Dr. Henry M. Harlow of the Maine Insane Hospital suggested separate asylums for foreign and native patients; most of the foreign born at his institution were from the lower classes and not fit companions for Americans.[70] Dr. Merrick Bemis reported experimenting with the separation of foreign and native inmates at the Worcester Hospital. He wanted to classify them according to their religious and social backgrounds. The trustees approved his policy because they thought that segregating the Irish from the native born would eliminate the need for private mental hospitals to house the latter.[71]

The *Report on Insanity and Idiocy in Massachusetts* endorsed the concept of different institutions for immigrants and natives. Jarvis wanted to build a separate asylum for the state paupers who—unlike paupers supported by the towns—were primarily rootless foreigners. Since gradations among different classes in the United States were slight and even the poor might have education and refinement, he argued that native-born town paupers could be kept in one asylum regardless of economic status. Foreigners could with all propriety be sent to institutions for their exclusive care. Besides, the object of classification was to offer accommodations and companions that were similar to those the patients had known before they became ill. Therefore, the foreign pauper insane would not suffer with plain, cheap facilities and a smaller expenditure for their daily maintenance and management, and the native born would not have to be disturbed by them.[72]

Apparently Jarvis' prejudice was sufficient to prevent him from accepting his own statistics when they were favorable to the Irish. He noted that foreigners added fewer idiots to the population of Massachusetts than native Americans did and that the idiots constituted a very small proportion of foreigners whose minds were "defective or deranged." But, he explained, "there is probably a large portion of these native idiots who are children of foreigners, though born in this country." [73] Idiots were persons who had been born intellectually deficient. The mental disorders of the insane usually were acquired rather than congenital, and sometimes a considerable part of their intellectual powers were retained during their illness.

Ray criticized the *Report* for not combining the figures for the idiots and the insane. Because most people confused the two, he wrote, one could not be sure that those reported to the commission as idiots were not insane and vice versa. The separate figures showed that the proportion of native-born insane to the total native population of Massachusetts was smaller than that of the foreign-born insane to the total foreign population. This finding helped Jarvis to explain why Massachusetts seemed to have the highest total incidence of insanity in the United States: he could lay the blame on the foreigners. But, Ray argued, if Jarvis had combined the statistics, the proportion would be greater for native Americans than for foreigners, thus belying the assumption that insanity was more prevalent among the foreign born. However, even Ray seemed to have been affected by the nativism of the period, for he approved the *Report*'s arguments and recommendations for separate hospitals for immigrants. He thought that native Americans and foreigners had too much distaste for each other in normal life to get along well in asylums, where it was important to have a congenial environment. Foreigners would respond more favorably in hospitals run by their compatriots.[74]

Psychiatrists gave various reasons for the alleged high incidence of mental disease among the Irish. Jarvis ascribed it to poverty, lack of education, intemperance, inability to adapt to American conditions and customs, and the consequent discouragements and anxieties. Others mentioned poor adaptability as well as homesickness.[75] Choate thought that frustration of the hope of gaining wealth in America made the Irish especially susceptible to insanity. The disappointment that followed was too much "for their minds, uncultivated and narrowed as they [were] by education and religion." Other factors, according to Choate, were the physical effects of the long sea voyage and the change of climate.[76] Chandler attributed the large number of Irish in the Worcester Hospital to their "want of forethought" to save earnings in case of illness, their excessive indulgence in alcohol, and "their strong love for their native land." [77]

The Irish also allegedly had a low rate of recovery. According to Harlow, everyone who had experience with the insane Irish observed that "they, from some cause or other, seldom recover." [78] The few Irish patients who recovered in Bemis' asylum came from the "better classes." [79] McFarland found that all of his "stubborn cases" were Irish and wondered if something in their nationality led to an unfavorable prognosis.[80] A partial explanation, Choate thought, was the "broken-down condition to which the vices and privations incident to a residence in the metropolis" reduced so many of the Irish.[81] Other obstacles to their recovery were supposed to be the difficulty of obtaining their confidence and their problems in understanding "our language." [82]

Not everyone agreed that the Irish were more susceptible to mental illness and more difficult to cure than native Americans. Dr. Cutter, superintendent of a private asylum in Pepperell, Massachusetts, said that he had "always considered [the Irish] less liable to attacks of mental disease than others," since he knew of no Irishmen in his community who were insane. According to Kirkbride, the numerous Irish inmates at the Pennsylvania Hospital recovered as readily as others; Butler had the same experience at the Hartford Retreat.[83] The resident physician at New York City's asylum on Blackwell's Island, M. H. Ranney, found that many Irish patients recovered their sanity within six months of the onset of illness and noted the great value of moral therapy in their treatment. Before admission they had felt friendless and, if treated kindly in the asylum, responded very well.[84]

Ray remarked that the Irish poor, although disproportionately numerous in American insane asylums, were no more prone to mental illness in their own country than other groups. They filled American asylums because public charity was more easily available to them in the cities where they congregated than in their rural homeland, and they were not embarrassed to seek aid here. He believed that they were "preeminently incurable," but he did not know why. Perhaps the Irish who emigrated to the United States did not fairly represent their countrymen but included many chronically and incurably insane persons. It was possible that during lucid intervals many took advantage of their temporary sanity to migrate to "a more friendly shelter." [85]

Ray thought the treatment of Irish patients presented special problems. Attendants who understood the Irish and could approach them on their own level of expression were required. Otherwise, even if kindly treated they did not recover, for the "confidence of uneducated, superstitious, and impulsive minds, is obtained, not so much by discoursing of our good intentions, nor even by actual kindness of treatment, as by touching the inmost springs of feeling by means of the cant phrase, the playful allusion, and all those familiar turns of expression which are known only to the Irish native." Better results with Irish patients might be achieved in separate asylums for foreigners.[86] Chandler also commented upon the difficulty of approaching the Irish, who seemed "to be jealous of our motives." Ranney noted that the Irish in Blackwell's Island asylum appeared distrustful of kind words and relied on action as a trustworthy indication of the psychiatrist's attitude.[87]

6

The Irish shared their reputation for a comparatively high incidence of insanity with a group of native Americans, the free Negroes of the North. Widely publicized figures from the 1840 census indicated that free northern Negroes had a higher frequency of insanity than either the entire white population of the nation or the Negro slaves of the South.[88] Their freedom allegedly made them tenfold more prone to mental illness than Negroes who were slaves,[89] a belief that had widespread political as well as psychiatric implications.

When the 1840 census results first appeared, the facts seemed indisputable, and the only way of explaining the great proportion of free Negroes listed as insane seemed to be by assuming that freedom and a higher state of civilization, with all of its tensions and temptations, were especially conducive to mental illness among Negroes.[90] But the spectacularly high rate of insanity reported among northern Negroes convinced Jarvis, a statistician, that something was wrong. He investigated further and uncovered gross errors in the census figures. At his instigation and on the basis of his work, the *Philadelphia Journal of the Medical Sciences,* the *Boston Medical and Surgical Journal,* and the Massachusetts Medical Society issued analyses of the census that showed its unreliability. In 1845, a committee of the American Statistical Association, headed by Jarvis, challenged the accuracy of the statistics concerning insanity among Negroes and petitioned Congress to correct this part of the census.[91]

According to prevailing psychiatric theory, the northern Negroes might have been supposed to have a higher rate of insanity than the southern Negro slaves. At the same time it was believed that their comparatively uncivilized character—they were emancipated recently and only a few generations away from a primitive African culture—might guarantee better mental health for them than for whites. This advantage, however, could be offset by the poverty and anxiety that allegedly accompanied their freedom.

Despite the demands of psychiatric theory, discrepancies in the census figures were so glaring that it is understandable why Jarvis, an opponent of slavery, questioned their validity, especially since they furnished good arguments for pro-slavery advocates. In a critique of the census figures, he complained that the *Southern Literary Messenger* offered the uncorrected statistics as a "new reason for the conservatism of the peculiar institutions of the South." He feared that "this apparent exemption of the slave from one of the most terrible disorders that has visited humanity, and the ten-fold liability of the free black to the same, may become not only a fundamental principle in medical science, but also one of the elementary principles in political economy." [92]

Southerners were indeed quick to exploit the political and sociological implications of the census figures. The writer in the *Messenger* expressed the generally accepted view that insanity was "very often the result of evil, moral or physical, brought on by vicious habits and uncontrolled passions." The vast disparity between the insane Negro population of the free and the slave states was the consequence of "moral causes, arising from their situation and in no degree the effect of climate." He taunted the abolitionist "fanatics" about the crime, insanity, and immorality allegedly found among free northern Negroes. "General emancipation," he concluded, "would be attended with most injurious consequences to the country where it took place, and eventually prove fatal to the emancipated race." C. B. Hayden, also writing in the *Messenger,* attributed the low rate of insanity among southern Negroes to slavery, which gave them security, a simple, healthy mode of life, and an easy old age. In contrast, the free Negroes in the North were in a condition of "social helotage, constituting the pauper caste and the heirs of all the ills which poverty entails upon its subjects." [93]

Another well-known southern journal, *DeBow's Review,* told the "weeping philanthropists of the North" not to waste their sympathy on the Negro slaves, for statistics showed that they were better off than other Negroes.[94] Similar arguments were presented by the superintendent of the Asylum of the State of Louisiana at Jackson:

> . . . it is exceedingly seldom that our slaves ever become insane, . . . you will [therefore] agree with me that this fact is a striking commentary on the *pseudo-philanthropy* of some of our Northern brethren. . . . it cannot be got around, that [the slaves'] great exemption from insanity is due to their situation, the protection the law guarantees to them, the restraint of a mild state of servitude, the freedom from all anxiety respecting their present and future wants, the withholding (in a great degree) of all spiritous and drugged liquors, and all other forms of excess into which the free negroes plunge.[95]

Dr. Chaillé, the New Orleans physician, declared that this testimony made a southerner "feel indignant" at being so often "the object of wholesale vituperations," especially since there was prejudice against insane Negroes in northern mental institutions.[96]

In 1844 the southern spokesman John C. Calhoun, then Secretary of State, cited the census in detail to justify the Texas annexation treaty to the British Ambassador. He argued against the abolition of slavery:

> The census and other authentic documents show that, in all instances in which the States have changed the former relation between the two races, the condition of the African, instead of being improved, has become worse. They have been invariably sunk into vice and pauperism, accompanied by the bodily and mental inflictions incident thereto—deafness, insanity, and idiocy—to a degree without example; while, in all other States which have retained the ancient relation between them, they have improved greatly in every respect—in number, comfort, intelligence, and morals.[97]

Jarvis' fears had been more than realized. He confessed to Dorothea Dix that when he wrote his critique he did not think that "so soon would the second officer of our nation make such use of the falsehoods of the census —and produce such an atrocious piece of sophistry as Mr. Calhoun has, in regard to slavery & Texas." [98]

As might be expected, anti-slavery politicians did not accept the thesis that slavery protected the Negro's mental health and emancipation threatened it. Basing their arguments on Jarvis' findings, they claimed that the census returns were inaccurate. Northern representatives, led by John Quincy Adams, entreated Congress to grant the American Statistical Association's petition to correct the census figures on insanity and idiocy among Negroes.[99] Although Calhoun and others in Congress were well aware of the critical analyses made of the census, Adams' efforts failed. "It is too good a thing for our politicians to give up," one southerner was reported to have told Jarvis. "They had prepared speeches on it, which they could not afford to lose." [100]

A northern free Negro, James M'Cune Smith, discussed the argument raised by the census in three long letters to the *New York Tribune.* "It is a prevalent opinion that Emancipation has made the Free blacks deaf, dumb, blind, idiots, insane, &c. &c.," he wrote. The *Southern Literary Messenger* had "quite a pretty theory on the subject," based on the census, a theory that was demolished by Jarvis and others. "Freedom has not made us mad; it has strengthened our minds by throwing us upon our own resources, and has bound us to American Institutions with a tenacity which nothing but death can overcome." Smith noted that the number of Negroes in mental institutions in New York City was smaller than their proportion of the total population. It seemed that there was "less insanity, among the colored than the white population." [101]

Using the census to support slavery provided an effective argument because it seemed to offer scientific proof of the inferiority of Negroes. Southerners, and many northerners as well, considered the Negro ethnologically inferior, even though they differed in their estimate of the precise degree to which freedom precipitated mental illness.[102]

The discussion of this question among northern psychiatrists did not reflect a deep concern for the free Negro. As Chaillé was quick to note, northern asylums discriminated against Negroes. The superintendent of the Indiana Hospital for the Insane, Dr. James Athon, criticized the institution's policy of excluding them on the grounds that they were not legal citizens of the state. He said it was neither merciful nor philanthropic, and he deplored the prejudice of the people of Indiana, who advocated the admission of Negro patients to asylums but demanded that they be segregated from the whites.[103] After talking to various superintendents, southerner John S. Galt had "reason to believe" that some asylums refused Negroes "because of the odium which might consequently attach itself to the institution, or because of the want of some separate compartment." He said that Dr. William M. Awl, of the Lunatic Asylum of Ohio at Columbus, seemed to think that there were not enough insane Negroes in the North to require any provision for them in hospitals.[104]

It is clear, however, that neither Awl nor any other psychiatrist knew much about the situation. In 1863, Samuel Gridley Howe, head of the American Freedmen's Inquiry Commission, requested all asylum superintendents in the Union to supply information about the number of insane Negroes in their respective states. The replies indicated that the majority of institutions did not accept them; a few asylums in which Negroes were sometimes admitted had a ratio of one to several thousand white patients.[105] Some superintendents suggested that the census provided the only reliable information [106]—evidently they did not know that the 1850 as well as the 1840 census should be used with care [107]—and Kirkbride told Howe that insane Negroes in Pennsylvania and in many other states might be found in almshouses, not in asylums.[108]

Despite the lack of reliable facts, several superintendents estimated that there were probably few insane Negroes in their states.[109] Butler noted that during the twelve years before 1863, the Hartford Retreat admitted only five colored patients; he thought that Negroes' constitutional cheerfulness made them less liable to insanity than others. Worthington believed that the poor education and less civilized nature of the Negroes accounted for their supposed low rate of insanity.[110] These psychiatrists did not seem to see the contradiction in ascribing the lack of Negroes in their hospitals to their alleged general immunity to the disease and at the same time admitting that hospitals did not ordinarily admit Negroes.

7

As the years passed, psychiatric emphasis on cultural factors in the etiology of mental disease was combined with a growing concentration on the importance of heredity. In the 1830's and early 1840's, before large numbers of poor native Americans and Irish immigrants flooded the eastern asylums and at a time when optimism about curability ran high, American psychiatrists stressed environment or precipitating causes. They considered heredity only one of several predisposing factors that weakened a person's ability to withstand the secondary or precipitating causes. Earle expressed the still widely held opinion in 1848:

> According to our belief, wherever this natural condition [hereditary predisposition] exists, the person will retain the healthy action of his mind until he is subject to some other influence, more immediate, more active, more potent, and the tendency of which is to derange the physical functions of the system, so as to impair the manifestation of the mental powers.[111]

Some psychiatrists, who assumed that an exciting cause was essential, felt insanity could be avoided if a person's mode of life were wholesome, whatever his heredity. To support this contention Kirkbride reported that only 20 out of 176 patients of his had inherited a predisposition to insanity.[112] Although Brigham considered hereditary predisposition the most frequent cause of insanity, he wrote, in 1837: "In those born of insane parents, much may be done towards preventing the developement [*sic*] of the disease, by attending to their education, both physical and mental"; he also thought that many persons would escape the disease if they shunned liquor.[113]

Some years later, however, Brigham expressed a growing conviction among American as well as European psychiatrists when he suggested that the tendency of parents to transmit insanity to their offspring had "more influence in producing that disease, than all other causes combined." Most of the supposed exciting causes would be unproductive, he declared, if there were not an inherent constitutional tendency. He claimed that people predisposed to inherited insanity often had repeated attacks from different causes.[114] In 1845 Bates stated that close to half the patients admitted to the Maine Insane Hospital had a family history of mental illness; in 1861 Ray gave a similar report about Butler Hospital.[115] These estimates greatly exceeded Woodward's statement in 1837 that only one-third of the patients at the State Lunatic Hospital at Worcester suffered from hereditary insanity.[116]

By the 1860's many psychiatrists believed that most mental cases were primarily the result of hereditary predisposition. They emphasized heredity so much that at times the role of inciting causes was nil. In the Friends' Asylum there were over one hundred cases of insanity whose causes were indeterminate. Worthington took this as proof of the significance of remote or predisposing causes that created a constitutional tendency to mental illness. The strength of this propensity, which was generally inherited, might provoke insanity from slightly exciting causes or from none at all.[117] McFarland stated that continued observation of the insane led to the conclusion that special or exciting causes had "less weight in the production of mental disease in the mass of cases, than such as are predisposing or constitutional. What is frequently given by the unskilled observer as the cause of the disease, is merely one of its accidental manifestations." [118] In the 1840's Brigham had insisted that hereditary predisposition could not produce insanity without the presence of exciting psychological causes.[119] A decade later, his successor at Utica said: "The influence of the predisposition may be so powerful as to produce insanity, without any other apparent cause." [120] Kirkbride was almost alone in maintaining his original position as late as 1858. He wrote that hereditary predisposition existed "in a very small proportion of all the cases," and even where it did, a person who avoided excesses and had happy domestic and social relationships might be much better off than those who had no hereditary taint but led a less regular life.[121]

The outlook of the editors of the *American Journal of Insanity* was more common. They criticized as unscientific asylum reports that claimed that anyone, regardless of constitutional make-up, was subject to insanity. On the contrary, the *Journal* editors argued, the events and emotions understood to be exciting causes affected most people but precipitated only a few into insanity. Those who did succumb had a hereditary tendency; statistics showed that inherited mental disease was the most important single cause of insanity.[122] "The little yet known of the laws of heredity just suffices to indicate the immensely greater importance of transmitted influences in determining the physical and mental condition of man." [123] In 1869 Ray declared that more than nine cases out of every ten involved a hereditary factor, which operated even when no acknowledged hereditary predisposition existed and when the supposed cause was a blow on the head, sunstroke, violent fever, or alcoholism.[124] Earle thought that a "natural idiosyncrasy or peculiarity of constitution which facilitates the invasion of insanity" was enough to predispose a person; this inherited peculiarity probably existed in the nervous system, not, as Rush had believed, in the blood.[125]

Even if no ancestors seemed to have been afflicted with the disease, psychiatrists assumed that at some time in the past a forbear acquired a mental deficiency, excitability, or weakness. This idea resembled the old belief in the transmissibility of acquired characteristics; climatic effects, diet, and experience were supposedly incorporated into the body and passed on to descendants.[126] Psychiatrists also believed that these characteristics either disappeared or grew in strength from generation to generation, so that a tendency that began as an excitable or "nervous" temperament might lead to insanity several generations later. This concept is similar to the Frenchman Benedict A. Morel's theory of degeneration, which was developed in the 1840's and became well known in America by the 1860's. Expounding Morel's ideas in 1863, Ray tried to discredit the popular idea that a disease had to pass fully developed directly from parent to child if it were to be called hereditary. Morel showed that inheritance in humans, as in animals and plants, might involve the slow growth of mental and physical weaknesses by repeated transmission from parent to child, until the full-fledged mental disease appeared—a sort of evolution in reverse that gained a quasi-scientific credibility from Darwin's theory. Supposedly, the bad trait sometimes disappeared; this was nature's way of preserving the race.[127]

This approach provided support for the moralistic attitude toward the insane, particularly those of the lower classes, that appeared more frequently in the writings of asylum superintendents as the immigrant poor crowded into their institutions. Not only did their illness presumably derive from some bad and often sinful ancestral trait, but, according to some superintendents, it might have been avoided by leading a wholesome and regular life.

The belief that society created conditions conducive to mental disease enabled psychiatrists with liberal social attitudes to be less condemnatory. They placed ultimate responsibility for undesirable hereditary mental traits upon the environment instead of the individual.[128] Men like Ray, Brigham, Woodward, Jarvis, and Bell thought that modern society encouraged unhealthy pursuits and failed to educate people how to live properly. Those who inherited defective brains could not be "held to a rigid responsibility for the consequences of [their] misfortune," Ray wrote. Improved ventilation, sewerage, water supply, and measures to prevent tuberculosis, rickets, and scrofula—all of which led to poor inheritance—would do the poor and depraved more good than missionary tracts.[129] Ray counseled those with a predisposition to pay special attention to their physical health, but he believed that prevention lay mainly in eugenic measures, particularly since the frequency of familial insanity usually doubled in succeeding generations.[130]

In comparison with their European colleagues, some American psychiatrists were optimistic about curing patients supposedly suffering from hereditary insanity. Although the Europeans gave it a poor prognosis, leading American asylum superintendents, especially during their institutions' early years, believed it was curable as well as preventable. For example, in 1843 Bell forecast a good prognosis for patients with hereditary insanity because the disease was usually functional, not organic.[131] Nevertheless, after 1850 the increased emphasis on the role of heredity in the etiology of insanity indicated a growing pessimism about cure, particularly among psychiatrists working in the older eastern asylums, where the number of incurable patients steadily increased. Even if hereditary insanity seemed to present no special problems in treatment and cure, the predisposition was thought to be so strong that insanity could occur without precipitating causes or as a result of minor ones, so that frequent relapses were common. The patient could expect no more than a life on the borderline of sanity.[132]

As psychiatrists attributed more and more cases to hereditary predisposition, heredity and incurability became linked together. Hereditary predisposition was a catchall for cases for which causes could not be found and in which prevention and cure were almost impossible. It was, after all, tempting to pass the blame to the patient or his ancestors. This was especially true for the poor, who seemed to recover less frequently than the middle- and upper-class patients receiving better care in select corporate and private institutions. The gradual and subtle shift from almost unqualified optimism to a less hopeful attitude, noticeable in American psychiatry from the 1850's to the end of the Civil War and beyond, occurred in large part because the bright hopes about cure were not fulfilled.

THE PRICE OF AMBIVALENCE

1

Discouragement was just beginning in 1850, and it would be a mistake to characterize the mid-nineteenth century as a time of disillusion and defeat in American psychiatry. The widespread hopelessness about cure that persisted until the end of the Second World War did not develop until much later. On the contrary, from 1830 to 1850, confidence among many psychiatrists about the possibility of cure reached such heights that Albert Deutsch called it the "cult of curability." [1] Dorothea Dix began her great reforms in the care of the indigent insane, and moral treatment achieved its fullest use in the corporate asylums. Before 1825 asylum superintendents had been concerned mainly with organizing their new institutions, introducing the fundamental principles of moral treatment, and attempting to integrate these principles with traditional medicine. Afterwards, asylums expanded and improved their tech-

niques, abandoned others, and experimented with new ones in an effort
to find the best ways of managing patients.

In his classic history, *The Mentally Ill in America,* Deutsch wrote
about these hospitals:

> It is significant that the greatest reforms in the care and treatment of the
> insane in the first half of the nineteenth century lay rather in the substitu-
> tion of kind for cruel treatment than in scientific therapy. Even the most
> advanced hospitals of the day resembled well-conducted boarding houses
> rather than hospitals. They had little more to offer the mentally ill than
> food, clothing, pleasant surroundings, neat apartments, and perhaps some
> means of employment and exercise.[2]

The evidence does not support this evaluation. The care of patients in
the best institutions practicing moral treatment before the Civil War
went beyond "well-conducted boarding houses." In some respects—doctor-patient ratio and daily doctor-patient contact, for example—these
asylums had advantages over most mental hospitals of today. More
important, the early institutions achieved for a time, at least, a therapeutic approach similar to the one currently being introduced into
modern mental hospitals under the name of milieu therapy.

Perhaps the best way to show how moral treatment worked is by a
brief description of one of the best early American mental hospitals, the
Friends' Asylum at Frankford, Pennsylvania. Through a series of daily
diaries kept by the superintendent and supplemented by annual reports
and other documents, one may see in detail how moral treatment was
administered in an asylum well suited to its practice and strongly committed to its theory.[3] The history of the Friends' Asylum was distinguished by two main periods: the first, from 1817 to about 1834, was a
time of sectarianism and some experimentation; the second, from about
1835 to 1865, was one of extensive innovation and improvement in
moral management and marked changes in conventional medical practices.

At first only persons of the Quaker faith who could pay for their
upkeep were admitted. Even after the religious qualification was abol-
ished, the asylum, failing in its efforts to subsidize poor patients,
remained largely a middle-class institution. Each patient had a private

room, and common day rooms served as indoor gathering places; men and women ate in separate dining rooms. The Friends sought to create an intimate, or, as they called it, "family" atmosphere. Because the superintendent's administrative duties were light and the asylum population small—less than thirty until the 1830's—he and his wife, who acted as matron, and their few assistants became well acquainted with each patient. Convalescents were accepted into the superintendent's family circle; they ate at his table, visited his personal quarters, and spent much of the day in his office.

Believing the mentally ill to be more capable of rational activity, logical thought, and normal feeling than was generally realized, the asylum personnel attempted to show respect for patients and to inspire in them a sense of self-esteem. This attitude is revealed in the arrangements for eating, working, religious worship, and recreation. Patients ate with knives and forks that were not chained to the table, worked in open fields without fences or guards, frequently attended Friends' religious meetings in town, and walked and rode under a minimum of surveillance.

In addition to creating a pleasant environment, the asylum gave attention to the specialized needs of each patient and to the nature of his psychosis. The depressed inmate was cheered and his fears allayed; the volatile patient was humored to avoid "irritating" him. The superintendent sought to understand each patient's character and personality in order to treat his particular illness more effectively. Like many of their colleagues in other mental institutions, the successive superintendents at the asylum recognized the importance of interpersonal relations in the hospital, especially between doctor and patient, but scarcely appreciated the role of family relations in the cause and cure of mental disease.[4]

Grouping patients according to their behavior and degree of illness and providing occupational therapy were basic to the practice of moral treatment. For various reasons, however, the asylum did not adopt a satisfactory system of classification until the 1830's. Before then it had separated patients only by sex and extent of violent behavior. All patients were urged to work three or more hours a day, the men at farming and gardening and the women at household tasks. Labor supposedly diverted the mind from morbid thoughts, exercised the body, and helped to restore a proper balance between the physical and nervous systems. By inculcating the habits of regularity that the insane lacked, it also served to prevent idleness and sloth. Yet the asylum failed to employ all able-bodied patients, for many men regarded manual labor as degrading and refused to work. Women presented less difficulty; with little protest they sewed and knitted, shared in household tasks, and worked in the garden.

Until the late 1830's the asylum relied upon manual labor as the main therapeutic technique, but it also provided amusements to aid recovery and keep patients occupied. The staff was not only expected to be kind to the patients but to be "active in their employment and amusement." [5] Patients played ball, drove a circular railroad in the yard, took walking trips, rode in the carriage, visited local townspeople, and enjoyed watching the rabbits and other animals kept on the grounds. Male and female inmates frequently met at parties, on trips to places of interest in the neighborhood, and at religious assemblies in Frankford.

Although still required to follow asylum rules, convalescent patients enjoyed great freedom, received callers, and occasionally left the grounds to visit relatives and friends. This liberty made escape fairly easy. Those working outdoors escaped most frequently, for they were given considerable latitude of movement as both an incentive and a reward. The continued emphasis upon outdoor labor despite the frequency of "elopements" indicates its importance. The asylum's lenient attitude extended to the escapees themselves, who were not always punished; those demonstrating remorse usually regained their former privileges. Succeeding superintendents believed that this liberal policy, though resulting in repeated escapes, helped eventually to develop the patients' sense of responsibility and self-respect.[6]

Despite their belief in kindness as the most effective means of restoring mental health, the asylum staff considered restraint necessary at times. If cajolery, promises of privileges for good behavior, and appeals to honor and pride proved unsuccessful with unruly or violent patients, they might be threatened with various punishments—confinement in bed or a dark room, a strait jacket, hand and foot straps, or a cold shower bath. The superintendents did not use whips or chains, and claimed never to have struck a patient. Usually the patient's promise to behave saved him from punishment. One superintendent experimented with other techniques of control and at times succeeded in preventing outbursts and calming patients without using force.[7]

Like other American mental institutions the Friends' Asylum did not rely exclusively on moral therapy but employed orthodox medical treatment extensively and considered it auxiliary to moral management. Although placebos were occasionally given for their psychotherapeutic value, "resident" physicians and even lay superintendents usually applied medical means for their alleged curative effects on the insane's supposed pathological bodily condition. They bled, blistered, and cupped difficult patients repeatedly and often ordered low diets, drugs, cold and warm baths and showers, and occasionally electric shocks from a static electricity machine. Nevertheless, the asylum considered moral or psychological treatment as its chief curative technique regardless of any theoretical conflicts between somaticism and psychological therapy.

The years after 1834 saw many changes in both moral and medical treatment at the asylum. Partly because of a new non-sectarian admissions policy, the number of patients rose and better classification became possible. By the 1860's the patient population reached about sixty and the ratio of attendants to patients, one to four. The asylum had four divisions or wards for each sex. The superintendent wanted a finer separation of patients, but this was delayed many years.[8]

Inmates received increasingly varied and specialized therapy to suit their individual needs. Manual labor still proved to be "the most effective of the 'moral means,' for the promotion of a cure in the curable," and for making the incurables "more comfortable and contented." As an alternative to farming or gardening the asylum offered broom making, basket weaving, and carpentry. Many patients who resisted farm labor consented to woodworking, and in 1844 more than one-third of the asylum's male population engaged in some kind of manual labor; this was a considerable increase over past years. The women continued with their needlework and domestic chores.[9]

Innovations appeared in the use of recreational and educational therapy. "The more the sources of amusement and employment," wrote the superintendent in 1839, "the more readily are we enabled to meet the peculiarities of every case placed under our care" and effect a cure.

Social gatherings were encouraged and a stereoscope was donated for the amusement of the patients. At the superintendent's urging, patients organized a Restorative Society in 1838. This organization, he believed, would bring them under a system that combined employment and amusement and would expose them to the "powerful beneficial influence" of moral treatment:

> By association of the patients thus together, it was expected, (and we have not been disappointed) that they would act as a collective body in every employment or amusement set before them, rather than in their individual capacity as they had previously done; so that the industrious might stimulate the indolent, that the grave might check the boisterous, that the amiable might restrain the vindictive, and that the gay might cheer the sorrowful and divert their minds from any train of reflection likely to produce gloom and despondence.

Members fished, walked, threw quoits, played ball, and flew kites; every Friday evening they held a lecture or debate.[10]

Observing that many patients' intellectual capacities and interests could be stimulated, the staff encouraged intellectual activity. In 1838 a collection of books, maps, drawings, and natural history specimens was gathered, which became quite popular. Approximately half the inmates attended a series of chemistry lectures in 1841, and three years later a class was started for inactive demented women to encourage orderly behavior and awaken their interest in their surroundings. Successful experience with educational programs indicated that mental occupation as well as manual labor promoted the recovery of the curable and the comfort and well-being of the incurable.[11]

More liberal policies were adopted after 1834; by the 1840's and especially the 1850's, the asylum discarded almost all means of restraint. Superintendent Worthington noted in 1856 that even the milder mechanical restraints, such as "sleeves" made of soft material, had not been used for the previous six months; bed straps were employed only in exceptional cases. A few years later he wrote that he almost never ordered solitary confinement, painful medical means, or mechanical restraint because patients regarded them as punishments.[12]

In some respects conventional medical therapy changed more radically than moral therapy. With the increased emphasis upon moral therapy and the replacement of the theory of brain inflammation with that of irritation as the chief explanation of insanity, depletion was supplanted by measures to build up the patient's strength and to calm him with opium and other sedatives. The most advanced mental hospitals in the United States abandoned the old techniques; [13] this paralleled the general trend in medicine away from bloodletting and heavy dosing. The objectives of both depletion and sedation remained the same; to subdue the violent, excited, noisy patient; to cure the supposed pathological condition of the "brain and its members"; and to make the patient susceptible to moral treatment.

Even this sketchy description of treatment at the Friends' Asylum should make it evident that patients received more than good boardinghouse care. The asylum administration always used a therapeutic approach and in striving for cures it adopted and experimented with the most advanced psychiatric practices known.

The practice of moral treatment at its best involved psychological therapy that was costly and required considerable emotional commitment on the part of asylum personnel. The success of moral management at Friends' provided the greatest impetus to the introduction of additional psychological and humanitarian techniques and reduced reliance upon medicine. Year after year the asylum announced high percentages of cured patients—about 50 per cent annually, excluding those who relapsed. During the late 1830's and 1840's other hospital superintendents glowingly reported annual recovery rates of 80 to 90 per cent of patients brought in soon after falling ill, or 40 to 60 per cent of all patients admitted in a single year.

Until recently historians have tended to accept Pliny Earle's criticism that these recovery rates were inflated.[14] In 1956 an American psychiatrist, J. Sanbourne Bockoven, analyzed Earle's statistics and challenged his conclusions. Bockoven maintained that at the Worcester Hospital the announced recovery rate of approximately 40 per cent of patients admitted in a given year was, despite some discrepancies noted by Earle, substantiated by the evidence.[15] This is not the place to revive the controversy, but it does appear that Earle was overly pessimistic and did an injustice to his colleagues of former years. Although the whole question is complex and generalizations should be made with great caution, the evidence seems to show that under moral treatment at its best many more patients recovered than the 4 per cent Earle estimated.

In the early nineteenth century, when few mental patients had ever been cured and the majority of them were still confined to jails and almshouses, almost any number of recoveries would be cause for gratification. In 1819 the Friends' Asylum reported with pride that eleven out of thirty-eight patients had recovered during the second year of its operation.[16] In the 1830's, northern superintendents claimed that out of every one hundred recently ill patients admitted to mental hospitals, eighty to ninety or more could be and sometimes were cured. The millennium in psychiatry seemed near.[17]

There were warning voices. Bell, who distrusted statistics, wrote:

> As things now are progressing there is infinite danger that the public may arrive at such views and expectations as to the curability of insanity, as will eventually react most unfavorably on our successors in these holy, though arduous avocations, if not upon ourselves.[18]

Brigham disagreed: If the statistics showing high recovery rates had not been published, "several of the best establishments for the insane in the country" would not have been built. Perhaps some superintendents did exaggerate their success, he said, but this was necessary in order to stimulate the founding of new mental institutions.[19]

Statistics showing high rates of recovery also served as publicity for the corporate institutions in their competition for wealthy patients. Because these hospitals depended heavily upon private patients' fees for their income, they tried to solicit patients who could afford high rates. The striving for patients also encouraged a reduction in the use of unpleasant medical and moral means. Superintendents claimed to have abandoned rough methods, and their reports depicted their asylums as virtual vacation resorts. Some reports were so indecorous and roseate in their appeals that even Brigham was moved to criticism. They gave an impression, he wrote, "akin to that made by the puffs of Mineral Springs and Water Cure establishments; as if the various Lunatic Asylums were rival institutions endeavoring to attract customers." [20] This tendency seemed to have diminished in time. In 1855 Bell remarked on "the very great improvement in the style of [mental] hospital reports" away from the previous inclination "to run the race of self-glorification," a change he ascribed to the establishment of the Superintendents Association.[21]

2

The de-emphasis on restraint, especially in the better institutions, reflected the successful British effort to abolish the use of mechanical contrivances. The non-restraint movement, led by the English physicians Robert Gardner Hill and John Conolly, had become well known among both psychiatrists and interested laymen in the United States. Partly as a result of British influence, some American asylum superintendents introduced it. Brigham told Earle: "I have determined to try the disuse of mechanical Restraints *à la Conolly* & have hired additional help and got all . . . ready to cooperate and will earnestly and fairly try it." [22] Bell and Kirkbride also reduced restraint in their institutions, and the superintendent of the Insane Asylum of Louisiana reported favorably on the results of similar policies.[23] Study of the British system encouraged Worthington to eliminate restraint at the Friends' Asylum in the 1850's.[24]

The majority of American psychiatrists, however, continued to rely heavily on mechanical controls, and even those who came close to adopting non-restraint in practice refused to accept it in principle.[25] They insisted upon the right to use restraint when necessary, a position that most English advocates of non-restraint actually believed compatible with the acceptance of their system.

An 1846 article by Ray included most of the points raised in the American attack on the theory. He claimed that the British could employ non-restraint because five-sixths of their patients were quiet incurables; in the United States most patients had become ill comparatively recently and were more violent. He maintained that the British insane were growing less violent as the years passed, and cited a Glasgow asylum superintendent's statement to that effect. A more significant factor, however, was that the great majority of Britain's insane came from the lower class, and hospitalization relieved them of unremitting toil and suffering, provided kinder treatment and better food than they had ever received, and did not create family hardship, for they probably had been unemployed before commitment. Besides, in Europe class divisions were more sharply defined than in the United States, and the poor tended to be timid in the presence of superior rank represented by asylum personnel. "This feeling is seldom extinguished by insanity."

Ray also asserted that patients were no calmer in European institutions practicing non-restraint than in those depending upon mechanical means. European asylums had only a small number of morally insane patients, generally a very disturbing element. He suggested that these patients were more numerous in America because of its republican form of government.[26]

If Europeans were more docile patients than the freedom-loving Americans, why were Irish immigrants more violent in the United States than at home *and* more violent than Americans? Ray answered the first but not the second question. He said that Americans were characteristically restless, boisterous, and impetuous because of climatic conditions. These traits not only "favored the development of insanity," but also accounted for the fact that insane patients in the United States—particularly in the northern and eastern states, and regardless of national origin—were more excitable than those in Europe.[27]

In a paper "On the Care of the Violent Insane" delivered at a meeting of American asylum superintendents, Tyler justified his belief in restraint by maintaining that patients in New England were more violent than those in the western and southwestern states or in Britain. At another meeting McFarland declared that "unquestionably, latitude and longitude have much to do in modifying the excitability of the insane"; differences between the insane on the Atlantic seaboard and those in the Mississippi Valley might influence attitudes toward the use of restraint.[28]

Jarvis, a cautious man, was unwilling to accept his colleagues' sociological and geographical explanations. In 1860, discussing a recent trip abroad, he termed European psychiatry worthy of serious consideration. Widespread use of varied occupational therapies, frequent mixing of the sexes, the practice of keeping patients in common dormitories instead of separate rooms, and the tendency to discard means of restraint were regarded there as signs of progress. Americans had to discover, he suggested, whether differences between their practices and the Europeans' were based on the inherent character of the patients, and, if not, whether American mental institutions could profitably adopt some of the European techniques.[29]

Jarvis' approach was a refreshing change from the usual defensive, negative attitude of most American psychiatrists toward non-restraint. They regarded the unfamiliar characteristics of lower-class patients as a barrier to effective treatment instead of trying to adapt their techniques to these characteristics; they explained their inability or unwillingness to endorse non-restraint by making invidious comparisons between American and European patients. "Live Yankees," one wrote, could not be controlled by the same means used on the "canaille of France" or the "stupid pauper population of Great Britain and Ireland." [30] In effect, they made a virtue of the alleged greater violence of Americans by boasting about it as evidence of a more democratic society and by contemptuously attributing the quiet of European patients to their subservient attitudes. The "weakness" of European mental patients, however, evidently permitted the introduction of a more humane form of treatment. In time American superintendents found that a reduction in the use of restraint lessened the violence of even their patients.

The Americans of course gave other reasons for rejecting the principle of non-restraint. They said British advocates were guilty of hypocrisy and fraud; they contended that the true issue was mechanical restraint versus manual restraint and seclusion rather than restraint versus non-restraint. The Americans were unsympathetic to ideas urged upon them by foreign colleagues and lay reformers at home. They wanted no outside interference in their affairs.[31]

Although it is difficult to measure the importance of the opposition to non-restraint in dispelling the optimistic attitude of the 1830's and 1840's, it does not seem an exaggeration to say that the failure to adopt the principle of non-restraint was a major setback for American psychiatric theory and practice. This was an area in which American psychiatrists did not keep up with advances in Europe.

3

Perhaps a more important factor in generating pessimism was the limitation of moral treatment to the upper classes. The founders of moral management probably had meant it for everyone regardless of class or national origin, and later practitioners agreed in theory. But until the 1840's and 1850's—when many state governments built asylums for the poor, and the existing state hospitals began to fill with immigrant patients—only persons with financial resources could afford to enter hospitals practicing enlightened psychiatry. The lowest rates at the progressive corporate asylums continued to be prohibitive for most people, and fewer charity patients and wards of the state were admitted as more state hospitals became available. When the corporate asylums did subsidize patients, they chose, if possible, those of middle-class origin. Superintendents and trustees believed it was their Christian duty to make some provision for cultivated patients who had once been wealthy and for the hard-working "worthy poor," who might have owned small farms or stores or worked as self-employed artisans. For a brief time the admissions policy of even some publicly supported mental hospitals favored middle-class patients.[32]

As in the early days, the corporate hospitals practicing moral treatment usually gave paying patients better care and segregated them from other patients; those paying the highest rates received the best accommodations and special attention. The difference in this later period was that superintendents justified these conditions—which are common in general hospitals up to the present time—by the theory that moral treatment required a consideration of the background of each patient. They concluded that the educated and well-to-do should, as far as possible, have the luxuries and kinds of companions to which they had been accustomed in normal life. The following principles of patient classification adopted by the Bloomingdale Asylum represented the policy of most hospitals accommodating upper-class patients:

> The division of patients into classes is made according to the conduct, habits, education and station in life and state of mind. . . . In general, it

is attempted to place such individuals together whose society will, if possible, be of mutual benefit, or at any rate will be no disservice to one another.[33]

Even Woodward, who believed that the poor should be in the same asylum with the well-to-do, implied that the two groups received different treatment. The kind of care given to the "better classes is contagious, and reaches [the poor patients] and their attendants." [34] In his own hospital at Worcester, a state institution, patients from the middle and upper classes received special privileges. At the Friends' Asylum, where the superintendent believed that everyone should have equal treatment and accommodations, the poor were effectively excluded because efforts to subsidize them failed.[35]

Prior to the great influx of the urban and immigrant poor, middle-class and even some lower-class Americans benefited from moral treatment in the better public asylums built before the late 1840's. But these institutions could handle only a comparatively small number of the mentally ill; the mass of the insane poor still languished in jails and almshouses. Afterwards, with the establishment of numerous state and city asylums, superintendents were faced with the problem of extending moral treatment to the poor on a large scale.

As a group, psychiatrists—native-born, Protestant, and middle-class or upper-class in origin—could not free themselves from their prejudices about the poor, especially the immigrant Catholic poor, whom they neither knew nor understood. It was difficult to achieve the warm, close relationship, based on mutual respect between physician and patient, that effective moral treatment required. Some psychiatrists were not sure how much moral treatment the poor needed in order to recover, or if they deserved any at all.[36] A vicious circle developed. The poor and foreign born did not receive the same care as the well-to-do; since they recovered less easily, doubt about their ability to recover ensued, and fewer efforts were made to treat them therapeutically, which again reduced their rate of recovery and engendered further pessimism. Of course, it is possible that there were variations in the forms of mental illness according to the patient's social class and that the rate of recovery for upper and lower classes would have differed even if all groups had received similar treatment.[37] Unfortunately, this hypothesis was neither suggested nor tested.

In any case, as the publicly supported institutions grew to outnumber the private and corporate ones and to harbor the overwhelming majority of the hospitalized insane, the attitudes and experiences of the superintendents of the state asylums increasingly influenced the direction of psychiatric thought. It was particularly important for the preservation of an optimistic and therapeutic approach that these asylums be curative. Some of them were at first, but gradually they became mainly custodial; many were custodial to begin with. Psychiatrists were aware of this development and, though they did not like it, thought that institutions for the poor must inevitably be custodial. Bell, discussing the appropriate number of patients in an asylum, wrote:

> In institutions like those designed for the pauper and other insane of the State, where the great proportion of the inmates are received merely for comfortable and economical custody, and amelioration, there need be no particular limitation of the number to which adequate justice can be done. The best moral treatment can be most successfully applied to only such a number as the Director of the Institution can himself know thoroughly and intimately.[38]

However crucial a proper attitude on the part of psychiatrists was to the retention of psychological medicine and a hopeful spirit, it was by no means the only requirement. Even with the best intentions, they found that lack of adequate financial support made it impossible to practice moral treatment in most state hospitals. State legislatures wanted to build custodial institutions for the insane poor and subordinated all other considerations in the interests of economy.[39] Generally, state hospitals received operating expenses from fees paid by each patient's home county; county officials consistently tried to pay the lowest rates, often keeping mentally ill persons in almshouses and jails rather than sending them to state hospitals, where the cost was higher.[40] Opposition to building mental hospitals for the poor sometimes came from almshouse administrators, who used the insane as cheap labor.[41] Everyone agreed, Woodward commented, that almshouses were not the place for the insane, but when money was sought to give them hospital care, there were objections to the expense.[42]

The inferior physical plants and facilities, poorly-trained and insufficient staff, lack of land and equipment for the employment and amusement of patients, and, worst of all, overcrowding prohibited any attempts to practice moral management. Woodward's successor at the Worcester Hospital, George Chandler, believed that it was economical to house large numbers of poor patients in big institutions. Ninety per cent of the hospitalized insane were poor, and taxpayers were beginning to fret about paying high rates for their support. "Dollars and cents," he wrote, "are mighty in controlling the action of those who hold the destiny of the poor insane in their hands." [43] A committee investigating the conditions of the pauper insane in a Baltimore asylum commented that the practice of appointing temporary inmates as nurses and attendants was an economic measure, but it "also greatly reduces the chances for desirable curative results." [44] Leading psychiatrists warned that ultra-economy in an asylum, including the trend toward overcrowding, would lower the quality of mental hospitals and bring them to the level of poorhouses.[45]

With a few exceptions—notably Williamsburg Asylum, headed by Galt, and the Western Lunatic Asylum of Virginia, under Dr. Francis T. Stribling—hospitals in the South were particularly bad. Until the 1840's, southern asylums usually were designed for the violent and dangerous insane and often were headed by laymen. From the letters, reports, and public statements of superintendents, it is clear that the mental institutions below the Mason-Dixon line did not have facilities for middle-class and upper-class patients. They had to go North for better accommodations and treatment. For the most part southern asylums were pauper institutions lacking funds, proper facilities, and professional medical administration.[46]

Conditions in the northern public asylums were not uniformly unsatisfactory, especially when they first opened; even the asylums' later role as custodians did not mean a return to the harsh treatment of pre-Pinel days. Only a minority of the poor were admitted into the better state hospitals, but the thousands who were treated improved considerably. The evolution of patient care at the Worcester Hospital from 1833 to the mid-1850's typified in many ways the situation at the better state hospitals and indicates the kinds of problems that eventually made moral treatment a nullity even there.

What happened at Worcester is particularly significant because under the leadership of Woodward and backed by such men as Horace Mann and Samuel Gridley Howe, it was the model state mental institution in the United States. Woodward, who retired in 1846, was a highly respected and beloved figure in American psychiatry and a strong advocate of moral treatment. Under his administration the hospital tried to give therapeutic care to all but a comparatively few incurable violent patients. Even Woodward was sometimes repelled by these patients, who were mainly lower-class persons previously confined in jails and almshouses; he described them as vulgar and abusive.[47]

In the beginning many of the patients at Worcester were from the lower middle class and could pay a moderate fee. There were so many paying patients that Howe advised the asylum "to confer its benefits more exclusively upon the poor and destitute, and less upon those who have money and friends." [48] Ten years later the situation was reversed. The proportion of poor Irish immigrant patients in 1844 was only 10 per cent; by 1854 it had risen to 31 per cent.[49] The number of indigent, pauper, and criminally insane, many of them chronically ill, also multiplied, partly because of legislation designed to remove the insane from prisons and almshouses. The trustees—including Howe, who was no nativist [50]—complained that the presence of so many "incurable foreign paupers," mainly the uncivilized, brutish Irish, was "seriously impairing [the hospital's] usefulness as a curative institution." Native middle-class patients were so repelled by the Irish that they would not come, and the hospital became filled with immigrants and the criminally insane. Unless something was done, its benefits "will soon be denied to our native population, except to such as may be paupers or criminals." [51]

The trustees also blamed lack of funds, the decay of the physical plant, inadequate space, and overcrowding for the marked deterioration of the hospital. During Woodward's time, in the 1840's, these conditions had begun to undermine the hospital's therapeutic aims; [52] by the 1850's the situation became acute. Overcrowding was particularly serious. Equipped to house only 327 patients—the ideal number for effective moral treatment was 200 to 250—it was at times bursting with as many as 552,[53] with inmates swarming into the yards during the day and sleeping in the halls at night. Classification was most elementary. Individual attention by the superintendent was impossible, and physical restraint was used to ease the burden of overworked attendants. Worcester Hospital had become a place for the safekeeping of the mentally ill, with little opportunity for moral treatment. The trustees wrote in 1854: "Now, however high among kindred institutions [it] may have ranked, however excellent it may have been considered . . . it must be ranked low by competent and impartial judges." [54]

The opening of a second state hospital at Taunton in 1854 made little difference. The number of insane persons needing treatment was too great, and adequate staff, appropriations, and physical plant were not forthcoming for either asylum. Conditions at Taunton were worse than at Worcester. Built with minimum funds and planned to run on a minimum budget, it could never be more than custodial. The quarters for violent patients resembled jails with barred windows, insufficient light and heat, and no bathing or toilet facilities.[55] Even before it opened the staff seemed inadequate, the plumbing didn't work, and the oven wouldn't bake. Because the halls had no ventilating ducts, foul air had to pass through the patients' rooms. The grounds were a "waste of sand." [56]

Moral treatment did not have a chance in the crowded and poorly equipped public hospitals, and it is little wonder superintendents eventually despaired of curing patients. This pessimism lasted for a century. Until only a few years ago nearly all state hospitals, which still house most of the hospitalized psychotics, remained almost wholly custodial.

4

What of the fate of moral treatment in the corporate asylums, where conditions remained suitable for its practice? Though always in need of funds, these few hospitals did not have the acute problems of the public institutions. They were not overcrowded and understaffed; they did not have an "undesirable" clientele. Their superintendents could experiment more easily with a variety of therapeutic techniques, including educational and occupational therapy, non-restraint, and a degree of freedom. Yet, by the late 1850's there were signs that they were beginning to abandon some of the most touted measures of previous years and that optimism about curability was on the wane. At McLean Asylum, perhaps the wealthiest of the corporate mental hospitals, Bell discontinued mechanical and agricultural labor, an open-hospital policy for patients, and the mixing of the sexes at dances and religious meetings.[57] The increasing emphasis on heredity as a cause of insanity symptomized a feeling of discouragement. This concept helped to absolve the psychiatric profession of its inability to fulfill the claims of the 1840's about curing 90 per cent of new cases of insanity.

The dilution of moral treatment and the accompanying decline in optimism reflected a growing recognition that many cases of insanity were incurable. Despite the sizable achievements of moral treatment, it failed to attain the high rates of recovery that were anticipated. As proof of the alleged extreme pessimism that Deutsch contends appeared in the 1850's, Bell is quoted as saying in 1857: "I have come to the conclusion that when a man once becomes insane, he is about used up for this world." [58] Actually, this statement was unique at that time. The evident hopelessness about the curability of some patients, did not apply to all cases of insanity. Even in the public asylums established in the 1850's and 1860's—especially where none had previously existed—considerable optimism prevailed at first.[59] Bell's hopelessness, though anticipating a view that became widespread after the Civil War, exceeded that of his contemporaries. But if his remark represented little more than his own opinion, by the 1850's indications of disillusionment were appearing in the East. Understandably, few asylum superintendents openly proclaimed their declining faith. Their feelings are discernible in their statements about curability.

The Friends' Asylum may be used as an example again. Even though moral treatment flourished beyond the 1860's and non-restraint was introduced with success, the number of incurables rose to constitute the "great majority" of the asylum population as early as 1844.[60] The development of a less sanguine outlook is evident in Worthington's comments. Increasingly, in the 1850's and '60's he explained in the daily diary and annual reports why the recovery rate did not go much beyond 70 per cent even for recent cases. The theory that every case of less than one year's duration could be cured was incorrect, he declared. Incurables in the Friends' Asylum included about 28 per cent of all recent patients admitted since 1842; this figure made the asylum's reported recovery rate of 72.25 per cent of all recently ill inmates admitted between 1842 and 1851 about the best attainable. Worthington regretted that the presence of incurables prevented the achievement of "100 per cent of cures" among recent cases. Recovery could not take place even in patients who had become ill recently, he said, if structural changes had occurred in the brain as a result of inflammation or if general paralysis or emotions such as fear and grief had caused insanity.[61] His reports continually drew attention to the growing size of this group, whose presence lowered the over-all rate of recovery. He decried the public's and the psychiatrists' exclusive interest in curability and stressed the mental hospital's function of caring for chronically ill patients, a subject seldom discussed by asylum superintendents in earlier years. In brief, he sought to reduce public pressure and asylum competition for unobtainable high rates of recovery. Of course, the restoration of 40 to 50 per cent of all cases admitted each year and 60 to 70 per cent of recent cases did not warrant a hopeless view, and it would be an exaggeration to call the Friends' Asylum staff pessimistic at mid-century. Nevertheless, considering that psychiatrists had believed moral treatment was a panacea for mental illness, the puncturing of the curability bubble was cause for some disillusionment.

The disenchantment deepened. The indication of the fifties grew into a trend by the seventies, and by 1900 moral treatment was reduced to a minor form of therapy in the corporate asylums. Notwithstanding differences among hospitals and superintendents, the same forces eventually influenced all of them to devalue it. This happened so gradually and subtly that it went almost unnoticed in psychiatric literature. Superintendents worked mainly on a pragmatic basis and were not always logical in their theories; they showed little awareness that they were shifting their position. The story of this change, outlined briefly in the following

pages,* is not one of overcrowding, financial stringency, or social prejudice. Two other primary forces were at work in the corporate hospitals:
an apparent continuing decline in the recovery rate, which engendered
a pessimism deadly to moral treatment and led psychiatrists to search for
other kinds of therapy, and the influence of somaticism on a new generation of psychiatrists, less creative than the first and more interested in
making their specialty "scientific." Additional factors, such as the inherent difficulty of applying psychological therapy, the routinization of psychiatric techniques, and the bureaucratization of the psychiatric profession, as well as various community pressures, were involved but to a
lesser extent.

By 1877, when Pliny Earle first published his widely quoted critique
of ante-bellum curability statistics, some asylum superintendents had
begun either to look for a cure-all other than moral treatment or to
despair of ever finding one. Earle's work, which seriously questioned the
validity of the high rates of cure claimed by pre-war superintendents
practicing moral treatment, confirmed what post-war asylum chiefs were
thinking. By the 1870's the corporate asylums found themselves unable
to match their initial rates of cure. Earle explained the discrepancy as a
difference in statistical methods. The early superintendents exaggerated
their figures, he said; the comparatively poor showing of the post-war
period indicated greater care in gathering statistics. Moreover, the criteria for recovery—always a problem because it is difficult to tell when a
mental patient is cured or what cure is—had become more stringent.
Success with the insane had never been overwhelming, and the post-
Civil War figures were different only in their increased accuracy.[62] The
majority of physicians in corporate hospitals did not agree with this
interpretation. They were less willing to challenge the ability and integrity of the men whose pioneering work had gained national and international reputations for their institutions. Without denying that the early
recovery rates may have been magnified or uncritically compiled, they
saw a real disparity between their achievements and that of their prede-

* The analysis of the course of moral treatment through 1900 is made to complete the picture of moral treatment rather than to give a full description of post-1865 developments.
My remarks, based on psychiatric periodical literature and annual reports, should be regarded as tentative, although I believe they are valid. Further and more detailed research,
however, might modify this account.

cessors. In 1875 Dr. H. P. Stearns, superintendent of the Hartford Retreat, wrote that the recovery rate of 45.8 per cent for all admissions from 1824 to 1869 compared with 37.8 per cent for 1869 to 1875 supported this contention. He noted that there had been a steady decline in recoveries after Todd's death in the thirties.[63] Worthington stood almost alone in his later years when he declared that asylum statistics showing lower recovery rates were misleading. In his asylum, he wrote, curability remained the same in the 1870's as before; it seemed lower because more persons suffering from incurable brain disease were applying for hospital care and because alcoholics, who were easily cured, were no longer admitted.[64]

The apparent decline in recovery rates was not blamed on psychiatric techniques; it was explained by the theory that insanity was becoming more incurable. Why was this happening? Causes were changing or becoming more intense. Organic alteration in the cells, connective fibers, and blood vessels of the brain and spinal cord were supposedly more involved in producing insanity than before. These conditions resulted from the changing habits of an advancing civilization and a growing neglect of hygiene in general and mental hygiene in particular. One superintendent contended that alterations in the human constitution, in habits of life, and in the ways of business, together with delays in placing patients under proper care, accounted for the growing incurability.[65] A few years later his successor concluded that insanity "may have to be regarded as largely incurable." [66] Contributing to this pessimism was the presumed increase in types of insanity that no available means could cure. These included senile dementia, general paralysis—which was not firmly established as of syphilitic origin until the twentieth century—and so-called hereditary insanity.

Searching for new means to check the downward trend, asylum superintendents turned away from a psychological approach. Although many of the outward appearances of moral treatment remained and superintendents still thought that they were using it, this therapy gradually was downgraded and transformed. The features that suffered most were characteristic of it—techniques that catered to the patient's psychological needs. Therapy designed to operate on the intellect, emotions, or psychology lost its former importance, and the virtual disappearance of optimism removed the rationale for developing a close doctor-patient relationship. During the height of moral treatment the superintendent visited each patient every day. By 1879 the head of the Hartford Retreat saw only "those cases daily, who for any reason may appear to require his personal attention." [67] The unfortunate consequences of leaving the care of patients to inexperienced or unsuitable attendants were described in Clifford Beers' classic account of his mental illness, *A Mind That Found Itself*.[68] In the late nineteenth century there was an effort to train attendants in order to improve patient care. This was important because patients were being removed from contact with the superintendent and placed under the control of attendants more than ever before. The old concept of hospital personnel and patients constituting a "family" disappeared. Instead a hierarchy developed in which the most highly trained and responsible members were not always accessible to the patient. The modern institution made its appearance.

For reasons having little to do with psychological therapy, superintendents continued some practices associated with moral treatment. In the first place, no acceptable substitutes were immediately available.[69] Second, the corporate asylums' upper-class clientele demanded individualized attention and comfort. Superintendents had to provide a pleasant environment, recreational facilities, entertainment, and a large staff, even if they doubted that these conditions would produce cures. In certain ways care improved: The practice of non-restraint was extended, and limited open-hospital policies were adopted sometimes. Finally, and most significant, these measures served not only to keep the patient comfortable and content, but to build up his supposedly broken-down physical state, especially his defective nervous system. Activity was assumed to be one of the best remedies for functional brain disorder, halting its deterioration into incurable organic disease.[70] Entertainment, dances, reading, lectures, music, riding, games, and especially education, massage, labor, and systematic physical development—applied on an individualized basis—stimulated "the impoverished nerve-cell" of the insane.[71]

Asylum reports relate a growing reliance upon massage, exercise, rest, diet, and drugs. Although the early psychiatrists seldom gave up conventional medical means and always maintained a somatic concept of pathology, they had stressed methods of reaching and changing the patient's psyche. The post-Civil War approach was the converse; psychiatrists hoped, like the orthodox physicians of the eighteenth century, to eliminate the psychical symptoms by physiological remedies. Therapy now followed theory: The disease was somatic and so was the treatment. As the introduction of moral treatment led to a reduced dependence upon medical techniques, so the renewed emphasis on somatic therapy encouraged a neglect of the patient's psychological needs.

Misgivings about concentration on a mechanical somaticism were expressed by the superintendent of the Hartford Retreat:

> I have sometimes thought that in our rebound from the old idea that insanity is a spiritual disease, and due to spiritual or moral causes . . . there exists danger we shall land too far over on the other side. The psychical and physical are united by the closest of bonds; they act and react upon each other, and any system which ignores, or treats the one to the neglect or exclusion of the other, is radically faulty.[72]

The approach of Dr. John B. Chapin, superintendent of the Pennsylvania Hospital for the Insane, was more typical. In 1890 he wrote that he relied chiefly on measures that produced sleep, improved general health, and added pounds. He attributed his increased success in curing new cases of insanity to a system that stressed advancement in neurological investigations, the role of deficient nutrition, and the degeneration of the nervous system. His regimen included a program of liberal feeding, prolonged administration of tonics, and new hypnotics. He also discussed the value of improved moral techniques. Several years later he predicted that future advances in psychiatric treatment would be made through special care of curable patients; study of the relations of functional disorders and bodily illness to mental disease; and the recovery of nervous systems disordered by overwork, strain, and excesses. Mental disorder, he believed, was only one manifestation of neurasthenia, or nervous exhaustion.[73]

The renewed emphasis on somatic therapy appeared among a generation of psychiatrists imbued with the spirit of the "scientific" medicine being developed in France and Germany. Some of these men had been trained by the leaders of the moral treatment school but lacked their strong faith in moral methods. The successors of Luther V. Bell, Isaac

Ray, Amariah Brigham, and Samuel B. Woodward became deeply discouraged by the apparent failure of moral treatment, and they wanted to find more objective, presumably more scientific, techniques.

The importance of research or modern scientific methods at the end of the nineteenth century is revealed in the 1904 report of the Friends' Asylum:

> It is pleasant to bear witness to the fact that mental medicine has been entering upon a new era during the past few years, and in consequence the purview of asylum practice has largely changed. . . . If the time shall come when cases can be definitely grouped in accordance with bacterial infection, specific auto-intoxication, pure psychological deviations, organic disease, etc., then may the pioneers of mental morbid research be amply repaid for the minute study of these manifestations of disorder which to-day are so diligently sought.

These investigations, combined with laboratory research, the report noted, made asylum practice more effective and stimulated the staff. The superintendent of McLean Asylum called for research as a way for psychiatry to break away from institutional routine and take part in the general movement for progress in medicine. Only through research into the physical functions of life could physicians hope to increase the number of insane restored to health.[74]

The trend away from a psychological psychiatry was further strengthened by the unrelenting campaign for somaticism conducted in the *American Journal of Insanity*. A more significant factor was the research of late nineteenth-century European alienists like Emil Kraepelin, famous for his classic delineations of mental illnesses. Concerned with diagnosis and description rather than the individual patient, Kraepelin thought that insanity probably had a physical origin and its victims a preordained, hopeless fate.

Although hospital psychiatrists on the whole leaned increasingly toward a total somaticism, the most outspoken and uniformly somatic approach to mental illness was found not in psychiatry but in the rapidly developing specialty of neurology, which had received great impetus in the United States during the Civil War. As pessimistic as superintendents became about the possibility of curing insanity, neurologists became even more so.[75] The attitude of the latter was important in shaping the outlook of all physicians concerned with mental illness during the late nineteenth century. Neurologists not only took over some of the patients who had been under psychiatric care, but also became the experimentalists and innovators in psychiatry as well as neurology. The work of Silas Weir Mitchell with his "rest cure" and George M. Beard with his theory of neurasthenia was especially influential.

American psychiatrists had long sought full acceptance by the medical profession and had struggled to ensure mental illness a place among legitimate physical diseases, even when moral treatment was at its peak. Their later emphasis upon "scientific" methods and somatic therapy seemed to bring psychiatry into the mainstream of medicine at last. This generation was no less pragmatic than its predecessors: late nineteenth-century psychiatrists also used whatever techniques seemed effective. The various shifts in psychiatric theory and practice partially reflected the lack of a body of scientifically established facts about the causes, nature, and cure of insanity.

The speed and extent of the change from a psychological to a more purely somatic therapeutic approach varied among the corporate hospitals. The superintendent seems to have set the pace. For example, at the Pennsylvania Hospital, it was not until the death of Kirkbride, chief for over forty years, that moral treatment clearly lost its predominance. It did not completely vanish in any of these institutions, and in some the superintendents retained at least a verbal commitment to it.[76]

Despite variations among individual institutions and physicians, moral treatment faded into comparative insignificance in the corporate hospitals; the features that remained tended to lose their psychological content. If it lost importance among the majority of American superintendents because of unsuitable conditions in the public hospitals, it definitely disappeared as a significant force in American psychiatry when the corporate hospitals shifted their emphasis. This process was so complete that until very recently only a few persons remembered that moral therapy had ever existed. It has been suggested that the "lack of inspired leadership after the death of its innovators was probably the most important factor in the deterioration of moral treatment in the United States." [77] There is much to be said for this appraisal, but the complicated reasons for this deficiency—medical, social, and financial—seem more important. In the crowded and poverty-stricken state hospitals, the extra-medical factors worked against moral management; in the few corporate hospitals, the spirit of contemporary medicine combined with disappointing recovery rates to defeat it.

5

Although American psychiatrists discussed at length the major problems in their field and generalized about the characteristics of patients and the nature of insanity, they conducted little scientific investigation to verify their ideas or validate their practices. The scientific spirit in medicine that developed in France and Germany during the mid-nineteenth century was slow in permeating the United States,[78] and for a long time psychiatry was composed of practitioners who were not interested in research. This is true for the periods before and after the Civil War, although the concern here is with the former. While the French, British, and Germans were performing autopsies, trying to correlate symptoms with pathological anatomy, studying the physiology and anatomy of the nervous system, and experimenting with various kinds of psychiatric treatment, the Americans for the most part were occupied with the everyday problems of administering mental hospitals and treating patients. They were aware of the work in Europe and were influenced by it, but with a very few exceptions did not attempt to duplicate it. From 1840 to 1860 four men—Bell, Brigham, Ray, and Joseph Workman of Toronto —were responsible for most of the psychiatric research in the United States and Canada.[79]

If American psychiatrists seldom engaged in research—that is, the attempt to study data objectively, systematically, and in a verifiable way —they did have a fondness for compiling statistics about mental patients and seemed to regard it as research. Certainly they hoped that this work would make a significant contribution to understanding the etiology of mental illness. Their statistical efforts cannot, however, be equated with serious research.[80] Most of their work—such as listing patients' sex, age, occupation, alleged reasons for illness, and color of hair—was assembled so uncritically that it was virtually worthless for any scientific purpose.

Despite the criticism of their methods from within the profession [81] and the existence of appropriate statistical techniques, psychiatrists continued to collect data that they themselves often recognized as valueless. For most of them this pursuit served as a means of proving the scientific nature of their institutions and—when recovery rates were involved—their success in curing patients. To do more than amass gross figures would have required the kind of effort that busy superintendents were either unwilling or unable to make.

Of course, few American physicians engaged in medical research before 1865.[82] But asylum superintendents had more opportunity, for they controlled the hospitals in which they worked. Brigham thought that the chance to study mental illness, particularly through "autopsical examination," was an advantage gained from the establishment of asylums. He considered autopsies "one of the most important methods for obtaining a knowledge of the functions" of the brain and nerves.[83]

At the same time, it might be assumed that the overcrowding, insufficient funds, understaffing, and physical isolation in many asylums would place insuperable obstacles in the way of scientific investigation. Yet both Brigham and Workman superintended large public hospitals; Brigham conducted scientific experiments while administering one of the best state asylums in the United States, editing the *American Journal of Insanity,* and writing numerous articles. In the corporate hospitals, which were not usually overcrowded, understaffed, or desperately short of money, psychiatrists did little more research than their colleagues in state institutions. A number of eastern asylums were in or near cities, and their chiefs were well acquainted with the intellectual leaders of their day. Conditions in most asylums were not ideal for research activities, and, indeed, discouraged such work as time went on, but a few highly motivated men did not find them insurmountable.

The correspondence of Woodward, Earle, Kirkbride, Chandler, Mann, and Dix contain few complaints that asylum superintendents or their assistants lacked time for research. In these collections, which include thousands of letters from virtually all the psychiatrists of any note in the United States, little is said concerning original experiments or research. (One can, however, find superintendents writing about the great strain and labor involved in running a mental hospital.) The

American Journal of Insanity, for many years the only American journal
devoted to psychiatry, published few articles reporting results of American scientific investigation. This is also true of the annual reports of asylums.

Although the precise reasons for this indifference probably varied
from person to person, some general comments may be made. Many
practical problems took precedence over scientific study of theoretical
questions. Superintendents placed great stress upon the therapeutic role
of physical layout and the proper administration and organization of
mental hospitals. Usually they devoted time and effort to problems such
as classification of patients, perfection of heating and ventilation systems, and establishment of working programs of occupational therapy.
Kirkbride, for example, believed that good ventilation was essential to
the restoration of mental health and was an expert on this topic as well
as on the construction of mental hospitals in general. He and others sub-
jected the technical aspects of these matters to a certain amount of
experimentation, and Kirkbride's book on hospital buildings and organization became the standard text throughout the nineteenth century.[84]

Under great pressure to show high rates of recovery, psychiatrists
understandably devoted themselves to measures that would bring
immediate results. Therapeutic success not only improved their status
within the medical profession, but also greatly helped to gain legislative
and public support for mental hospitals. It removed the practical impetus to do research, since existing methods supposedly could cure nine
out of every ten recent cases of insanity, at least during the 1830's and
1840's. With this prospect, psychiatrists naturally pushed forward to per-
fect a system of treatment that gave promise of quickly eliminating mental illness as a significant medical problem. They resembled most physicians in their practicality and emphasis on results; however, physicians
demanded utility instead of research at a time when utility in medicine,
in contrast to psychiatry, could offer least in terms of cures.[85]

The psychiatric attitude is evident in a letter from as original a
thinker as Isaac Ray to Earle in 1872. Ray noted with pleasure that
Earle, unlike many other superintendents of the day, emphasized occupational therapy:

I hope you will neglect no opportunity to let superintendents who visit you, see what can be done in this direction. If thus you can make your example followed, you will have accomplished a greater good, than you would by abolishing restraint or making 100 autopsies every year.[86]

The criticisms from Europe of American inattention to autopsies and rejection of non-restraint may perhaps explain Ray's sentiment.

Theory did not greatly interest Americans, but they needed some theoretical structure to explain and organize what they observed, so they tended to retain old, unscientific ideas. Since philosophy and religion as well as medicine shared a common interest in maintaining a preconceived approach, these traditional concepts were exalted to the position of unquestioned "fact." Psychiatrists were not likely to challenge ideas that seemed axiomatic: The mind is immaterial and cannot be diseased; the brain is the mind's material agent within the body; insanity always involves some brain damage.

Yet their indifference to theory enabled psychiatrists to accept, on the basis of practical experience, the use of moral treatment as an exclusive cure for insanity even though it was a departure from somaticism as understood at that time. Their interest in psychological therapy might have led psychiatrists, while retaining an essentially somatic outlook, to free themselves from the theological and philosophical commitments that hampered a more critical approach to psychiatric problems, but it did not. The difficulty was not that they believed in a narrowly defined somatic pathology as much as that religious and philosophical ideas weighed so heavily in their somaticism. Earle expressed the attitude of many of his colleagues when he wrote:

The longer I live, the more am I impressed with a belief in the all-controlling supremacy of mind over matter, of the far-reaching, mysterious power of the divine intelligence within, and of the limited bounds of present knowledge, compared with what is to be known when mind shall have thrown off its fetters of clay. Science is proud, even presumptuous; but how much cause for humility in the fact that it cannot trace one particle of its knowledge upward, through effects, to the original cause and center of all things! Science is lost at once in the mazes of uncertainty and ignorance, whenever it attempts to fathom mind itself.[87]

It would be unfair to infer, however, that psychiatrists did not understand the requirements of a scientific approach. Rather they did not
apply a scientific attitude to certain problems. Answering criticism of
phrenology as having a "deplorable moral influence," Brigham wrote:

> To first enquire what according to our feeble understandings are to be the
> moral results of certain statements in matters of Science, or whether they
> are in conformity with our interpretation of the Bible, appears to me a
> futile method of proceeding, and very liable to lead us into error. . . .
> Whether a scientific statement is true or not, seems to be the first inquiry.
> If it is true we may feel confident it will be found to harmonize with all
> other truth.[88]

Yet Brigham, who directed some scientific research himself, admitted
that in attempting to prove the harmfulness of revivalism to mental
health he had "constantly appealed to the Scriptures for the correctness
of what [he had] advanced, and referred to them as authority not to be
questioned." [89]

Endeavoring to be empirical and "scientific," but also attempting to
work within conventional moral and religious limits, American psychiatrists found it difficult to challenge accepted ideas with the freedom of
some of their European colleagues. I do not suggest that belief in the
conventional mind-body dualism, for example, made experimental work
impossible. Except for the doubts expressed by Ray about the adequacy
of this theory, even those Americans who made contributions to psychiatric knowledge adhered to it. But the most fundamental research conducted in psychiatry before 1865—in pathological anatomy—often involved findings that questioned by implication the validity of the mind-
body dualism. Thus, if the unquestioned adherence to the mind-body
dichotomy did not prevent certain kinds of research, it certainly
removed some of the impetus to it. This was especially true in pathology, in which many of the advances of medicine during the first half of
the nineteenth century took place. Why examine problems to which
answers were already known, particularly if contrary evidence would be
rejected because it contradicted religious beliefs?

The concepts and practices of American psychiatrists were subject to
changing circumstances, social and religious pressures and prejudices,

and shifting philosophical and medical theories. With a few notable exceptions they tended to present ideas not on the basis of systematic investigation but on unverified impression and experience. In this way they resembled their associates in general medical practice. Because psychiatry dealt with the mind, however, it not only had inherent difficulties in research, but also exposed psychiatrists to problems upon which regular physicians could perhaps more easily refrain from taking untenable positions.

Part Three

The Spread of Psychiatric Thought, 1825–1865

GENERAL MEDICINE

LAGS BEHIND

1

In 1860 the editors of the *American Journal of Insanity* came to an unhappy conclusion about the more knowledgeable physicians' lack of confidence in psychiatry. This situation, they complained, weakened popular faith in mental institutions, for the family doctor was usually the first to see the insane, and his advice was influential. The specialists in mental illness had only themselves to blame. "When we glorify our specialty and its institutions in the same manner and spirit, almost in the same terms, in which the whole host of quacks advertise their vulgar theories, their 'water cures' and 'hygienic institutes,' can we wonder if by many intelligent physicians we are partially included in the same category?" [1]

This is a harsh judgment, and the evidence does not support it. On the contrary, the more literate and intelligent the general practitioner, the more respect and approval he had for moral and medical treatment of the insane and, by implication, for psychiatrists.[2] This chapter analyzes the views of general practitioners and discusses medical cultists, who were both numerous and influential among physicians and the general public.

The terms "general practitioner" and "physician" include the tens of thousands of regular physicians who were not psychiatrists; they cover various opinions and levels of medical competence.[3] No doubt many of these doctors lacked formal medical training; others held degrees from the numerous diploma mills established everywhere in the United States, without state or professional regulation. The physicians who made any attempt to keep abreast of medical progress probably represented a minority of the medical profession. This group comprised teachers in the respected medical schools, graduates of these schools, and prominent physicians trained under the preceptor system. They tended to be the intelligent, literate, and articulate members of their profession. Often they were in a position to influence laymen through personal contact and contributions to journals and newspapers.

This chapter concerns mainly this group. Though fragmentary, the evidence is probably representative of many practitioners in New England, the Middle Atlantic states, and the bigger southern cities. The main sources of research are the written comments of psychiatrists, medical journals, general medical texts, newspapers, and testimony by physicians at criminal trials where the defense pleaded insanity. The Friends' Asylum admissions papers, in which physicians requested the admittance of mentally ill persons, also revealed some of their opinions on insanity.

2

The most obvious difference between the mid-nineteenth century physicians and those of the early years of moral treatment was the increased and more widespread awareness of psychiatric advances. By the 1850's and 1860's general practitioners were still not greatly concerned with mental illness, but they were becoming aware of the new psychiatric theories. Psychiatric knowledge was no longer confined to a handful of highly educated medical leaders. Various developments probably account for this change: the increased general consciousness of the problem of mental illness, particularly after Dorothea Dix and others began agitating for reform; the establishment of asylums in many states; the widely advertised successes of reputable private and state mental institutions; and the increased interest of medical journals in psychiatry.

Medical schools on the whole continued to ignore psychiatry in their formal curricula, although professors at the better schools kept up with the latest advances in the field. Several psychiatrists delivered lectures on mental disorders at New York's College of Physicians and Surgeons and the Harvard Medical School, and Earle served as a Professor of Psychologic Medicine at the short-lived Berkshire Medical Institute. However, no systematic, consistent instruction in psychiatry was available from Rush's death in 1813 until 1867, and psychiatry probably received little mention in regular medical lectures.[4] At best, interested teachers gave some attention to mental illness in courses devoted to other subjects, such as medical jurisprudence. Psychiatrists, working exclusively in mental hospitals, remained largely isolated from medical schools. Their institutions were seldom used for teaching purposes, although some well-known psychiatrists did get training there as resident physicians. Even when the opportunity arose to teach at medical schools, asylum superintendents, overburdened with work and often not sufficiently aware of the need to educate the general practitioner, found it difficult to leave their institutions for any length of time. For example, despite the contention of Professor Jonathan Knight that the medical profession would continue to neglect psychiatry unless psychiatrists taught in medical schools, Eli Todd refused to lecture at Yale because of the pressure of his duties at the Hartford Retreat.[5] Medical students had no practical experience with mental illness and little theoretical training.

It was possible, however, for students and practicing physicians to learn about mental disease from medical publications. By the mid-nineteenth century, the importance of general medical texts declined and emphasis shifted to publication of texts devoted to special aspects of medicine. If a physician was interested in reading at length in psychiatry, he would be apt to turn to the works of Esquirol and Pinel, among others. Aside from Rush's classic, which by the 1840's was quite out-dated, no general psychiatric text by an American physician was pub-lished until 1883. The reason, it has been suggested, was the British publication of John C. Bucknill and Daniel H. Tuke's *Manual of Psy-chological Medicine* . . . which quickly became the standard work in the field.[6] Isaac Ray's *Treatise on the Medical Jurisprudence of Insanity* was also highly regarded by the medical profession and extensively reviewed. Of course, many physicians probably read none of these works. Dr. Bates, of the Maine Insane Hospital, declared in 1846 that not half of the medical practitioners in Maine possessed a standard, scientific work on insanity,[7] and Earle wrote a few years later that "it [was] safe, perhaps, to assert that not one in ten of the graduates of [American med-ical schools] has ever read a treatise upon mental disorders." [8] An impor-tant source of information about mental illness—at least for progressive physicians—were asylum reports, which were widely circulated among physicians and laymen and frequently reviewed in lay and medical jour-nals.[9] New psychiatric ideas doubtless were popularized through the medical journals; they proliferated rapidly in the thirties and forties and were becoming increasingly significant as repositories of medical news and progress.

The major American medical journals began to print more articles on psychiatry from 1800 to the 1840's. In 1844 a decline set in, probably because of the appearance of the *American Journal of Insanity*. The articles and book reviews in the general medical periodicals were often written by well known psychiatrists and discussed mental illness in terms similar to those found in the *Journal*. They expressed psychiatric ideas on pathology, etiology, and treatment; supported moral treatment and the establishment of mental hospitals; and encouraged physicians to entrust mental patients to the care of psychiatrists in these hospitals.[10] Another indication of the recognition that psychiatry received from the medical profession was a request from S. V. C. Smith, editor of a medical almanac, for an article from Woodward on "Statistics of Insanity in the United States." Such a paper, Smith wrote, "would be exceedingly acceptable to the profession of this country. The work circulates exten-sively in this & other countries, being a sort of medical directory." The object of the article was "to interest medical men everywhere in encouraging people to build up hospitals for lunatics, &c." [11]

The emphasis on the need to hospitalize mental patients, plus the erection of many new asylums and the tendency of superintendents to monopolize the field of psychiatry, meant that ordinary physicians had little contact with the insane beyond initial treatment and referral to an asylum. As they became better informed about moral treatment and the value of hospital care, they lost practical experience with psychiatry. One asylum superintendent commented in 1853 that the majority of physicians did not study mental illness in school or in general practice. Since the medical profession agreed that the insane should be treated only in asylums, physicians were not "willing to undertake to conduct the medical treatment of a case of insanity . . . at home." [12] After fruitlessly experimenting with various medicines for a few weeks, the local doctor would send the patient to an asylum if he could afford it. If a mental hospital were nearby and had been in operation for a while, the general practitioner might have gained enough confidence in its usefulness to send insane patients directly there, without attempting to treat them at all.

The degree of faith in asylum care generally varied with the physical accessibility and age of the institution. At the twenty-two mental hospitals whose history was studied in detail, the following pattern is typical. When asylums first opened, superintendents invariably complained that they received many patients only after months or years had been wasted in vain attempts to cure them at home. Within five to ten years, the number of these cases declined, and superintendents noted that the public, at least in the immediate vicinity, had become more aware of the need for haste. Since most mental hospitals received inmates from neighboring communities, often on the advice of physicians, the relative speed with which patients arrived at the asylum after the onset of illness was a rough gauge of physicians' attitudes toward institutional care of the insane. Of course, many other factors were involved, but it is likely that when the local doctor thought a mental hospital was the proper place for insane persons, the public was apt to patronize asylums early in the course of the disease. At the same time, it is possible that physicians' attitudes reflected public opinion, which was slowly altered by the efforts of reformers and asylum superintendents.

3

It would be unwarranted to assume that because many physicians came to acknowledge the beneficial effects of asylum care, they also adopted all the tenets of moral treatment. Local doctors still attempted to treat mental illness by traditional methods before they gave up and sent the patient to an asylum. Long after most mental hospitals had discarded venesection, superintendents complained about new patients who were exhausted from excessive bleeding by their local physicians.[13]

Psychiatrists attempted to persuade regular physicians to stop depleting mental patients excessively. In 1842 Ray advised the general practitioner that mental hospitals in New England and probably elsewhere no longer bled their patients, and if this were more generally known local doctors might reduce, if not eliminate, this much overworked technique.[14] In an article written expressly for the general practitioner in the West, Dr. John R. Allen, superintendent of the Eastern Lunatic Asylum at Lexington, Kentucky, deplored the American predilection for venesection and warned against excessive bloodletting and purging of mental patients.[15]

By the fifties and early sixties the use of venesection by general practitioners diminished, particularly in the eastern cities.[16] This trend probably resulted from the decline of bloodletting in general medical practice rather than from the few efforts by asylum superintendents to educate physicians. Public pressure also may have influenced general practitioners to change their methods. There is no doubt that laymen's opposition to harsh treatment of their mentally ill friends accounted in part for the reduction of restraint and heroic therapeutics in asylums. The same pressure may have influenced the general practitioner's treatment of the insane, especially at a time when his techniques for the treatment of all diseases were under fire from both laymen and professionals.

Samuel Thomson, the founder of a popular system of botanical medicine, satirized medical practices in this verse:

RECIPE TO CURE A CRAZY MAN

Soon as the man is growing mad,
Send for a doctor, have him bled:
Take from his arm two quarts at least,
Nearly as much as kills a beast.

But if bad symptoms yet remain,
He must tap another vein,
Soon as the doctor has him bled;
Then draw a blister on his head.

Next he comes, as it is said,
The blistered skin takes from his head;
The laud'num gives to ease his pain,
Till he can visit him again.

The doctor says he's so insane,
It must be dropsy on the brain,
To lay the heat while yet in bed,
A cap of ice lays on his head.

And lest the fever should take hold,
The nitre gives to keep him cold;
And if distraction should remain,
He surely must be bled again.

The bowels now have silent grown,
The *choledocus* lost its tone;
He then, bad humours to expel,
The jalap gives with calomel.

The physic works, you well must know,
Till he can neither stand nor go;
If any heat should still remain,
The lancet must be used again.

The man begins to pant for breath,
The doctor says he's struck with death;
All healing medicine is denied,
I fear the man is mortified.

.　.　.　.　.　.　.　.　.　.　.　.

What sickness, sorrow, pain, and wo,
The human race do undergo,
By learned quacks, who sickness make,
I fear, for filthy lucre's sake.[17]

It is doubtful that physicians' growing faith in asylum techniques was based on a real understanding of moral treatment as psychological therapy. Most of them probably thought of it as synonymous with kindness and the elimination of whips and chains. Not all physicians agreed with psychiatrists that the majority of mentally ill persons should be sent to hospitals. A few doubted the somatic nature of insanity and denied the effectiveness of any medical means; sometimes this led them to advocate the exclusive use of moral treatment. In 1837, the resident physician at the Friends' Asylum, R. R. Porter, complained that it was "not uncommon to hear physicians speak of insanity as purely a mental affection; and, in consequence of this view . . . , regard the employment of physical agents in its treatment either as hazardous or useless." Occasionally medical men, strongly imbued with the idea that mind was independent of matter, requested the Friends' Asylum not to use medical means in treating their insane relatives. These physicians thought that medication had no value and merely caused the patient needless pain and torment. Porter warned that this negative approach could lead to a repudiation of medical means in favor of moral means alone, with less chance of cures. Besides, such a doctrine might undermine the influence of medical men in asylum affairs: The head of a well-known asylum told Porter that "several years ago he and his colleagues were so prejudiced against the use of medical measures, as to object even to the election of physicians in their board, being fearful they might effect some innovation." [18]

This tendency among laymen was also noted by Worthington as late as 1863. People often rejected asylum treatment for their relatives "in a fruitless effort to benefit the patient at home by moral remedies" while the physical disorder went unchecked.[19]

4

Study of testimony at trials that involved pleas of insanity furnished concrete expression of physicians' attitudes, particularly small-town practitioners who did not contribute to professional journals and whose ideas may not have been represented there by others. Court records also supplied information about definitions of insanity and physicians' approach to specific cases, for usually they were called to certify the sanity or insanity of the defendant.

A defense plea of insanity became more common as time went on; it seemed to increase in frequency as psychiatric knowledge broadened. In contrast to the few reports of such cases found before 1825, there were over fifty in the later period that contained relevant material.[20] These sources are difficult to unearth, and no doubt many other similar records exist. Besides numerous psychiatrists, over one hundred and seventy-five general practitioners testified at more than forty trials studied in detail. In fact, psychiatrists were indignant that non-specialists served so frequently as expert witnesses on mental illness. One psychiatrist charged the prosecution with calling obscure physicians as witnesses because they were easier to influence and would testify as the counsel desired.[21]

Regardless of their own competence or the influence of the prosecution, physicians acting as witnesses and making judgments about the insanity of a defendant exercised greater caution in the courts than in their own offices or in academic discussions. This applied especially to murder trials. Medical witnesses tended to be intimidated by a public and a court demanding vengeance; with the possible exception of a few psychiatrists, there was no movement among physicians to explain antisocial acts as the result of mental illness. Physicians who supported an accused murderer's claim of insanity flouted public opinion. A majority of the trials took place in the town where the crime had been committed, at a time when popular feelings were still inflamed.[22] Sometimes special interests would have suffered if the physician had testified in favor of the accused. In one case, if the plea of insanity had been sustained, it would have reflected unfavorably against the town's main source of income, the Auburn State Prison of New York; this case also became a subject for Democratic-Whig controversy.[23] In Massachusetts, a verdict of insanity for a defendant discredited the state prison administration.[24] This does not mean that physicians knowingly gave false testimony to protect their own positions or others', but in most cases they were asked for opinions rather than facts, and various pressures probably tempered their readiness to declare a defendant insane.

It seems clear that although trial records provided firsthand information about the general practitioner's concepts of insanity, his testimony was not necessarily unbiased. This was particularly true in the important cases in which psychiatrists—without exception—supported the plea of insanity while general practitioners did not.

The testimony of physicians, excluding psychiatrists, can be divided into two large groups: those who revealed scant knowledge about mental illness and those, including eminent professors, who seemed to be well informed about psychiatric matters. In diagnosing insanity, the former group looked for general irrationality coupled with overt gross acts that would convince anyone that insanity existed. One doctor said that a defendant—an obvious paranoid who was acquitted by the jury as insane —was feigning insanity. He claimed to have a pain in his head and to be incapable of controlling his mind, but he did not walk carefully in order not to disturb his head. The defendant was calm, had not rebelled at being ordered to work, had not mentioned hearing voices. He had exhibited nervous excitement, and seemed to be an onanist, for which the doctor prescribed work.[25]

Physicians did not always see violent or excitable behavior as a sign of mental derangement. A defendant's excitability and violent temper convinced one doctor that he was a "dangerous, reckless man," but "it never occurred" to him that he was insane.[26]

Another doctor commented that a person's state of mind, affected by confinement in prison, might show signs of dementia, but not really be deranged.[27] Delusions did not always convince physicians that insanity existed, for even where "there are delusions, there may still be the power to discriminate between right and wrong." [28] It appears that physicians surrendered their right to diagnose insanity to the courts, which tested sanity by the ability to distinguish right from wrong.

These examples, which could be multiplied indefinitely, show that virtually nothing could convince some doctors of a defendant's insanity. These physicians proved ingenious in discounting evidence, and they were the prosecution's delight.

Few general practitioners had the same incentive to study psychiatry as a Kentucky physician, Harvey Baker, who had to testify at his brother's murder trial. The latter claimed that his wife had intercourse on the floor of their bedroom with his sister's husband and that an armed Negro woman prevented him from interfering. He subsequently murdered the brother-in-law. Despite the implausibility of his stories, the murderer spoke rationally and had a reputation for honesty, so it was difficult for his brother to believe he was insane. But after reading psychiatric books and consulting experts, he discovered the existence of monomania, in which the victim might be irrational on only one topic and even then, if the false premises were granted, his subsequent arguments might be logical. Dr. Baker's testimony shows that prior to the murder he knew very little about mental illness; despite his formal medical training, he had shared many of the popular misconceptions about insanity.[29]

Some physicians with little knowledge of mental illness combined unfounded opinion with prejudice in their court testimony. During the Packard trial in Illinois, a physician testified that at first he had thought Mrs. Packard insane because of her unconventional religious opinions, but later reconsidered his position. "I have thought perhaps I was not a proper judge, for I am not much posted on disputed points in theology, and I find that other people entertain similar ideas. They are not in accordance with my views, but that is not evidence that she is insane." [30]

At the celebrated trial of William Freeman, a Negro who had senselessly killed a whole family of strangers and was clearly in an advanced stage of dementia, several general practitioners testified that he was not insane. One can only marvel at what kind of evidence these doctors would have considered sufficient to pronounce a man mentally ill. Of course, considering the tremendous public pressure to convict and hang Freeman, perhaps these physicians were just being prudent. But while they did not declare Freeman insane, to their credit they did not conclude that he must therefore be sane; they made no decision about his mental condition.[31]

Some general practitioners took a more sensible approach and were more concerned with medical than legal definitions of insanity.[32] They did not look for total irrationality or a history of violent behavior as the only signs of insanity but accepted more subtle types of evidence.[33]

A Brooklyn doctor was unsure about the sanity of a prisoner who declared that he committed murder after spirits bewitched him. According to his physician, the murderer had "some queer ideas about spiritualism," but in other ways he reasoned "like any other rational man." A closer examination was needed, for "deception is so very easy." Another physician did not believe the murderer "could dissimulate so much." His pulse rate was good; he did not drink; he spoke calmly. Nevertheless, this doctor thought he had been insane for a long time: "He is in a state of alienation of the mind in consequence of physical disease and religious mental aberration." The physical disease, "a nervous debility," stemmed from masturbation, which was "enough to make anyone crazy." [34]

At a Connecticut murder trial one doctor concluded the defendant was insane on the basis of his appearance and demeanor. He was melancholy, disliked society, answered questions irrelevantly, stared vacantly, was indifferent to cold weather and to his state of health, had peculiar eating habits, and, finally, regarded the human race as his enemy. The doctor had never seen a case of monomania, but believed that such a disease existed.[35]

Physicians who had extensive knowledge about insanity may also be divided into two groups. The first and much smaller one consisted of a few professors who maintained that only a loss of virtually all mental activity was proof of insanity.[36] This position was so unusual among knowledgeable doctors that one can only conclude that its advocates were more concerned with obtaining public approval and making sure that crime did not go unpunished than with making objective medical judgments.[37]

More typical of educated medical opinion was the testimony of Dr. Charles Van Epps at the Freeman trial. Van Epps, a medical practitioner for twenty-one years, believed Freeman, whom he had known as a child, was demented or idiotic. Freeman's replies to questions and his "appearance generally" convinced Van Epps that Freeman was insane. He answered only "yes" or "no" to questions, read like a child, counted no higher than twenty-eight, and repeated things as if he had learned them by rote. Besides, his uncle had been mentally ill, and Freeman might have inherited the disease. "One powerful argument in favor of his insanity" was his truthfulness, which, Van Epps noted, was typical of insane persons in his condition: "When they have committed desperate acts they glory in them." [38]

On the whole, the more knowledgeable medical witnesses, including eminent professors at medical schools, agreed with psychiatrists on most psychiatric questions. The over-all impression from trial records and other sources is that specialized knowledge helped physicians to recognize insanity, especially in borderline cases. By the mid-nineteenth century, general medicine had caught up with psychiatry, and informed physicians went to the books of Pinel, Ray, Bucknill, and Tuke for information about mental illness and bowed to superintendents like Woodward, Bell, Earle, Brigham, Ray, and others as experts.

The less erudite physicians, especially in outlying districts, were not nearly as sophisticated in their understanding and treatment of mental disease. Psychiatrists did not help the situation, for they gave only slight attention to the education of the general practitioner. Articles like those by Brigham [39] and Allen,[40] which told the local doctor how to recognize, manage, and perhaps prevent insanity, were exceptional.

Psychiatrists as a rule believed that the local physician did not need to know more about psychiatry for his ordinary daily practice than the general public, that is, how to identify insanity and the location of the nearest mental hospital. In fact, most of the educational and propagandistic literature issued by asylum superintendents did not include the family doctor. Relatives and friends were assumed to be capable of diagnosing mental illness and deciding when to take the patient to the asylum. It may be that psychiatrists placed little faith in the ability or willingness of general practitioners to handle mental cases. More likely, the need to educate the public, many of whom might not consult a physician, was considered of first importance.

5

In addition to an increase in the number of regular physicians during the pre-Civil War years, there was also a rise of medical sectarians. Many of these men were trained physicians with community stature; in many ways they provided a healthy counterbalance to the dogmatic, unhygienic, and largely ineffective ministrations of ordinary physicians.[41] Some of the sects, such as hydropathy and phrenology, were on the border of the medical world. Although physicians were among the leaders, these movements were greatly influenced by laymen and had a broad following among the general population. For the sake of convenience, however, they are included among the medical cults.

One of the most fashionable fads was hydropathy, or the water cure, which first became popular in Europe, then spread to the United States. It involved the use of water both externally and internally. Hydropathists exhorted the public to prevent and cure all ills by drinking mineral water, bathing and showering in cold and warm water, applying wet packs, and taking steam baths and water injections. Dr. Thomas L. Nichols, a hydropathic theoretician, explained that all disease was a form of inflammation and would be relieved by cold water, which would draw the blood away from the inflammation and open other paths for the excretion of morbid matter.[42] In offering a monist theory of generalized pathology, Nichols, like other cultists, was considerably behind the times; "systems" in medicine had begun to give way to eclecticism and therapeutic nihilism during Rush's lifetime. Nevertheless, hydropathy became popular and in the 1840's hydropathic establishments flourished all over the United States, especially on the eastern seaboard.[43]

Leading hydropathic physicians approved of asylum care for the insane but recommended use of the water cure. Nichols wanted asylums to adopt "a daily bath, pack, and injections" and a pure vegetable diet for the patients. He believed that hereditary predisposition increased the risk of insanity and that the disease seemed to be caused by exhaustion from masturbation, disappointment in love, grief, and disorders of the passions.[44] Dr. Joel Shew, America's most famous water curist, discussed mental illness in his *Water-Cure Journal* and other books. The most obvious characteristic of his remarks is their close resemblance to contemporary psychiatric thought. Like many water-cure enthusiasts, Shew was also a phrenologist, which probably explains why Amariah Brigham, who was phrenologically inclined, was presented as a psychiatric authority par excellence in the *Water-Cure Journal*.[45]

Shew thought an asylum was the ideal place for the insane, but because of the stigma attached to confinement there he suggested treatment at home as a second-best solution. Although sympathetic to a psychological approach, Shew recommended the use of water cures for insanity. Despite his tendency to discourage asylum care, he described many of the latest psychiatric concepts of insanity.[46]

Dr. Sylvester Graham and his many followers also advocated simple, clean living, but emphasized health foods instead of water cures. Graham explained mental pathology as the result of nervous irritation, which caused the patient's preoccupation with certain associations. If the irritation were reduced, the patient would be cured. Although Graham did not discuss moral treatment, his theories did not contradict its use.[47]

Thomsonianism was even more popular than hydropathy and Grahamism. It flourished in the Midwest from 1822 to 1837. Samuel ("Recipe to Cure a Crazy Man") Thomson, the movement's founder, advocated botanical as opposed to mineral remedies.[48] Thomsonians generally did not discuss mental disease, but one of them emphasized hereditary or constitutional predisposition as the cause of insanity and recommended both psychological and medical treatment which, though dated and tending toward mysticism, was fairly similar to the position of psychiatrists.[49]

Perhaps the most enduring of the non-orthodox medical systems of the nineteenth century was homeopathy, which led the attack on the old *materia medica* and eventually merged with scientific medicine. Founded early in the century by Samuel Hahneman in Germany and introduced into the United States in 1825, it quickly spread through the country, particularly where Thomsonianism had been strongest.[50] In the words of a modern medical dictionary, homeopathy is:

a system of therapeutics . . . based upon the observation that certain drugs, when given in large doses in health, will produce certain conditions similar to those relieved, when occurring as symptoms of disease, by the same drug in small doses. This is called the law of similia . . . like things are cured by like things.[51]

Homeopaths showed much interest in mental illness and often were perceptive in their insights. Dr. George E. Shipman's *Homoeopathic Family Guide* advised doctors that the sufferings associated with hysteria were just as real as the illness itself.[52] Dr. J. Kost agreed and suggested that hysterics were often woefully neglected because of the erroneous popular view that the patient himself was responsible for his condition. Kost attributed many cases of hysteria to a morbid predisposition that not even the strongest mind could resist.[53]

Dr. John C. Peters devoted a whole book to "nervous derangements and mental disorders," based on T. J. Rückert's "Clinical Experience in Homoeopathy." In addition to homeopathic physicians, Peters cited Pinel, Jarvis, Chandler, Kirkbride, Bell, Ray, and other psychiatrists in his discussion of insanity, which he thought was the result of an irritation of the brain. He described insanity as basically an excess or perversion of one of the natural passions or propensities of the mind. Like Esquirol, Peters thought mental derangement was the inability to direct attention; the impressions of the insane were so vivid and their ideas so numerous that they could not focus on each object or idea. He agreed with Ray that perverted education led to insanity and that mental and moral training and control of the imagination were important in preventing it.[54]

Understandably, phrenology was the cult most concerned with insanity, for its theoretical basis was brain structure. Popular phrenologists, like phrenological physicians and psychiatrists, dealt with the localization of brain functions, the principle of exercise, and the importance of environment and education, but they emphasized the reading of character and intelligence by the shape of the head.

Although stressing physical cures, phrenologists and other faddists supported the movement to build mental hospitals and wrote approvingly of moral treatment.[55] According to Orson S. Fowler, the most famous commercial exploiter of phrenology and author of widely read phrenological works, mental disease consisted "solely in functional derangement caused by organic disease." The mind was "as capable of being sick as the body." [56] Insanity was a manifestation of excessive excitability and overaction of the brain and nervous system that resulted in brain inflammation; it could be prevented and cured by reducing the overaction.[57] Fowler emphasized the hereditary origin of mentality. He perpetuated the idea that insanity affected only intelligent persons. Mental disease was "the very *excess* of . . . talent and sensibility. . . . Nor can a simpleton well be crazy." [58]

For the most part, the *American Phrenological Journal,* the chief organ of popular phrenology, discussed mental disease in the same terms as the *Water-Cure Journal.* They cited Brigham and his *American Journal of Insanity* as exemplary authorities, described insanity as a somatic disease subject to cure, and advised hospitalization.[59] Popular phrenology differed from most other medical cults in the continued support of venesection by some of its leaders, including Fowler.[60]

It is somewhat surprising to find that the leading medical sectarians held views about mental illness that in many ways were more advanced than those of physicians. The cultists pleaded for the use of health nostrums in the treatment of mental patients, but they did not deny the value of regular psychiatric practices. Moral treatment, though practiced by psychiatrists who were conventional physicians, apparently was accepted by the leaders of medical movements whose very existence represented a condemnation of the orthodox medical profession. It seems likely that the kindness with which cultists looked upon psychiatric practices was based on the mildness of psychiatrists' medical remedies and their stress upon psychological methods. Water-cure advocates could and did point with pride to the use of baths and showers in asylums as proof of the value of their system, and phrenologists claimed that the best asylum superintendents in England and America followed Gall's system. Homeopaths were pleased by the trend toward reduced dosages of drugs, while Graham and his followers, as well as all of the other schools, approved the emphasis upon exercise and "wholesome" food proposed by psychiatrists for both prevention and cure. In brief, faddists usually found justification for their system in one of the few areas of medicine that appeared to be successful.

No doubt many cultists were interested in mental illness to the detriment of patients. Psychiatrists objected to their neglect of hospital care. Ray and others complained that some patients had been treated, with injurious effects, by physicians, vegetable doctors, and homeopaths, the last doing the least harm.[61] Although there was criticism of the Thomsonian devotion to vegetable drugs, the homeopathic emphasis on tiny doses of medicine raised little protest. In general, psychiatrists did not seem to object as much to cultist leaders or their quack followers as to the practices of medical men, probably because of the latter's predilection for venesection.

The great majority of the insane had little access to the ideas of the faddists and the nostrums of medical quacks; they were too poor and were likely to be shut away in prisons, almshouses, or asylums. Wealthy patients were treated in hospitals or by family physicians. It does not seem likely that many persons realized that they were becoming mentally ill; except for the hypochondriac and hysteric, who probably served as a good source of profit for cultists and their commercial exploiters, they would not be looking for cures.

Then, too, the phenomenal success claimed by asylum superintendents undermined the effect of the cultists, who gained much of their popularity as a result of the failures and inadequacies of orthodox medicine. Old medical theories and systems were discarded by scientifically oriented physicians, but no new ones appeared in their place. With only therapeutic nihilism as an alternative, many American physicians continued to apply the ancient and increasingly discredited techniques, and a disillusioned public turned to those who offered them something new and promising. Despite their reluctance to surrender medical therapy and a somatic philosophy, psychiatrists were far ahead of the conventional practitioners of their day in rejecting the heroic medical methods of the past.

E N L I G H T E N E D   T H O U G H T   A N D

T H E   R E F O R M   M O V E M E N T

1

Sharing psychiatrists' advanced ideas were the leaders of the lay movement to reform the care of the insane in the United States. Professional reformers, educators, politicians, and clergymen participated in this effort, and numerous prominent men served as trustees of mental hospitals. At first, the movement primarily was involved in founding, with some government support, privately endowed hospitals that gave moral treatment to those who could pay for it. Small groups of persons sought to have the state governments establish asylums for the poor, but their activities remained local and, with some exceptions, ineffectual. After 1841 Dorothea Dix entered the scene; then the struggle for reform took on a national character and its participants gained some unity and substantial success. In many of the twenty states that responded to her appeals, Miss Dix brought to fulfillment previously formulated demands for new state mental hospitals or for the expansion of old ones. She devoted most of her life to this cause.

Miss Dix and her fellow reformers made up a small but influential group, which gained understanding of psychiatric theories through efforts to help the insane. In comparison with the earlier period, lay reformers did not become expert in the practical management of the insane but were no less sophisticated in their knowledge of the field. At that time an intelligent person could master most of psychiatry's theoretical content, which was available in professional psychiatric literature and in leading general periodicals. The situation resembled the twentieth century, when many non-medical persons have been able to read widely and comprehensively about Freudian theories without knowing how to practice psychoanalysis.

Few books on psychiatry for the layman were published before 1865, but well over a hundred articles and book reviews concerning mental illness appeared in several dozen general American magazines during that time; almost all of them were edited in northern cities.[1] Statistics of insanity and quotations from asylum reports also were published in the *American Almanac*. A few important journals, such as the *North American Review* (Boston), *Littell's Living Age* (New York), *Eclectic Magazine* (New York), and the *Museum of Foreign Literature, Science, and Art* (Philadelphia), accounted for over half of this material. Of the entire group of articles, about half were reprinted from influential British periodicals,[2] and many others came from American journals, books, and newspapers. Only the *North American Review* consistently published original articles by Americans. The authors, including American, British, and sometimes continental psychiatrists and reformers, wrote with intellectual sophistication. They covered a wide range of subjects, with special attention to the causes and treatment of insanity and to medical jurisprudence. Almost any question upon which psychiatrists disagreed found both supporters and opponents in the periodical press. This was particularly true of moral insanity, though it received more condemnation than praise. On this subject the liberal members of the medical profession came under sharp criticism, but on most other questions the periodical literature generally strengthened the position of psychiatrists.

The phrenologically inclined reformers, like Samuel Gridley Howe and Horace Mann, found much of psychiatric thought congenial to them. Perhaps phrenology affected reformers even more than psychiatrists. It helped to form a theoretical foundation for the strong humanitarian element in their activities. Phrenology supplied a rational, "scientific" theory of progress and improvement; it countered Calvinist theories of the sinful nature of man with a concept of human perfectibility based upon changes in the environment. This improvement in turn would affect the structure and functioning of the brain and result in better behavior in future generations.

Of course, the emphasis on environment in personal as well as societal ills was not unique to phrenology. Before the Civil War many Americans believed in human progress through human efforts and had unbounded optimism in the ability of men to control their surroundings and destiny. Far from being unchangeable and evil, man's nature was seen as potentially good and subject to molding. Isaac Ray, evaluating the reform movement of the 1830's and 1840's, gave three reasons for its emergence: the example of the corporate hospitals' successful treatment of the middle and upper classes; the increase in the number of insane, along with the increase in population, and the consequent magnification of the problem; and the work of Dorothea Dix. But, Ray declared, these forces sufficed only because of the "spirit of the age"—"a remarkable moral and intellectual uprising that reached every department of thought and action." [3]

The reform movement of the mid-nineteenth century differed from previous movements in leadership as well as objectives. Before 1825 upper-class citizens championed the establishment of corporate mental institutions but did little to found hospitals for the masses. Bloomingdale, McLean, Hartford Retreat, Friends', and Pennsylvania asylums received aid from sympathetic state legislators and men of wealth and influence. Obtaining asylum care for the poor was much more difficult. Only once did someone give Dorothea Dix a large private donation of money, and it was for an asylum that accommodated mainly the middle and upper classes, Butler Hospital of Providence, Rhode Island. Funds for asylums for the poor had to come from the state, and parsimonious legislators resisted demands. The struggle to improve the conditions of the poor insane, unlike the earlier movement to found mental hospitals, almost exclusively involved efforts to persuade state and national legislatures to build asylums. The men and women who led this fight generally came from the middle class, and the most famous and successful was Dorothea Dix.

2

Estimates of Miss Dix's understanding of psychiatry and her influence on its practice vary. One of her biographers, Francis Tiffany, contended that in her search for ways to aid the mentally ill, Dorothea Dix mastered "the whole question of insanity, its origins, its stages of development, the relations of body and mind, its treatment, its legal and moral rights, and . . . put herself abreast with the most advanced thought on the subject." [4] She made her greatest contribution, however, as a crusader who instilled in others some of her own fervid spirit.[5] Helen E. Marshall, a more recent biographer, agreed and, like Tiffany, stressed Miss Dix's accomplishments in improving the state of the insane poor.[6] Other non-medical writers also dwelt upon the humanitarian aspects of her work and did not give much attention to her ideas about insanity and its treatment.[7] The emphasis of these authors upon sentiment and a religious sense of duty as the forces driving Miss Dix has tended to obscure her psychiatric knowledge.

Others, concerned with the scientific treatment of the insane rather than with the philanthropic motives for reform, have been critical of Dorothea Dix, mainly because of their dissatisfaction with the custodial nature of the hospitals she helped to build. F. B. Sanborn, editor of Pliny Earle's *Memoirs* and a longtime chairman of the Massachusetts State Board of Charities, noted that the many hospitals established through her efforts soon deteriorated therapeutically. According to Sanborn, Miss Dix failed to see—almost unavoidably under the circumstances—that hospital custody in itself might do little to cure patients. She did not often perceive the weaknesses of superintendents at the hospitals she helped to found and did not become aware of the need to train attendants until near the end of her life.[8]

More recently, Dr. J. Sanbourne Bockoven has written:

[Miss Dix's] immense emphasis on eliminating gross abuse of the insane had the most unfortunate effect of driving into the background serious considerations of the requirements to be met in securing positive active treatment. The forced inundation of mental hospitals with long standing chronic cases completely ruined moral treatment.

Care, not cure, was the object—in fact if not in theory—of Miss Dix's campaigns. Bockoven thought Miss Dix's greatest weakness was her excessive concentration upon the humanitarian aspects of reform. The very effort, moreover, to care for all of the insane incurables as well as the curables overtaxed asylum facilities and prevented the implementation of therapeutic policies. This stress on the conditions of the poor insane in jails and almshouses enabled those who built the state hospitals to ignore the fact that good physical surroundings alone would not cure insanity. At the same time no provisions were made for training enough physicians in the philosophy and practice of moral treatment. The decline of moral treatment followed inevitably from Miss Dix's failure to understand psychiatric thought sufficiently.[9]

Even Deutsch, who wrote that Dorothea Dix, "by the sheer force of her personality . . . had awakened public opinion to the sufferings and needs of the mentally ill to a degree unparalleled by any other individual before her time or for many years after," quoted Sanborn's criticism with evident approval. Although Miss Dix had succeeded in forcing recalcitrant public officials to accept definite standards of care and treatment, Deutsch said, she could not "*organize* that enlightened opinion on a permanent basis so as to safeguard adequate standards, in addition to obtaining immediate gains." This "was beyond the capacity of any individual at that time, even of such a rare person as she was." [10]

Unfortunately none of these writers discussed Miss Dix's psychiatric knowledge in any detail. Before passing judgment on her responsibility for the custodial nature of mental hospitals, certain questions need to be answered: How thorough was Miss Dix's understanding of the psychiatric ideas of her day? What did she really think about the nature of mental illness and its curability? What did she consider desirable in a mental hospital? Did she have different standards for the poor and for the rich? How did she conceive her role in reforming the care of the insane? The scope of this study precludes an analysis of any but the first two questions; by studying her ideas about insanity, however, some light may be shed on all of them.

A problem in analyzing Dorothea Dix's psychiatric thought is the propagandistic nature of her writings. It is possible that she expressed some ideas for their effect on state legislators rather than for their inherent merit. Nevertheless, when pieced together, her writings, mostly in the form of letters and memorials to state legislatures, undoubtedly represent her beliefs about mental illness.

She first learned about the medical approach to insanity from psychiatrists Woodward, Bell, and especially John S. Butler, the first superintendent of the Boston Lunatic Hospital, which opened in 1839.[11] Her memorials show that she was also acquainted with English and French as well as American psychiatric literature.[12] She seemed to accept the ideas she read about, and her concepts were indistinguishable from those of most leading American asylum superintendents, whom she knew personally. Although a solitary worker, Miss Dix carried on an extensive correspondence with men like Ray, Kirkbride, Butler, Nichols, Bell, and Curwen and constantly traveled from asylum to asylum, talking with superintendents and observing their work.

Like many psychiatrists, Miss Dix's psychological approach was probably associationist, her concept of etiology psychosomatic as well as somatic, and her view of pathology somatic, with the usual mind-body dualism. Insanity sprang from civilization and increased annually in the United States.[13] Uncivilized people seldom became insane; the South produced fewer cases of insanity than the North because it had fewer foreigners and, more important, because of its large number of uncivilized Indians and Negroes, who rarely went insane.[14] Although mental disease struck all classes of people,[15] the educated were particularly susceptible.[16] She blamed society for almost all insanity and, like Howe, viewed the insane as the victims of vicious social institutions and observances, such as revolutions, party strife, capricious legislation causing commercial speculation and disaster, and false standards of worth and rank. Society was responsible for its victims; the insane should be the wards of the states and the national government.[17]

Miss Dix believed that insanity was curable if treated before organic lesions developed and that isolation in a hospital away from family and

friends was the most successful means of treatment.[18] Along with many
New England psychiatrists, she thought the foreign born were the most
difficult to cure.[19] She wanted to establish therapeutic hospitals, not
places of custody, and she believed that moral treatment was as important as medical treatment, perhaps more so.[20] She was not unaware of
the need for proper care of the insane in hospitals. As early as 1844 she
criticized Blackwell's Island Asylum in New York City because it did not
provide employment for patients and lacked enough competent attendants.[21] Nor did she condone large asylums for the poor; she attempted to
establish small institutions in which individualized care would be possible. She maintained that more hospitals, not larger ones, were needed.[22]
However, she proposed building less costly hospitals for the poor than
for paying patients,[23] a position also taken by some leading asylum superintendents. In support of an active therapeutic program at state asylums
Miss Dix sent musical instruments, books, pictures, and money for the
purchase of games and the construction of libraries; she appealed for
hospitals with good physical facilities and sufficient land for farming.[24]

Although not a thoroughgoing advocate of non-restraint,[25] Miss Dix
wanted mechanical restraints—most prevalent in custodial institutions—
reduced to a minimum. She believed that the insane possessed normal
characteristics in distorted form and that they reacted violently if treated
like beasts. Nichols, whom she had recommended as superintendent of
the Government Hospital for the Insane (now St. Elizabeths) in Washington, D.C., described to Kirkbride her vexation and mortification at
hearing that a manufacturer of bed straps was advertising Nichols' "un-
limited approval" of his product. Nichols wrote Miss Dix a long letter
of denial and explanation. He assured her that he occasionally used only
mild mechanical restraint, applied when it would help the patient. The
letter concluded with a lengthy defense of his objections to the British
non-restraint movement.[26]

From this brief summary it is clear that Dorothea Dix's psychiatric
views resembled those of most psychiatrists of her day. In theory, and
often in practice, she sought to found therapeutic mental hospitals for
the poor. Since her knowledge of the subject compared favorably with
that of many asylum superintendents, it would be difficult to attribute
the decline of a therapeutic approach in state hospitals to her lack of

understanding. It may be true, as Bockoven suggests, that by focusing on the conditions of the insane poor in jails and almshouses, Miss Dix influenced people to be concerned exclusively with the physical well-being of the insane. But it seems a dubious conclusion that her activity alone largely accounted for the custodial nature of many state asylums. To attribute the decline of moral treatment to her because she sought successfully to have many of the poor insane sent to mental hospitals seems unwarranted. It was the state legislatures that did not provide the funds and legislation necessary for the proper care of the insane poor. Besides, she noted with disapproval what had happened to many asylums, and she objected to the signs of deterioration that she found on her periodic inspection trips.[27] Her main interest, however, lay in building new asylums.

Psychiatrists themselves applauded Miss Dix's activities and praised her memorials; [28] the Association of Medical Superintendents of American Institutions for the Insane officially commended her several times.[29] Appreciation is indicated in their public pronouncements and personal letters. Kirkbride, Ray, Butler, Nichols, Curwen, Awl, Earle, and other psychiatrists seemed to have no basic criticism; on the contrary, they highly respected her. They knew that many of the hospitals she helped to build fell below the standard they desired, but they did not hold her responsible. Bell declared: "We owe a majority, perhaps, of our largest and best institutions for the insane to [Miss Dix's] efforts." [30] Even Ray had trepidations when she came to visit, for fear that something in his institution might not meet her high standards.[31] Psychiatrists, who were burdened with additional problems as a result of the influx of the poor into asylums, did not blame Dorothea Dix but deplored the parsimony of public officials and the characteristics of the patients.

3

If Dorothea Dix is judged deficient, then Horace Mann must be as well, for he had been the guiding spirit of the State Lunatic Hospital at Worcester, which badly declined after Woodward's retirement. He chose Woodward as superintendent, and when Woodward received tempting offers to head the Hartford Retreat, it was Mann who probably convinced him not to desert the Worcester asylum.[32] But despite the efforts of Mann, Howe, and other prominent Massachusetts citizens, the Worcester Hospital degenerated from a therapeutic to a custodial institution. Yet no one has charged Mann with responsibility for its failures. And no one can say that Miss Dix's understanding of psychiatry differed from Mann's in any significant way. She accepted and promulgated Mann's belief that the pauper insane were the wards of the state.[33] Possibly the most important difference between Dorothea Dix and Horace Mann as reformers was that Miss Dix gave her life to reforming prisons and founding asylums while Mann's main efforts embraced educational reform. She helped to found over thirty insane hospitals and he, only one.

Mann's letters and writings show that his interest in theories about insanity may have been more profound than Miss Dix's, even if his general outlook was the same. He apparently learned much about mental illness from his friend Samuel B. Woodward.

Mann sought Woodward's advice about many problems related to the education of children, such as how many hours the very young should be confined in school each day.[34] It also appeared that Mann applied what he learned about insanity to his theories of education, for he sought to have children, like the mentally ill, "governed by moral means" rather than by force and fear.[35] These, of course, were also Woodward's ideas.[36]

Mann emphasized phrenology because he believed that for the first time reformers had a scientific theory upon which to base their work for the betterment of man and a means with which to counter pessimism about man's future.[37] Miss Dix did not seem to be influenced by phrenology; her approach was humanitarian, with a religious rather than a phrenological basis.

Samuel Gridley Howe, close friend of Mann, trustee of the Worcester Hospital, and chief aid of Miss Dix in her work in Massachusetts,[38] shared their humanitarian zeal. A physician, he was familiar with current psychiatric thought. Like Mann and the phrenologists, he thought that mental illness, including idiocy, resulted from some violation of the natural laws. But since society created destructive conditions, it must care for its victims.[39] He tried to obtain improved care for the insane and pioneered in educating the deaf and the blind. Under Woodward's prodding, he also campaigned successfully to establish a school for the mentally deficient.[40]

In an impassioned plea for expanded asylum care for the insane poor in Massachusetts, Howe lashed out at the upper class. Admitting that his proposals would not provide for all the insane in the state, he declared:

> But the pressure will fall mainly on the paying patients. . . . if any must be sent from the State hospital to the jails and almshouses-cages for safe-keeping, let it be the rich man's son or daughter, and not the poor man's child. Indeed it might not be ill, that the rich should suffer a little what the poor have been and are still suffering; for one or two cases only would raise a clamor, which would at once provide sufficient hospital accommodations for all. . . . Come, ye who are filled with sickly sentimentality, who weep over imaginary sufferings or imaginary beings, who sigh for some opportunity of doing heroic deeds, who are speculating upon human progress; here are realities to be grappled with, here is misery to be alleviated, here is degraded humanity to be lifted up.

Although every insane pauper was a ward of society, "prostitutes, criminals, foreign vagabonds, inebriates, &c., [had] a claim altogether secondary and inferior to that of the virtuous poor" and should be separated from them.[41]

Howe was more critical of psychiatric practices in the United States than Miss Dix or Mann. He expressed great admiration for the system employed in Gheel, Belgium, where the insane lived with village families, worked on nearby farms, and enjoyed extensive freedom. By comparison he found New England's system a "great restraining machine," without sufficient freedom of movement or contact with the sane population; he believed that many mental patients could safely be at liberty. According to F. B. Sanborn, Howe was the first American to recommend experimentation with the Gheel system.[42]

Though Miss Dix, Mann, and Howe were the most prominent workers on behalf of the insane poor, they were not the only ones. During the thirties and forties, local citizens initiated campaigns all over the country to improve the condition of the insane. Among the best known was educator Henry Barnard, who sponsored legislation on behalf of insane asylums, prisons, and common schools.[43] Eli Todd had been his family physician and had interested him in the educational work of Pestalozzi [44] and possibly in mental illness as well. While eulogizing Thomas H. Gallaudet, a pioneer teacher of the deaf and first chaplain of the Hartford Retreat, Barnard discussed the types of patients at the Retreat in 1852. Since the Retreat had been established, he declared, investigation had shown that insanity sprang from natural causes, which could be "hastened or retarded in their effects, and . . . [could] be known and counteracted entirely." Prevention, an urgent need at a time when mental illness was increasing at a "fearful ratio," lay in recognizing the many causes inherent in American civilization, with its freedom, instability, and materialism.[45] Barnard expressed ideas that were common among psychiatrists from Rush's time to the 1840's. By 1852 emphasis on environment had diminished somewhat in favor of heredity; nevertheless, Barnard was presenting theories still advocated in his day.

This short sketch of the outlook of American reformers cannot do more than suggest that they were aware of and accepted the ideas of leading psychiatrists. In effect, the reformers supplemented the work of psychiatrists by publicizing modern theories and convincing legislators to appropriate money for asylums. They did not entirely succeed in developing the best type of curative mental hospitals, but this was due to a complex of factors, many of which were out of their control.

4

Political and social pressures forced many politicians to acquiesce in reform measures. They did not necessarily agree with or attempt to understand psychiatric arguments, but acted through necessity and probably a mixture of humanitarianism, state pride, or fear of condemnation.

When Dorothea Dix conducted a campaign to build asylums for the poor, some of the politicians to whom she appealed agreed to assist her. Occasionally they served on legislative investigating committees set up to determine the truth of her exposés. Although most of them accepted the medically established concept of insanity as an illness that should be treated in asylums and some felt sympathy for the plight of the insane, it is likely that they took Miss Dix's views as authoritative without thinking too much about them.

In the United States Congress Miss Dix's bill passed after it had been introduced three times, then was vetoed on constitutional grounds in 1854 by President Pierce. There was debate on the political, economic, and constitutional issues but little on insanity and its treatment. Most speakers in favor of the bill, which provided that money from sales of certain public lands would be used for building mental hospitals, indicated their confidence in Miss Dix and medical specialists and then went on to argue the other questions. Some supporters inserted emotional appeals. Representative Richard Yates, of Illinois, declared: "It may be a weakness in this business age of finance, steam, and railroads, a *sickly sentimentality*, perhaps, yet I confess that . . . appropriations for these sacred objects is my first desire, and I would rather see all the projects for grants of the public lands fail than these." [46]

Opponents of the bill did not publicly question or reject any of Miss Dix's assertions; some of them obviously were careful to express sympathy for the insane poor and for her efforts. Senator Clement C. Clay of Alabama had to explain his position to his constituents, many of whose "sympathies have been deeply enlisted in behalf of a scheme for ameliorating the condition of that most unfortunate and pitiable of all classes of men, who, bereft of reason, sit in moral darkness more appalling than death." He was against the bill and in favor of presidential veto on the basis of strict interpretation of the Constitution.[47] He and other southern states' righters, supported by the President, sought to limit the power of the Federal government. Representatives of western states did not want to see the eastern states share in the proceeds of land sales in other states and were afraid as well of the effect of the bill on land prices and settlement. Congressional debate over the bill continued for several years, and by 1853 its implications for Federal land policy led to unsuccessful attempts to tie it to a homestead bill, which the western states wanted. These political and economic issues, rather than disagreement with the object of the bill, accounted for the veto and the failure of Congress to override it. Congressmen said little about insanity.[48]

The situation seems to have been similar in the state legislatures, where Miss Dix's efforts were, however, successful. Some insight into the reactions of the state representatives as well as the public can be gained by examining Miss Dix's memorials.[49] She sent a different one to every legislature; each was designed to fit the local situation (which she usually had surveyed thoroughly) and to overcome possible objections. Before formulating her memorials she often spoke to members of the legislature and read the proposals of her predecessors. Investigating the conditions in a state also gave her some idea of the local thought about insanity. Her final appeal reflected in part the expected resistance, and she anticipated her opponents' arguments.[50]

She always discussed the appalling conditions of the insane poor and the economy of placing them in hospitals where some might recover. She stressed both the humanitarian and practical reasons for establishing asylums and tried to correct misunderstandings by pointing out the successes of existing asylums and the kind treatment patients received.[51] Sometimes she appealed to state pride and emphasized the curability of insanity, particularly in the South, where one has the impression that there were strong remnants of older pessimistic and uninformed attitudes even among state legislators. In the North, especially in New England, Miss Dix concentrated on the issue of economy and the fact that, despite existing facilities, many of the insane poor were still not properly cared for. Some northern states already had one corporate mental institution, and she tried to convince politicians that financial wisdom compelled them to construct additional state-supported ones. Insanity could readily be cured in mental hospitals, she argued, so that in the long run the cost of building them would be less than the current system of jails and almshouses.

On the whole, newspapers supported her cause.[52] That the praise heaped upon her by the press offset the effects of its sensational reporting of crimes involving insanity and of charges against asylums by former patients is doubtful. In one way, favorable newspaper coverage of the reform movement helped to make Dorothea Dix a national and international heroine and enlightened some readers about the need for asylums and for a humane approach to the insane. At the same time, newspapers helped to perpetuate old prejudices and misconceptions by printing advertisements for quack remedies and lurid accounts of crimes committed by insane persons and of alleged abuses in asylums.

5

In addition to the active reformers, a large group of educated persons gave support to the movement. They frequently were involved in some humanitarian cause and were sympathetic to the plight of the insane once they were aware of it. Some of the most famous persons in American cultural, intellectual, and political life knew prominent reformers and psychiatrists. Intellectual society was still small enough so that everyone, particularly in New England, knew everyone else and had some insight into each other's interests and work. Every superintendent of an asylum, especially if state-supported, came into contact with politicians and public officials and with the leaders of local society who sat on boards of trustees. Howe and Mann served in the Massachusetts legislature—and Mann in Congress—and both sought to advance the cause of insane asylums. Miss Dix was a friend of the Unitarian leader, the Rev. William Ellery Channing, educator George B. Emerson, and philosopher Francis Lieber, who was a supporter of prison reform and one of her ardent admirers.[53] At her request, Charles Sumner, later a United States Senator, visited jails and almshouses around Boston; he was a close friend of both Howe and Mann and a supporter of their work on behalf of the insane.[54] Sumner was probably well aware of current psychiatric ideas. If his brain had been deranged organically rather than functionally by the severe beating he had received from a Southern Congressman, he told Howe, "then, as you know, death would have been my best friend." [55] Years before, Sumner had helped Isaac Ray gather many of the books used to prepare *Medical Jurisprudence of Insanity,* and later Sumner had read and criticized the manuscript.[56]

The prominent Democratic politician and governor of New York, Silas Wright, was concerned about the plight of the insane. At different times several of his relatives and acquaintances were patients at the state asylum at Utica, and he was a frequent visitor there.[57] In New York City, the well-known philanthropist Philip Hone served as a trustee of the Bloomingdale Asylum and seemed to be familiar with contemporary psychiatry; he visited the Boston Lunatic Asylum and thought its system of classification superior to Bloomingdale's.[58]

Educated people accepted the profession of psychiatry and the existence of mental hospitals and held leading psychiatrists in esteem. Psychiatrists worked long hours for low salaries. They were benefactors of mankind, with little possibility of reward or recognition from the people they assisted; they helped those who could not help themselves and who in many cases could not repay them. John Greenleaf Whittier dedicated his poem "Moll Pitcher" to Eli Todd.[59] The popular American novelist Catharine M. Sedgwick told Woodward: "You must be one of the happiest of men, for what greater happiness can there be than to be the source of physical, intellectual, and moral good to the most wretched (save the guilty) of our fellow creatures!" In 1858, the writer assigned to do the article on "humanitarian topics" for the *New American Cyclopaedia* requested a biographical sketch of Pliny Earle: "We desire to do justice to the labors of those who have aided materially by deed or word in making man better and happier." [60]

A few American mental hospitals gained excellent reputations in Europe, and European travelers in the United States often visited at least one asylum, most often the Hartford Retreat. Captain Basil Hall, who found so little to praise in the America of the late 1820's, called the Retreat a credit to the American nation.[61] Another British visitor, writing in 1833, spoke of Todd as "a man who had obtained great celebrity by his skill in curing insanity." [62] Under Todd the Retreat came to be known as the most successful mental hospital in the Western world.

Prominent laymen often called upon psychiatrists for advice and information. The historian George Bancroft asked Woodward for his analysis of the insanity of King George III and the Rev. Seth Sweetser, a leading Congregational minister and school board member in Worcester, requested his views on coeducation.[63]

Catharine Sedgwick, concerned about insanity in part because her mother and brother had suffered from it, portrayed it in her fiction with sympathy and realism.[64] She wrote Woodward knowledgeably about Horace Mann's discussion of hereditary insanity in a report of the Worcester Hospital. She disagreed with Mann, who had advised against the marriage of persons with a hereditary taint of insanity. Mann had not weighed the chances of insanity being repeated in families against "the certain misery" of inflicting "the heaviest curse that could fall upon . . . those whose families have been thus afflicted—of marking them as lepers. . . . even in the worst case, where the disease is constitutional, and has broken out in different branches of the family may it not be averted by a judicious physical education, and by an observance of those sanative laws physical, moral, and intellectual that would finally extirpate all disease?" [65]

In contrast to the earlier Gothic novels, mid-century fiction did not often include supernatural events, although it still stressed flamboyant and violent forms of mental illness.[66] A notable exception was the work of Oliver Wendell Holmes, whose psychiatric novels gave a medically accurate and psychologically perceptive picture of mental illness.[67] Holmes was a physician and had a natural interest in psychiatry.[68]

Other novels describing mental illness expressed a concept of the disease that was fairly similar to the one held by psychologically oriented psychiatrists. While American psychiatrists were attempting to develop psychological explanations for insanity and were discussing moral insanity, fiction writers also became more concerned with psychological factors in both the etiology and pathology of mental illness. Novelists wrote about people devoid of conscience who murdered, robbed, and in general acted as though they were "morally insane." An inherent moral sense existed in these characters, but it had not developed to the point that it governed their behavior under all circumstances.[69] Writers, like some psychiatrists, modified the traditional religious and philosophical concept of an incorruptible moral sense.

Reformers working for other causes also became concerned with insanity as it related to their special interest. Temperance workers stressed the possibility, if not the certainty, that insanity was caused by excessive alcoholism. The American Temperance Society reported that out of 781 "maniacs" in two British hospitals, 392 had become insane through drink; the report declared that an inquiry in the United States would show similar results. Liberal use of liquor, according to the Society, also tended to predispose people to insanity, and this predisposition could be passed on to offspring.[70]

Insanity became a factor in the prison discipline reform movement, rocked by a schism over two different plans of prison management—complete separation of prisoners from each other in solitary confinement (Philadelphia system) and collective but silent work during the day and isolation at night (Auburn system). Champions of each side sought to prove, among other things, that their system was not detrimental to mental health. The advocates of the Philadelphia system—Sumner, Howe, and Lieber were among the most passionate—had to defend themselves on this ground, for many persons believed that total isolation, even though broken by visits from a chaplain, would lead to insanity.[71]

Frederick A. Packard, manager of the House of Refuge in Philadelphia, editor of the *Journal of Prison Discipline,* and participant in the campaign to build asylums for the insane poor of Pennsylvania, showed some insight when he answered charges that isolation caused the disease. He seemed to be cognizant of its often subtle nature and the difficulty of diagnosing it. In addition to producing testimony from prison physicians to the effect that separation did not cause insanity—masturbation, "especially among the lowest and most depraved class of colored prisoners," and heredity were the causes most often cited—Packard noted that frequency was likely to vary with the purposes of prisons. In the separate system, the object was rehabilitation, which required intelligence and capacity: ". . . if the mind is suffering alienation or decay, such a process of reformation will be quite likely to disclose the fact, as no other process will or can." But if the purposes were to punish the prisoner, restrain him from further crimes, and make him pay his way, then the prison administration would not be interested in his moral and intellectual state. They would believe that real cases were feigned, and they would not be able to tell the real from the false or to catch incipient conditions. Therefore under the congregate system, practiced at Auburn, the reported cases would be fewer than under the Philadelphia system.[72]

Howe, in a well-publicized report to the Boston Prison Discipline Society in 1846 that was endorsed by Mann and Sumner, admitted that the Auburn system gave "considerable mental stimulus, and considerable gratification of [the prisoners'] social nature, by marching together and working together," but at the sacrifice of the principle of non-intercourse among prisoners on which the whole scheme was based. In the Philadelphia system nothing prevented the prisoners from having "as much social communication with virtuous persons as is necessary for their mental health." Statistics about frequency in the Eastern Pennsylvania Penitentiary, where solitary confinement was the rule, were not reliable, and even if they had been, Howe would have blamed the high incidence of the disease on the administration of the system, not the system itself. Howe, later an avid abolitionist and worker for the welfare of the freed slaves, noted that allowance had to be made for the large proportion of mulatto prisoners in the Philadelphia prison. These men could not bear confinement as well as Anglo-Saxons.[73]

These discussions indicate that educated laymen interested in social welfare activities were concerned with the latest psychiatric ideas. They had to be, for this knowledge proved essential to the success of the many social reform movements that flourished before the Civil War.

R E L I G I O U S   O P I N I O N

1

Since mental illness had long been bound up with religion and many psychiatric concepts impinged upon religious doctrines, the Protestant clergy were also interested in insanity and played an important role in shaping public opinion.* From 1825 to 1865 more than seventy articles, many over twenty pages long, about insanity and related topics appeared in leading Protestant journals, especially those sponsored by Presbyterians and Quakers.[1] During that time clergymen wrote at least two books and one pamphlet devoted to mental illness and four other books that discussed it.

* This discussion of religious thought excludes the Roman Catholic church, which had little influence in the United States before 1865. Although the influx of Irish and German immigrants into New York and Boston in the 1840's and 1850's strengthened the Catholic church, the hierarchy at that time spoke for and to only a relatively small minority of the American people.

Because the range of opinion was wide, it is difficult to make valid generalizations. One may, however, group clergymen and other religious writers into three major categories, First, there were those with a nearly psychiatric attitude, gained through participating in the reform movement or ministering to asylum inmates. The second category consisted of the academic moral philosophers, who, though students of human psychology, left its pathological aspect to the medical specialists. Finally, there were the clergymen and religious writers interested in insanity mainly on theological grounds; they endorsed the new psychiatric practices but were critical of psychiatric theories. Of course, the overwhelming majority of clergymen left no record of their opinions about mental illness, although many must have read and perhaps been influenced by the articles in religious journals.

A typical example of the first group's outlook was found in a pamphlet written by the Rev. Robert C. Waterston, of Boston, to aid Dorothea Dix's first campaign in Massachusetts. A description of the condition of the insane in that state, it aimed to convince the legislature to act on behalf of the insane poor. Waterston described McLean Asylum, which did not use strait jackets, handcuffs, or chains, as an example. Patients knew that if they observed the rules and exercised self-control, they would receive extended privileges. Perhaps because he was appealing to the educated and wealthy, who might think that insanity was confined only to the poor, Waterston emphasized the old but still popular idea that gifted persons were particularly susceptible.[2]

Another work written by a clergyman was the Rev. D. S. Welling's *Information for the People; or, The Asylums of Ohio, with Miscellaneous Observations on Health, Diet and Morals, and the Causes, Symptoms and Proper Treatment of Nervous Disease and Insanity.*[3] This long treatise also more or less repeated current psychiatric ideas.

In the 1840's and afterwards, ministers of various Protestant denominations accepted permanent positions in asylums as chaplains or preached Sunday sermons to patients.[4] Asylum superintendents approved, though not without reservations. They were afraid clergymen would weaken their authority or disturb their patients. Ministers might preach depressing or condemnatory sermons, and their untrained efforts to console individual patients might cause harm. As late as 1869 some leading superintendents still questioned the usefulness of asylum chaplains.[5] However, since these psychiatrists usually expressed themselves reluctantly and with circumspection, the details of their misgivings are difficult to discover. More information about the relations between superintendents and ministers came from those who voiced satisfaction. In annual reports and elsewhere, many superintendents maintained that religious services aided greatly in therapy. Similarly, the chaplains strongly supported psychiatric practices and wrote of the great benefits that patients received from both religion and psychiatry.[6]

Through his work as chaplain of the Hartford Retreat, Thomas H. Gallaudet, a noted educator, especially of the deaf, studied the relation of the mind to the body, the elements of moral science, and methods of educating youth, all of which he applied to his educational activities.[7] Gallaudet thought that religious teaching should take place only in accordance with the superintendent's directions, "or in a way, at least, that meets his approbation".[8] Evidently he achieved this position at the Retreat, for he had a key and could go through the hospital when he pleased, unattended, and could talk with whomever he wanted.[9]

Sometimes clergymen would come to asylum superintendents for advice about relatives or parishioners.[10] President Francis Wayland of Brown University, the economist and moral philosopher who was a trustee of Butler Hospital, asked Woodward about a friend who suddenly exhibited extreme and unjustified jealousy of his wife and appeared to be more than usually excitable though rational on other subjects. This person's grandfather had committed suicide, and his parents, uncles and aunts, and two of his cousins had been insane. Wayland showed understanding of insanity as conceived by psychiatrists—a recognition of relatively subtle changes in personality combined with hereditary factors as signs of illness. He told Woodward that there had been several cases of insanity at Brown and he wanted Woodward's opinion on the liability of students to the disease: "I have read your reports with great interest and believe that your observations among the insane will teach us who profess to be sane much in regard to the human mind which we should not otherwise know." [11]

Wayland discussed the mind-body relationship in conventional terms in his book, *Elements of Intellectual Philosophy*. He wanted no part of scientific theories that did violence to religious beliefs: science progressed only by observing phenomena and their laws and by abjuring investigations of the essence or absolute substance of mind or matter, a limit fixed by God.[12] His attitudes represented those of many of his colleagues, the academic moral philosophers of the day. These men dominated higher education in the United States and wrote textbooks that were influential among the American middle class.[13] Although interested in the mind-body relationship and in psychology, they considered psychiatry out of their purview. President Noah Porter of Yale, author of a textbook on *The Human Intellect,* wrote: "It is no part of our duty to give a scientific theory of insanity." [14] Francis Bowen, Harvard professor and editor of the *North American Review* and the *American Almanac,* gave considerable thought to mental illness and showed he understood the subject. But he, too, deferred to the experts; he cited approvingly the work of asylum superintendents and quoted from their reports.[15]

One of the moral philosophers wrote a book on mental disorder. In 1840 Harper and Brothers, responding to the need for a popular work on mental disease, published a volume on the subject in their "Family Library." Despite the prestige of psychiatrists, they asked the Rev. Thomas C. Upham, professor of mental and moral philosophy at Bowdoin College, to do the book. The result, *Outlines of Imperfect and Disordered Mental Action,* was a mixture of old and new ideas. Like many other moral philosophers, Upham, an adherent of the Scottish common-sense school, rejected the current growing medical belief in localized physical pathology and emphasized bloodletting.[16] He looked to Reid, Stewart, Brown, and the "Scottish school generally" for his belief in the internal senses and condemned Hobbes, Condillac, and Helvetius because their theories did not conform to nature.[17]

Nevertheless Upham agreed with Pinel, Heinroth, and Prichard that insanity could "include the moral or affective part of man's nature as well as the intellectual." He believed that men were born with a moral conscience, and the degree of its health determined the degree of guilt for anti-social actions.[18] In allowing that the moral faculty might be diseased or deranged, Upham seemed to accept the concept of moral insanity, which was anathema to most theologians.

2

The clergymen concerned with insanity from a theological point of view readily endorsed a humane attitude toward the insane, the desirability of mental hospitals, and the practice of moral treatment. On many theoretical questions, such as the influence of civilization and urbanization on mental health, they shared psychiatrists' views. But they were quick to challenge psychiatric theories that seemed to conflict with religious doctrines. In dealing with such controversial problems as causation of insanity, moral responsibility, and the origin of religious melancholia and mania, they often sought to counter allegedly dangerous psychiatric ideas. There was little unanimity among them; each writer had his own conception of the relationship of religion to psychiatric theory.

Leading ministers as well as most of the public no longer believed in the idea of demonological possession or divine visitation as the cause of insanity. This was particularly true of the Unitarians; led by Channing, Dorothea Dix's mentor, they repudiated the concept of depravity and emphasized brotherly love and humanitarian works. A few religious writers of orthodox persuasion still contended that insanity might be attributed to satanic agency.[19] More common were the ideas cited by the Rev. Joseph H. Jones, a Presbyterian minister in Philadelphia, who admitted the theoretical possibility of demonological possession but denied its actual presence in the mentally ill.[20] This position enabled clergymen to accept the concept of somatic pathology and to sanction medical treatment of insanity.

If Satan did not cause insanity, could religion? Many psychiatrists thought so, and as a result the question of the effect of religion upon unstable minds was discussed by religious writers anxious to defend the faith. Psychiatrists did not believe that religion was an underlying cause of insanity, even of religious mania, but they did think that excessive religious zeal was responsible for precipitating the disease in persons who were predisposed.[21] Brigham thought some clergymen unsuitable for service in asylums because they were "too austere, denunciatory, and prone to dwell on the 'terrors of the law,' rarely preaching in a way calculated to console and encourage those who hear them." [22] He was so concerned about the frequently injurious influence of religion upon mental and physical health that he wrote a book about it.[23] This work, a consideration of religious observances from a medical viewpoint, seemed sacrilegious to many persons and received numerous unfavorable notices. The clergy and the press attacked Brigham as a materialist and a phrenologist so sharply that he felt obliged to defend himself as a believer in God and religion.[24]

The Rev. Lyman Beecher substantiated psychiatrists' claims in his description of the mental anguish involved in Calvinist soul searching. Hearing a sermon on "The harvest is past, the summer is ended, and we are not saved," Beecher felt as if a "whole avalanche" fell on his mind, and he went home "weeping at every step." To relieve "people without number out of the sloughs of high Calvinism," Beecher developed a "clinical theology," a hopeful view of the world.[25]

Few religious writers agreed that the terrors of religion endangered mental health. They maintained that Christianity properly construed gave peace of mind.[26] A Presbyterian clergyman wrote that he "never knew the most pungent convictions of sin to terminate in insanity." [27] Others denied that either religious insanity (an illness marked by religious delusions and hallucinations) or melancholia characterized by fears of damnation (common among ministers) could be attributed to religion. These disorders arose from physical disease. The victims of religious insanity, according to one writer, often had a constitutional tendency to mental illness, which was exhibited in religious guise because of the interest that most people had in religion. When recurrently insane persons were well, they found their greatest source of enjoyment in religion, which proved that religion, even in its "gloomy" Calvinist forms, did not cause insanity. Religious feelings would precipitate melancholia, another author maintained, only in persons who had a naturally gloomy or fanatical temperament.[28] Frederick A. Packard, an editor of Sunday school publications and a proponent of sectarian education as well as a prison reformer, argued that properly revealed religion warded off insanity by engendering obedience to God through fear and love.[29]

An anonymous reviewer of Brigham's book in the *Christian Spectator* asserted the positive role of religion in the cure of insanity and accused

Brigham of disregarding it. Brigham had the "effrontery" to deal with matters which "his mind [had] never digested" and in which he had "no insight whatever." It was bad enough that he did not know what he was talking about, but, more important, his wholly negative attitude toward religion smacked of "moral obliquity." He ignored the "fact" that patients "religiously affected" were more likely to recover than others. Furthermore, patients often told their doctor that only the ministrations of heavenly support sustained them. When the physician's efforts failed, he frequently saw "a spirit of *supernatural* health and vigor still rejoicing in the poor rent tenement, and if not absolutely restoring it to soundness, yet holding it together long after his art has become useless." [30]

The clergy were worried about psychiatrists' charges that revivalism excited unstable minds and drove some persons insane. Ray noted that the "great awakenings" in the western states led participants to imitate abnormal muscular behavior that was detrimental to mental health.[31] Brigham condemned the tone of many evangelist newspapers, which catered to the tastes and prejudices of the most ignorant and credulous readers. These papers, he feared, "contributed largely to increase and perpetuate the love of the marvelous and mysterious, among this class of people." They contained "surprising accounts" of conversions of infant children, remarkable effects of reading religious tracts, fulfillment of pious persons' dreams, and immediate answers to prayers.[32] Fits and seizures were common among the audiences at revival meetings. In some cases the affected persons were clearly mentally unstable, if not insane, but credulous laymen as well as clergymen were diverted from recognizing them as such. In one example cited by Brigham, a religious paper reported the conversion of a man and woman through the Holy Spirit: the man fell to the ground, cold and still, as in death, while the woman "suddenly turned into a marble-like, cold and motionless statue; her eyes were fixed in her head, and many thought her to be dying; but all these were only dying unto sin, for soon they were made alive with God." To Brigham these were obvious cases of "catalepsy," a form of mental illness.[33] Even outside the hysterical atmosphere of the meetings, pathological behavior was often confused with religious fervor. Spiritualism, which was in vogue before the Civil War, produced similar effects.[34]

A few anti-revivalist ministers joined psychiatrists in denouncing evangelism as detrimental to mental health. A bishop wondered about the effect of "rhetorical flourishes" in evangelical journals upon "weak, credulous, and superstitious minds," [35] and the liberal clergyman Otis A. Skinner declared that the miraculous events reported by revivalists could be explained by the influence of the imagination, which irritated and excited the nervous system and sometimes produced insanity. Skinner cited Benjamin Rush and Sir Walter Scott to show that the mind not only influenced the body but that the body also influenced the mind. Revivals assuredly produced insanity; proof was the increase in the number of insane persons in asylums since the beginning of revivalism. He referred to a pamphlet written in the 1830's that contained accounts of one hundred cases caused by revivalism, and declared that asylum reports showed that "something like one sixth [of the insane] are made crazy by gloomy views of religion and terrific preaching!" One sermon by the eighteenth-century evangelist George Whitefield allegedly drove fifteen people insane. Nevertheless, Skinner was certain that true religion would not cause mental illness.[36]

Some clergymen who claimed that revivals were beneficial objected to certain aspects. The forms of hysteria, catalepsy, and epilepsy that occurred at revivals, one author observed, were not signs of grace, but the result of strong emotions that could become harmful if encouraged.[37] The Rev. Robert Davidson, a Presbyterian divine and former president of Transylvania University, agreed with Skinner that these convulsions resulted from the sympathetic connection of the mind and body, specifically, the influence of the imagination on the nervous system. By encouraging the seizures and thus aggravating the infirmities that produced them, western revivals produced "nervous disease, which was manifestly contagious" in some people.[38]

These objections apparently made little impression upon the evangelists themselves. Even when they acknowledged the danger of their practices to mental health, they believed that the effort to save men's souls was worth the risk. Charles G. Finney, one of the most famous revivalists of pre-Civil War days, declared:

It is very desirable that the church should go on steadily . . . without these excitements. Such excitements are liable to injure the health. Our nervous system is so strung that any powerful excitement, if long continued, injures our health . . . this spasmodic religion must be done away. . . . But as yet, the state of the Christian world is such, that to expect to promote religion without excitement is unphilosophical and absurd.[39]

Much later Finney insisted in his memoirs that revival meetings did not drive people mad: his preaching had even cured someone of insanity. "The fact is, men are naturally mad on the subject of religion; and revivals rather restore them, than make them mad." [40]

Brigham's critic in the *Christian Spectator* admitted that some of the reported cases precipitated by revivals had occurred, but probably there had been a strong predisposition to the disease. Besides, he was confident that for each one who succumbed, "hundreds" were saved from the "dreadful calamity" by evangelism. Furthermore, the majority of mankind needed some excitement to preserve bodily and mental health; the antiseptic quiet that Brigham advocated would drive the healthiest person insane. The reviewer could not resist repeating the rumor that one person had to be sent to a mental hospital as a result of reading Brigham's book.[41]

3

Although clergymen disagreed about the role of religion in causing insanity, they were virtually unanimous that irreligion threatened sanity. One author, for example, commenting on an insane murderer who disclaimed religious belief, wished to call the attention of his readers "to the marked influence of irreligion and immorality in producing insanity." A disposition to deny the truths of religion deprived the mind of "all rational and stable views in regard to the mysteries around and within us, sets it afloat without chart or compass," and might lead to insanity. This would most likely happen not to the "besotted, uneducated votaries of vice," but to educated people, because mental activity was a prerequisite. Especially dangerous was reading sentimental and immoral fiction.[42]

Religious writers were most critical of psychiatry when morality was involved, for they usually insisted on absolute standards of morality and on the existence of free will. The non-moralizing tendency of many leading psychiatrists appeared to deny sin and evil as the causes of immoral acts and met with practically universal opposition from clergymen. To the latter, the psychiatrists' clinical attitude reached its most flagrant expression in the doctrine of moral insanity. Even where "conventional" insanity existed, theologians were loath to ascribe immoral acts to illness which would free the patient from responsibility.

Clergymen who appealed for sympathetic attitudes toward the mentally ill were disturbed by their frequently objectionable moral traits.[43] The unchristian attitudes of the hypochondriac and melancholic (or even the criminal acts of the insane) might derive from disease, but they were also "precisely what would result from an impenitent heart waxing worse and worse. To which of these causes shall [the nervous invalid] impute the effect of his own case? If this be not a difficult question to decide, we know of none in the whole history of casuistry . . ." [44]

The criminal who pleaded insanity received the least sympathy. Clergymen complained about the frequency with which criminals used this defense to escape punishment when they were sane or at least not insane in the area relating to their crime. Physicians were scolded for saving such persons from death by testifying that "most cases of aggravated offenses [were] merely the results of undiscovered maladies" that required only medical care to restore the patient to society.[45]

The defense of moral insanity raised heated objections. Views of the conventional Protestant clergy and religious laymen were expressed in an article in a leading religious journal, the *Biblical Repertory and Princeton Review:* Moral insanity existed but only as a new word for sin.[46] The plea protected "desperate culprits, who [gave] no indications of insanity but the enormity of their crimes," said another writer in the *Repertory.*[47] He sought safety for society by demanding that the intelligent public, rather than physicians, determine when insanity reached the level at which moral accountability no longer existed. Physicians, though indispensable witnesses on questions of morbid states of mind or body, tended to be materialistic and were not especially competent in philosophy or ethics. Physicians could decide if insanity existed, but "the unperverted common sense of mankind will ordinarily give a safer spontaneous judgment" in deciding at what point a defendant should be freed from responsibility. Laymen would judge with "intuitive certainty" on these questions.[48]

When the good name of religion was at stake, religious writers could adopt as clinical an attitude toward mental illness as psychiatrists did; they saw that religious delusions were symptoms rather than causes. Why could not the same be true of non-religious manias in which the victim was impious or immoral? And why not attribute crime and depraved character to disease rather than to willful immorality and evil? In brief, the same logic that freed religion from the onus of causing insanity might equally free irreligion, immorality, and evil from the same blame. But the clergy did not follow this logic, for it would undermine Christianity's basic precepts.

Tensions between clergymen and psychiatrists were created when religious thinkers insisted that man committed immoral acts because of an evil heart, that he had free will to do otherwise, and that insanity rarely excused such acts. This doubtless helped to turn public opinion against the concept of moral insanity and was partly responsible for the theory's decline in American psychiatry. Evangelical religion, which encompassed practically all American Protestant sects, stressed that immorality was the natural condition of mankind. In advocating the theory of moral insanity, psychiatrists seemed to challenge the concept of original sin and to imperil evangelical religion.[49] Of course, some of them also saw man as essentially depraved, but many of the leaders of the profession had a more hopeful and relativistic view. And certainly the lay reform leaders openly repudiated the Calvinist concepts of depravity in favor of a belief in man's ultimate goodness. The conflict between religion and psychiatry should not be overstated, but it was, nonetheless, a real one. It involved a basic disagreement about the nature of man.

THE PUBLIC'S RESPONSE

1

The work for the insane, as in earlier years, activated only a comparatively small group of educated and socially conscious persons. The public in general, however, not only supported these activities, but gradually adopted a more enlightened look. Growing public acceptance of humane asylum care for the insane became readily apparent in the 1840's, when McLean, Hartford, Bloomingdale, Friends', and Pennsylvania hospitals began to receive patients from all over the country. Traditionally, hospital care had been the last resort for the destitute and dying, and it took time to convince people of its advantages. Many persons, unfamiliar with the principles of moral treatment, believed that mental patients were punished harshly.[1]

In time the existence of asylums that treated patients kindly produced favorable effects. By 1860 one superintendent reported that distrust was disappearing and that the public was beginning to look upon insanity not as a crime but as a treatable disease.[2] Discussing the growing number of rural patients sent to the Pennsylvania Hospital for the Insane, Kirkbride remarked that their return home accomplished "more in enlightening a whole neighborhood than volumes of essays or scores of statistical tables. [Recovery] is an argument which none can resist." [3] The asylums exploited this argument in their extravagant claims of success; Bell's warning about the danger of this practice was borne out when superintendents complained that some laymen expected quick and miraculous cures.[4]

To be sure, not everyone who committed a patient to a mental hospital or contributed money for a new asylum acted from humanitarian motives or the belief that insanity was curable. Relatives, jail keepers, and county officials often wanted to be rid of burdensome patients in their care, and local businessmen benefited from having a large institution in the neighborhood. If belief in supernatural agency disappeared —except perhaps in rural areas—many people still believed insanity resulted from some fault or vice and was at best a disgrace.

Trouble sometimes arose because the public did not always realize that cure usually required a long time and could not necessarily be equated with calmness. Relatives, eager to have patients at home and to eliminate the financial burden of hospital care, demanded their release as soon as they became rational, lost their delusions, and showed interest in family and financial affairs.[5] Inevitably many relapses occurred after premature removal and served to convince laymen that mental illness could never be fully cured.[6] Unrecovered former patients, particularly those committed against their will, sometimes maligned the institution in which they had been confined. Even patients who were presumed cured defamed asylums in an effort to convince others that they had never been insane.[7] The prejudice against Butler Hospital arose, Ray thought, "chiefly from idle gossip or a love of the marvellous, and occasionally from that mysterious malignity which mysteriously repays a favor with a curse." [8]

The curse sometimes took the form of public statements or sensational pamphlets written by former inmates trying to prove that they had been hospitalized unjustly and cruelly treated by hospital personnel.

Ray commented that these statements were "very characteristic of the insane," even after they had recovered. "Nothing is more common . . . than for the insane, in relating their experiences, to misconceive and consequently misrepresent what occurs around them, and especially whatever has reference to themselves." [9]

A former patient at the Maine Insane Hospital, Isaac H. Hunt, accused Ray, Dr. James Bates, and their assistants of cruelty. Hunt lectured to large crowds and distributed nearly four thousand copies of a pamphlet in which he claimed, among other things, that Ray tortured him with the fear of execution and a story about his son's horrible murder. He declared that the asylum staff had instilled in his mind the idea that they had killed his son and then served his body to him for dinner.[10]

In 1833 Robert Fuller published a thirty-page pamphlet describing "persecution" in McLean Hospital that allegedly almost killed him. He was aware that the hospital was "a popular one, and that any remark derogatory to it will be in opposition to the received opinion." Yet, "however benevolent and worthy may have been its original design . . . under its present administration, it is a reproach to the community." He played on the Jacksonian prejudice against paramilitary and aristocratic organizations by warning that every secret institution, whatever its name or character, was dangerous to society.[11]

These stories found willing listeners. Ray wrote:

> That many persons are ready to believe such statements about hospitals for the insane, is true, and pity 'tis true, because in consequence of them many are deferred from availing themselves of their benefits. But so it is, a plausible story plausibly told, will always find believers, even among the cautious and intelligent. If they were to decide the fate of our hospitals, what one would stand? For what one has not been the subject of such narratives. . . .[12]

Although occasionally newspapers helped to overcome distrust of asylums by printing favorable reports of their practices, they were much more likely to aggravate the situation by giving sensational publicity and support to former patients' accusations. In Philadelphia a man charged his family and the Friends' Asylum of confining him unjustly; before the defendants could answer, the *Public Ledger* ran a headline:

"A SANE MAN CONFINED AS A LUNATIC." The editorial that followed expressed no doubt of "a man's liberty having been abridged *without cause,* and himself confined in that most horrible of prisons, a lunatic asylum." The paper later called the defendants "a gang of barbarous, cold blooded conspirators" and suppressed evidence in their favor. Feeling against the asylum was so great that the judge came to its defense; the jury then convicted the family but acquitted the asylum physicians.[13]

A newspaper article characterized McLean Asylum as the "hobby of the Boston aristocrats" and a place where sane patients unjustly confined were unable to obtain a hearing. The hospital was a "bastille for the incarceration of some persons obnoxious to their relatives." [14] Similar charges led a Boston lawyer to petition the Massachusetts legislature for an investigation.[15] Part of the antipathy toward McLean Asylum as well as other corporate asylums sprang from their reputation as wealthy institutions that made a profit for their managers and catered to the rich.[16]

The popular periodical press, which came into existence by the 1850's, was less guilty than the newspapers of dwelling on the exciting aspects of mental illness or maligning mental hospitals. Magazines designed for broad circulation printed fewer and shorter articles on mental illness than the select publications and were more likely to stress its horrors and hopelessness. Nevertheless, their tone was generally sympathetic, if sentimental; insanity was assumed to have natural causes and to be subject to medical treatment. Compassion did not always extend to victims of non-violent forms of mental illness in which the intellect seemed only slightly impaired. Many articles poked fun at the hypochondriac and implied that if only he tried hard enough he could overcome his delusions. In contrast to the intellectual journals, popular periodicals aimed less to mold public opinion than to reflect it.

2

The criteria used by laymen to deem a person insane did not change in any spectacular way. The legal standards remained inadequate. In 1843 the M'Naghten decision in England decreed that the test of insanity was the ability to distinguish right from wrong. It supposedly set the pattern in the United States, but American courts did not succeed in formulating a consistent approach to the problem. Examination of judges' charges to juries indicates that the M'Naghten test was not always used and that the courts sometimes incorporated the findings of psychiatrists in their conception of criminal insanity—and on rare occasions accepted the concept of moral insanity.[17] A judge's definition of insanity usually depended upon other factors besides his acquaintance with the law: his psychiatric knowledge, psychiatrists' testimony, and public opinion. Even judges, concerned with protecting society and punishing crime, could not always remain aloof from the findings of medicine and from the humanitarian impulse of their time.

On the whole, however, the courts remained a stronghold of reactionary attitudes, and jurists did not usually base their opinions upon contemporary medical information, despite the increased use of psychiatrists as expert witnesses. Most people still expected an insane person to have no more reason or thought than a brute animal or to be totally wild and ungovernable. At times lawyers challenged the special competence of psychiatrists to judge legal insanity: The idea that the "ordinary man of fair capacity" could not understand insanity "substitutes the testimony of a physician . . . for the law of the land—expels the Judge from the bench and the Jury from the box—overturns the government, and places the Property, Liberty, and Life of any citizen in the hands of the Trustees and Superintendents of Lunatic Asylums." [18] As a result, there can be little doubt that juries found many insane defendants guilty. Some were so obviously ill that their sentences were finally commuted,[19] but others were executed despite appeals from outraged citizens.[20]

The public tended to suspect fraud in defendants' pleas of insanity, particularly as such pleas became more frequent. The newspapers fanned these feelings. "The more startling the crime, the greater the avidity, and the *effort,* by legal quibbles and false philanthropy, to protect the criminal," declared the *Albany Argus.*[21]

In New York City the defense of a forger on the novel grounds of moral insanity shocked the press and the public. The *New York Times* charged the defense lawyer with inventing a disease that was not recognized in books of medical jurisprudence. The theory of moral insanity "nullifies the idea of moral guilt, and resolves crime into disease." If the community accepted such a defense it "may be set down as indeed mad." [22] According to the New York *Evening Post,* leading lawyers, aided by physicians, would have the public believe that "scarcely any offense is committed which may not be attributed to the effects of insanity." It had become "alarmingly common" to enter the plea of insanity "in cases where it is difficult to rebut the testimony for the prosecution." [23]

There were crimes—usually a senseless murder of a respected citizen—that provoked such hysteria that almost everyone reverted to ancient and irrational feelings. In such an atmosphere a conviction was practically guaranteed, no matter how insane the defendant was shown to be or how authoritative the psychiatric testimony. When William Freeman murdered an entire family, excitement and fury in the upper New York State town of Auburn were so rampant that only a ruse saved him from being lynched by a frantic crowd including some of the "most substantial men" of the community. Many persons placed responsibility for the crime on the recent failure of a jury to convict a murderer whom former Governor William Seward had defended on grounds of insanity. After Freeman's act, a prominent lawyer ran down the street shouting, "Would that Seward were here to see this deed!" [24]

Although Freeman was obviously demented and sat grinning and silent throughout the trial, many people believed he was sane, and he was convicted and given the death penalty.[25] The established criteria for insanity were ignored in his case. Seward, who defended him, accused the prosecution, led by the former President's son, Attorney General John Van Buren, of implying that Freeman's character and intellect were in keeping with the low social and moral level of Negroes and Indians.[26] The district attorney called Freeman an *"unlearned, ignorant, stupid* and *degraded negro,"* and he and Van Buren repeatedly tried to link Freeman's crime to his racial origins, which were American Indian as well as Negro.[27] Many witnesses used standards for insanity that they regarded as valid only for Negroes, Asians, and Indians. One police officer, who had allegedly hoped to have Freeman lynched and his counsel tarred and feathered, said that if Freeman were insane "most of the negroes in Auburn are." Another did not think Freeman was crazy: "I thinks he knows as much as either of my dogs." [28]

The *Auburn Advertiser* was satisfied that Freeman, "this degraded, ignorant felon, who has consummated his wickedness by these atrocious murders," had received fair, unprejudiced trials. Well-known physicians testified to his insanity, but twenty-four men swore that he was sane, and "it is to be hoped that those who have heretofore doubted it will yield to an opinion thus carefully formed and solemnly expressed." [29] Another local paper probably was more indicative of public opinion about the trial: "A greater burlesque upon law and justice was never enacted, than the whole course of these labored technicalities, reported in this instance, it would almost seem, to shield one of the most atrocious murders ever committed!" [30]

3

Alongside old ideas and traditional prejudices were more progressive attitudes. Some people recognized mental illness in the absence of violent and flamboyant behavior or obvious irrationality. Although education helped to develop this awareness, the degree of intimate contact with the insane seems to have been equally, if not more, significant. A parent, spouse, or close friend might see signs of mental illness missed by others.

The well-known Parish case illustrates the difference that close and continued association with a person might make in an estimation of his mental state. Henry Parish, a wealthy New York merchant, suffered three strokes, the last paralyzing him and greatly impairing his speech. A few years later he died, leaving a fortune of about three-quarters of a million dollars. The trial, which took place in 1857, resulted from his wife's attempt to break a new will made after his third stroke and in which her inheritance was reduced. She claimed that Parish was insane at the time, and at least half a dozen prominent psychiatrists, including Earle, Bell, and Ray, wrote extensive concurring opinions.[31]

Several general practitioners and non-psychiatric medical specialists disagreed. But Parish's nurses thought he was insane before his death. They differed from the non-psychiatric physicians in that they had close day-to-day contact with Parish and a more thorough knowledge of his state of mind than the doctors, who saw him infrequently.[32] Other people who had been doing business with Parish for many years also thought he was mentally unsound before his death. The blacksmith and the poulterer, for example, believed he was unbalanced not only because he sometimes seemed violent, but because of his apparent inability to comprehend others or to make himself understood by them. The jury evidently believed the foregoing testimony and ruled in favor of Mrs. Parish.[33]

At the trial of Willard Clark, accused of murdering his former fiancée's husband, witnesses who had known him for a long time testified that he acted strangely and that his personality had greatly changed. A former landlord remembered that several years before, following a tragic love affair, Clark hung the girl's dress in his room and slept with it. He "never appeared [afterwards] as he did before—remained sad and cast down. . . . Before . . . he was as cheerful a man as I ever met." At times he spoke freely; sometimes he refused to converse with anyone. He would suddenly jump up after brooding a while and rush back and forth, rubbing his head, and then sit down; then he would repeat the performance. In conversation he skipped from topic to topic and spoke in a wild, wandering way, looking up and laughing about nothing.[34] To his former acquaintances Clark had been "not right," "strange," or possibly deranged long before the murder. These people had formed an opinion when they had no special reason to feel repulsion, fear, or hatred of him. Recent acquaintances did not call Clark deranged, but everyone noted that he seemed strange.[35]

At another trial several witnesses testified that the defendant, who killed a boy for stepping on his toe, was sane.[36] But many witnesses thought otherwise. Despite his rationality, "something was not quite right with the man." He was melancholy, his eyes flashed, and his passions were easily aroused. His habit of standing perfectly still for an hour in cold wet weather struck many as strange; he selected his food peculiarly, gazed into the fire, and appeared mentally lost. The opinion that he was insane was based not on any one of these characteristics or actions but on all of them. One woman thought he resembled her insane husband, who also could converse rationally.[37]

Determining the sanity of persons who retained considerable reasoning ability was so difficult that often only the closest family members could recognize mental illness. In the case involving the Friends' Asylum, friends testified that the plaintiff "was not crazy"; he managed his farm well and treated his family kindly. Although of sanguine temperament and lacking self-control, he was still sane. These witnesses did not know that he sometimes went through a performance of rolling on the floor, groaning, putting his hands to his face, and kneeling on a chair, and in general acting in a way unusual to sane persons. His mother had suspected him of being insane for years, and, together with his wife, placed him in the asylum.[38]

Those who evaluated the total personality of an insane person usually considered his level of education, social position, and, as in the Freeman case, race. When an educated, socially prominent man like Parish acted queerly and grew violent, observers were more apt to suspect mental illness than if he were poor and uncultivated. Violent response to a supposed insult, for example, was more expected from the ignorant than from educated, well-bred, and therefore supposedly less emotional persons. These considerations did not necessarily signify social prejudice but often good sense. In some cases, however, a poor or foreign-born defendant was held morally responsible for his act; though insane, he should be punished, for a good man would never have behaved as he did, even if bereft of his reason. In this respect, as in general, the poor were regarded as vicious and as responsible for their own circumstances.

4

The public concept of insanity remained generally vague and amorphous throughout the pre-Civil War period. People feared the mentally ill as violent and unpredictable but seem never to have formulated a coherent attitude toward these unfortunates. Probably for most of the population one cannot properly speak of their having more than formless impressions and feelings about the nature of mental illness.

The progress made in psychiatry and the work of the reformers slowly became known, so that by mid-century most Americans probably were aware of the great changes in the treatment of the insane, and the principle of humane hospital care for the mentally ill became widely accepted. At no time, however, was there established any organization with a mass following to carry out the work of reform. No means was found to insure that the successes of one decade might not be lost in the next. For brief periods and usually on a state level something approaching mass support for founding a mental hospital might be aroused and large sums raised among the public, but this feeling seldom outlasted the actual construction of the institution. The public did not participate en masse in the "cult of curability" or the great enthusiasm of many psychiatrists and reformers.[39] The "cult" reflected less of a spectacular public swing from pessimism to optimism than a moderately successful attempt by a relatively small group of people to re-educate laymen to a more hopeful and informed outlook and to enlist their support for mental hospitals.

(10)

S U M M A R Y   A N D   C O N C L U S I O N

From the time of Rush to the Civil War, American psychiatrists made advances in the definition and diagnosis of insanity, organized psychiatry into a medical specialty, and established public respect for their profession. Between 1789 and the mid-1860's a virtual revolution occurred in the treatment of the insane. Up until that period insanity had been considered incurable. Then moral management began to achieve an apparent record of phenomenal recoveries and seemed to be the panacea for mental illness. Even if superintendents exaggerated and sometimes deliberately distorted recovery figures, the new psychological treatment seemed to produce many cures. Reformers and physicians were convinced that insanity could be cured, or at least alleviated, with proper care in therapeutic institutions. But just as these reform efforts reached fruition, asylum superintendents began to lose their optimism and slowly slipped into a pessimism that persisted for almost a hundred years. Once again insanity was looked upon as a dread disease from which few recovered.

Moral management was never firmly established in the United States. It required optimism based upon belief in the goodness of mankind and upon successful therapeutic results, which in turn depended upon the attitude of psychiatrists and other asylum personnel and upon better scientific understanding of mental illness. Only a fortunate conjuncture of circumstances brought all of these factors into play. The philosophy of the Enlightenment and the revolutionary achievements of Pinel and Tuke and their American followers created the necessary optimism. The middle-class and upper-class origin of patients treated in the first asylums assured both the sympathy of psychiatrists and the income needed to keep the institutions small enough to provide individualized care. The initial success in restoring patients gave impetus to the further development of moral treatment and to the maintenance of a hopeful spirit.

The balance was disturbed when large numbers of the insane poor and later the foreign born entered the new state hospitals. For reasons of economy most of these institutions were built for custodial care, and there were not nearly enough of them. Before 1865 only as few as one-third of the insane could be crowded into the existing public asylums. Conditions there, combined with psychiatrists' prejudices or their inability to understand lower-class patients, defeated attempts at moral treatment and reduced the probability of achieving cures. Many superintendents concluded that patients in the public hospitals were untreatable and incurable; although they should not be treated cruelly, perhaps they did not deserve moral therapy. The result was that custodial institutions became filled with apparently incurable masses of insane inmates who came there to sit and eventually to die, forgotten.

At the same time, optimism also began to wane in the corporate asylums, which maintained an environment for practicing moral treatment. Despite increasing numbers of incurable cases, the novelty of moral management sustained enthusiasm for a while. By the late 1850's, however, some psychiatrists feared that its limits had been reached even in some of the best institutions. By 1900 moral treatment in the corporate hospitals had lost both its predominance and much of its psychological content. It seems that psychiatrists could not long remain hopeful and fully committed to moral treatment without seeing a continuing growth in the rate of cure. When the recovery rate declined, they were greatly disappointed, for they had seen in moral treatment not simply an effective therapeutic technique but a means of virtually eliminating insanity as a serious illness. The result was that even when they did not abandon moral treatment outright, they eliminated much that was crucial to its practice. This process did not lead, as it had in the state hospitals, to mere custody of patients. Therapeutic efforts continued, but they were mainly somatic; physiological methods became popular and pushed the psychological approach into the background.

Opinions about the nature of insanity also were changing. The rising proportion of apparently incurable cases among middle-class and upper-class hospital patients became more and more difficult to explain except by regarding insanity as hereditary, somatic, and inherently incurable. This outlook found support in the growing influence of the concept of local pathology in medicine and the strictly somatic approach to illness that it engendered. Psychiatrists began to apply these ideas to all aspects of insanity. Because the psychological approach seemed to have reached an impasse, they turned to explanations that were proving useful in other fields of medicine and that had long dominated their own thinking about the pathology of insanity.

The decline in emphasis upon the psychological elements in therapy and upon the psychological aspects of the nature of mental illness stemmed in part from the desire of psychiatrists to make their specialty as objective as the more advanced sciences of physics or chemistry. This may also help to explain the indifference of the medical profession to psychiatry; in practicing moral management, psychiatrists seemed to be dealing with illness in a "non-medical" way.

Beginning with Pinel, they found objective "medical means" so ineffective in dealing with insanity that moral treatment became their main hope. The subjectivity of this new therapy could be a source of weakness as well as strength, however. As long as the doctor-patient relationship had great importance in treatment, the individual psychiatrist's personality and attitudes influenced rates of recovery and the tone of psychiatric thought. If inexpensive chemical cures for insanity had existed, the personal traits and viewpoints of psychiatrists and the social, psychological, and physical environment in the asylums would not have mattered as much. The "low" state of scientific knowledge about insanity and its treatment gave great significance to the "non-medical" outlook of psychiatrists. Of course, even today no one understands the biology and chemistry of mental illness, and it may well be that the "subjective" methods are necessary. The social viewpoints as well as the personalities of psychiatrists and psychiatric personnel may indeed be crucial to successful therapy.

As it was, American psychiatrists of the mid-nineteenth century, especially those searching for an objective "medical" therapy, did not seem to realize how much their own "non-medical" ideas and attitudes affected their theories and practices. Psychiatry as a medical specialty owed its existence to the overthrow of traditional medical and popular prejudices. But psychiatrists, who were self-conscious and analytical about their "medical" ideas, accepted many of the prejudices of their socio-economic class and incorporated them uncritically into their theories about mental illness. This inclination was so great that at times they abdicated a scientific approach for a religious or moralistic one. By 1865 they had not yet adopted the idea, then gaining acceptance among scientists, that religion and morality were irrelevant to science and medicine.

Psychiatric theories about mental health and disease, based on alleged psychological and physiological laws governing the human body, revealed a conception about the "good life" that was typical of the Protestant middle class from which psychiatrists came. On the surface they gave approval to the Greek "middle way": Every man should conduct himself with moderation in all things; passions, desires for pleasure, intellectual activity, and physical exertion should be kept within bounds. The middle-class virtues of work, religious duty, self-control, and self-abnegation were extolled, and imaginative thought, sensual delights, business speculation, excessive search for fame and glory, and self-indulgence were condemned as dangerous to mental health. Psychiatrists objected to a life whose primary aim was self-aggrandizement and pleasure. They criticized civilization, saying it caused insanity, but their criticism was based in part on prejudice against industrial development and the classes associated with it—capitalists and factory workers. These classes seemed most guilty of leading self-centered lives untinged by moral and religious purposes.

Their emphasis on religious and moral righteousness and the need to obey natural laws conflicted with their desire to develop an objective attitude toward mental patients. This conflict was not resolved by the profession as a whole, but some psychiatrists—Woodward, Ray, and Brigham, for example—along with lay reform leaders tried to judge people by their heredity, upbringing, education, and social condition.

Despite some ambivalence, most psychiatrists and reformers taught that usually circumstances beyond the individual's control caused him to fall ill and behave in an abnormal fashion; he remained a human being, however unattractive, who needed compassion and care. This propaganda, together with the accomplishments of mental institutions, succeeded to the extent that the public gradually accepted the idea that insanity was a natural disease amenable to humane management in special hospitals. This did not mean that laymen switched sharply from negative to positive feelings; their knowledge of insanity was enlarged and they were willing to grant its victims the benefits of medical care.

American life before the Civil War came increasingly under rationalistic influences. Men were turning to natural explanations of phenomena, and the achievements of science and industry engendered optimism about man's ability to control his environment and his own physiological processes. This secularization of American society—a process occurring throughout the Western world—gave support to a shift away from traditional and superstitious concepts.

Of course, countertendencies existed, as shown in the resurgence of Protestant revivalism and the moralistic and religious elements in pre-Civil War reform movements. Considering the role that moralizing played in so many aspects of American life, it is not surprising that the public found it difficult to think in terms other than good or bad about persons whose "bad" behavior characterized their illness. Moreover, it may be unrealistic to expect laymen to have taken a clinical attitude when the medical profession in general and psychiatrists in particular often could not.

Ambivalent attitudes toward insanity arose in part from the clash of scientific with legal and religious viewpoints, a conflict that is still unresolved. The sharpest challenge to psychiatric thought came when physicians sought to apply their knowledge to problems that impinged upon the prerogatives of law and religion. To lawyers, judges, and those charged with law enforcement, the acceptance of psychiatrists as final authorities on mental illness seemed to endanger social stability. In matters of morality, the clergy would not yield to the psychiatrists, for the traditional concepts of guilt and sin were basic to orthodox Christian theology. These reservations, however, did not preclude the recognition by jurists and clergymen of the value of medical treatment for those they acknowledged as insane.

Ironically, the public institutions that played such an important part in disillusioning psychiatrists about the curability of mental illness tended to make the public more hopeful. The propaganda for state-supported mental hospitals did not explain that these institutions might not produce the same results attributed to corporate asylums, so that at the same time as psychiatrists began to doubt their initial claims to therapeutic success, the lay public was becoming more optimistic than ever before. Eventually the public caught up with the psychiatrists and reverted to a hopelessness that mental health specialists are again trying to overcome.

Today a new era in hospital psychiatry may be under way. Moral treatment has been revived in more expanded and complex form with the aid of tranquilizing drugs and with new names—milieu therapy, therapeutic community, total-push therapy, open hospital. Large scale research is being conducted into the physiology and chemistry of mental illness. New drives are being launched to motivate the public, which must give moral as well as financial support to reform efforts. Education is still necessary. Recent studies indicate that public conceptions of mental illness have changed little from the time moral treatment was in vogue, despite the propaganda of mental hygiene workers. According to these investigations,[1] the average American, though not grossly uninformed, has many lacunae in his knowledge of mental illness and still finds it difficult to recognize the less obvious or less extreme forms. The stigma attached to mental illness persists. Portrayals of the mentally ill in the mass media, geared to fit the requirements of commercial entertainment rather than public enlightenment, tend to reinforce traditional concepts: "The symptoms of mental illness are exaggerated, the causes and treatment greatly oversimplified and often erroneous, and mental illness usually appears in a context of 'horror,' sin, and violence." [2]

Obviously, the efforts of the past have not been effective in surmounting the public's ignorance and negativism. Because of the lack of progress in the care of mental patients, the Joint Commission on Mental Illness and Health was appointed by the Federal Government in 1955 to study and evaluate the needs and the resources of the mentally ill and to make recommendations for a national mental health program. It suggested that educational campaigns take into account the special nature of mental illness—the fact that it *is* different from clearly physical illness and difficult to understand, and that the mentally ill are repugnant to most people. The Commission also recommended that such programs should clarify the forms of mental illness, the average person's reactions to it, and the means of coping with it. Finally, the prevailing defeatism that hampers effective treatment must be overcome.[3]

Public opinion is important to insure therapeutic treatment for mental patients, but the outlook of laymen in positions of political and financial power is far more crucial. If they do not appropriate the necessary massive funds for hospitals, personnel, and research, little progress will be made in replacing custodial with therapeutic care. Another requirement is an improvement in the attitudes of psychiatrists toward the great number of mental patients from the lower classes. The study of the rise and decline of moral treatment in the nineteenth century does not appear to justify much optimism about the current wave of reform unless at least these prerequisites are met. Moral therapy was difficult to sustain over an extended time, and the conditions for its successful practice were complex, expensive, and sensitive to changes in the attitudes of the lay public and the medical profession. Those who are concerned hope that the attempt to reintroduce it will not meet the same fate as the original movement or have the same dismal consequences for the insane.

Bibliographical Note

In footnotes and bibliography the *American Journal of Insanity* is cited as *AJI*.

Citations from the periodic reports of mental hospitals have the following conventional form in footnotes: Name of hospital [standard name (see bibliography)]; place [if necessary for identification]; number of report [if available, i.e., 4th]; year to which report applies, or, when such information is complicated, the year of publication; page reference. A complete list of all hospitals whose reports were cited is given in the bibliography.

Introduction

1 Joint Commission on Mental Illness and Health, *Action for Mental Health, Final Report* (New York: Basic Books, Inc., 1961).
2 Oliver Wendell Holmes, *Currents and Counter-Currents in Medical Science, with Other Addresses and Essays* (Boston: Ticknor and Fields, 1861), p. 7.

Chapter 1

1 J. Sanbourne Bockoven notes that the naturalistic approach "had the effect of emphasizing those qualities which individuals have in common and the impossibility of an absolute

standard of individual responsibility. Logically then . . . all men could be looked upon as equal and forgivable for their evil actions" ("Moral Treatment in American Psychiatry," *Journal of Nervous and Mental Disease,* CXXIV [August, 1956], 172). See also Emil Kraepelin, *One Hundred Years of Psychiatry,* trans. from the German by Wade Baskin (New York: Citadel Press, 1962), p. 70.

2 Norman Dain and Eric T. Carlson, "Social Class and Psychological Medicine in the United States, 1789–1824," *Bulletin of the History of Medicine,* XXXIII (September-October, 1959), 454–465.

3 William Cullen, *First Lines of the Practice of Physic* (Philadelphia: Thomas Dobson, 1816), II, 155.

4 There were, of course, others who advocated reforms. But, as far as can be determined, the work of such men as the Italian Vincenzo Chiarugi, Abraham Joly in Geneva, and John Gottfried Langermann in Bayreuth, all of whom removed chains from the insane, was not familiar to many Americans at the time. The Spanish, unknown to most European and American physicians, had practiced humanitarian methods in the care of the insane before Pinel.

5 William Buchan, *Domestic Medicine; or, The Family Physician* . . . (Philadelphia: Printed by John Dunlap, for R. Aitken, 1772), p. 303.

6 Edward Cutbush, *An Inaugural Dissertation on Insanity* (Philadelphia: Printed by Zachariah Poulson, 1794), p. 14.

7 Buchan, p. 303; George Cheyne, *The English Malady; or, A Treatise of Nervous Disease of All Kinds, as Spleen Vapours, Lowness of Spirits, Hypochondrical, and Hysterical Distempers, &c.* (London: Printed, and Dublin: Re-printed by S. Powell for George Risk, George Ewing, and William Smith, 1733), p. 10; George Wallis, *The Art of Preventing Diseases, and Restoring Health, Founded on Rational Principles and Adapted to Persons of Every Capacity* (New York: Printed by Samuel Campbell, 1794), p. 432.

8 Andrew Harper, *A Treatise on the Real Cause and Cure of Insanity* . . . (London: Printed for C. Stalker and J. Walter, 1789), pp. 19–20. Harper did not consider the melancholic and hypochondriac states as insanity (*ibid.*, p. 20).

9 See, for example: Wallis, pp. 433–434. Many American physicians thought that the great socio-economic and geographic mobility in the New World were responsible for much of the insanity there (Leonard K. Eaton, *New England Hospitals, 1790–1833* [Ann Arbor: University of Michigan Press, c1957], p. 65). Democratic government was thought to foster insanity because it allowed freer rein to the individual's passions than despotic regimes; see remarks in Benjamin Rush, *Medical Inquiries and Observations upon the Diseases of the Mind* (4th ed.; Philadelphia: John Grigg, 1830), pp. 45, 63–67; and Alexander Anderson, *An Inaugural Dissertation on Chronic Mania* (New York: Printed by T. and J. Swords, 1796), p. 21.

10 Cheyne, pp. 36–38; David Macbride, *A Methodical Introduction to the Theory and Practice of Physic* (London: Printed for W. Strahan [and others], 1772), pp. 182–183; Richard Mead, *The Medical Works of Richard Mead, M. D., Physician to His Late Majesty King George II* (New ed.; Edinburgh: Printed for Alexander Donaldson and Charles Elliott, 1775), p. 366.

11 Cheyne, pp. 33–34. Thomas Trotter stated that two-thirds of all man's ills were of a nervous nature, as compared with Cheyne's estimate, seventy-odd years earlier, that one-third of the ills of the English were nervous disorders. Trotter also believed that the "inferiour orders" were becoming subject to nervous ailments at an alarming rate (*A View of the Nervous Temperament* . . . [Troy, N. Y.: Wright, Goodenow, & Stockwell, 1808], p. xiii).

12 Cheyne, pp. 34–38; Cullen, II, 51. Joseph Mason Cox thought that insanity was "peculiarly endemical" to England, the consequence of "early dissipation, unrestrained licentiousness,

habitual luxury, inordinate taste for speculation, defective systems of education, laxity of morals; but more especially, promiscuous intermarriages, where one or both of the parties have hereditary claims to alienation of mind." (*Practical Observations on Insanity* . . . [from 2d corrected and enlarged London ed.; Philadelphia: Thomas Dobson, 1811], p. v).

13 Cullen, II, 51.

14 Rush, *Medical Inquiries . . . upon the Diseases of the Mind*, p. 64.

15 John Reid, *Essays on Hypochondriacal and Other Nervous Affections* (Philadelphia: M. Carey & Son, 1817), p. 8.

16 These beliefs were widely held among physicians during the eighteenth and through the mid-nineteenth centuries. One student of medicine explained that children were not afflicted with insanity because they were not capable of abstract reasoning (Cutbush, pp. 8–10). Another generalized that "science, so far from considering imagination as, within certain limitations, a needful auxiliary, has viewed her agency as ever prejudicial" (Elias Marks, *Conjectural Inquiry into the Relative Influence of the Mind and Stomach: an Inaugural Dissertation* [New York: Printed by Van Winkle & Wiley, 1815], p. 2). "The transition from *poetic ardour* to madness is easy," wrote another physician, and recommended "a pleasing variety of employments" and the avoidance of concentration (Anderson, pp. 6, 18, 22 ff), Theodric Romeyn Beck claimed that "men of genious and talents seem, in many instances, to fall victims to the disease of insanity" (*An Inaugural Dissertation on Insanity* [New York: Printed by J. Seymour, 1811], p. 9).

17 Arthur O. Lovejoy, *Reflections on Human Nature* (Baltimore: The Johns Hopkins Press, c1961).

18 There were some, however, who rejected the purely somatic viewpoint in the late eighteenth and early nineteenth centuries. This was particularly true in Germany, where, influenced by romantic medicine, the psychological approach gained importance. See Erwin H. Ackerknecht, *A Short History of Psychiatry*, trans. from the German by Sulammith Wolff (New York: Hafner Publishing Company, 1959), pp. 31–32, 52–53.

19 For a concise discussion of medical theories in relation to mental illness at the close of the eighteenth century see William Logie Russell, *The New York Hospital: a History of the Psychiatric Service, 1771–1936* (New York: Columbia University Press, 1945), pp. 1–13.

20 Buchan, p. 66.

21 Kraepelin, pp. 51–52, 56–58.

22 See Harper, pp. 62 ff.; Reid, p. 6; Buchan, pp. 299, 301–303, 304, 306–308; Mead, p. 373.

23 Cullen, II, 51–52, 165–166; Buchan, p. 306; Robert Whytt, *Observations on the Nature, Causes, and Cure of Those Disorders Which Have Been Commonly Called Nervous, Hypochondriac, or Hysteric* . . . (2d ed., corrected; Edinburgh: Printed for T. Becket and P. A. De Hondt, London; and J. Balfour, Edinburgh, 1765), pp. 357, 439; *Encyclopaedia Britannica* (3d ed.; Edinburgh: Printed for A. Bell and C. Macfarquhar, 1797), XI, 283–284.

24 There were signs of optimism about insanity in America even before the work of Pinel and Rush at the close of the eighteenth century. In 1752 the founders of the Pennsylvania Hospital, appealing for state funds, expressed the unorthodox belief that insanity was curable and planned to admit the insane as patients (Thomas G. Morton, Assisted by Frank Woodbury, *The History of the Pennsylvania Hospital* [rev. ed.; Philadelphia: Times Printing House, 1897], p. 10). Benjamin Franklin thought, erroneously, that two-thirds of the "Mad People" admitted to Bethlehem Hospital (Bedlam) in England "and there treated promptly," were cured (*Some Account of the Pennsylvania Hospital from Its First Rise to the Beginning of the Fifth Month, Called May, 1754* [Philadelphia: Printed by B. Franklin and D. Hall, 1754], p. 4). The governors of the New York Hospital also

took the position in 1771 that mental illness was curable, although it is doubtful that they were as optimistic as Franklin (Russell, p. vii).

25 William G. McLoughlin, Jr., *Modern Revivalism; Charles Grandison Finney to Billy Graham* (New York: Ronald Press Company, c1959), pp. 9–10.

26 Ackerknecht, pp. 32–33.

27 See *ibid.*, pp. 30–37, for a brief discussion of this point.

28 Beck, pp. 27–28.

29 Bockoven, *Journal of Nervous and Mental Disease*, CXXIV (August, 1956), 175.

30 Philippe Pinel, *A Treatise on Insanity* . . . , trans. from the French by D. D. Davis (Sheffield: Printed by W. Todd, for Cadell and Davies, London, 1806), pp. 5, 110–111. Beck (pp. 24–25) referred approvingly to Pinel's position on this point.

31 Quoted from remarks of a visitor, Dr. de la Rive, to the Retreat, in Daniel Hack Tuke, *Reform in the Treatment of the Insane* . . . London: J. & A. Churchill, 1892), p. 36.

32 *Ibid.*, pp. 27–28, 34–38.

33 Quoted in *ibid.*, pp. 28, 36.

34 Rush wrote to the Board of Managers of the Pennsylvania Hospital on November 11, 1789: "Under the conviction that the patients afflicted by madness should be the first objects of the care of a physician of the Pennsylvania Hospital, I have attempted to relieve them." But he found this impossible to do. The cells were damp in winter, hot in summer; they were hard to ventilate and smelled offensively. Patients usually caught cold, and some died of consumption after being placed in these cells. (Benjamin Rush, *Letters of Benjamin Rush*, ed. L. H. Butterfield ["Memoirs of the American Philosophical Society, Vol. 30, Pt. 1–2"; Princeton, N. J.: Published for the American Philosophical Society by Princeton University Press, 1951], I, 528–529.)

35 Pinel's *Traité médico-philosophique sur l'aliénation mentale, ou la manie* appeared in 1801 (Paris: Richard, Caille, et Ravier, an IX [i.e., 1801]) and in English translation in 1806 (*A Treatise on Insanity* . . .). Rush read French and knew of a partial translation of Pinel's work probably available before 1806 (Rush to James Rush, March 19, 1810, *Letters of Benjamin Rush*, II, 1040). But even if we make the unlikely assumption that Rush first learned of Pinel's work in 1806, it would be interesting to know if it influenced his call in 1810 for separation of violent patients in isolated buildings, separate floors for the different sexes; labor, exercise, and amusements for patients; more attendants; isolation of patients from visitors; improved facilities for higher paying patients; and better sanitary conditions (Rush to the Managers of the Pennsylvania Hospital, September 24th, 1810, *ibid.*, II, 1064–1066). As for Tuke's work, it is difficult to believe that Rush was ignorant of the accomplishments of the York Retreat, but there is no direct evidence in Rush's book, *Medical Inquiries . . . upon the Diseases of the Mind.*

36 George Rosen, "Political Order and Human Health in Jeffersonian Thought," *Bulletin of the History of Medicine*, XXVI (January-February, 1952), 40.

37 Benjamin Rush, "The Influence of Physical Causes upon the Moral Faculty," *The Selected Writings of Benjamin Rush*, ed. Dagobert D. Runes (New York: Philosophical Library, c1947), p. 195.

38 Clifford B. Farr, "Benjamin Rush and American Psychiatry," *American Journal of Psychiatry, 1844–1944, Centennial Anniversary Issue* (n.p.: [1944]), p. 4.

39 I. Woodbridge Riley, *American Philosophy, the Early Schools* (New York: Dodd, Mead & Company, 1907), p. 422.

40 Rush, *Medical Inquiries . . . upon the Diseases of the Mind*, pp. 9, 14–15.

41 Riley, p. 452.

42 Richard H. Shryock, "The Psychiatry of Benjamin Rush," *American Journal of Psychiatry*, CI (January, 1945), 430.

43 Riley, pp. 452–453. Rush's favorite philosophical work was materialist David Hartley's *Observations on Man, His Frame, His Duty, and His Expectations,* from which he quoted frequently; in a letter to John Adams dated October 31, 1807, Rush called Hartley "the great good, I had almost said inspired, Dr. Hartley" *(Letters of Benjamin Rush,* II, 953). For a discussion of Rush's tendency toward materialism see: Joseph L. Blau (ed.) *American Philosophic Addresses, 1700–1900* ("Columbia Studies in American Culture, No. 17"; New York: Columbia University Press, c1946), p. 9; Joseph L. Blau, *Men and Movements in American Philosophy* ("Prentice-Hall Philosophy Series"; New York: Prentice-Hall, Inc., c1952), pp. 67–70; Herbert W. Schneider, *A History of American Philosophy* ("Columbia Studies in American Culture, No. 18"; New York: Columbia University Press, c1946), pp. 74–76.

44 Benjamin Rush, "The Progress of Medicine," in *The Selected Writings of Benjamin Rush,* p. 236.

45 Esmond Ray Long, in *A History of Pathology* ([Baltimore: Williams & Wilkins Company, 1928], p. 123), mistakenly calls Rush a Brunonian. Some thirty years later, Long, writing *A History of American Pathology* ([Springfield, Ill.: Charles C. Thomas, c1962], p. 17), devotes only three sentences to Rush's ideas. Other brief discussions of Rush's theory of pathology are given in: *The Autobiography of Benjamin Rush; His "Travels through Life" together with His Commonplace Book for 1789–1813* (ed. with introduction and notes by George W. Corner ["Memoirs of the American Philosophical Society, Vol. 25"; Princeton, N. J.: Published for the American Philosophical Society by Princeton University Press, 1948]); Nathan G. Goodman, *Benjamin Rush, Physician and Citizen, 1746–1813* (Philadelphia: University of Pennsylvania Press, 1934); and Richard Harrison Shryock, *The Development of Modern Medicine; an Interpretation of the Social and Scientific Factors Involved* (Philadelphia: University of Pennsylvania Press, 1936), pp. 28–29. My short discussion is a partial summary of my more extensive unpublished study of Rush's theory of pathology and is derived primarily from Benjamin Rush, "Outlines of a Theory of Fever," in his *Medical Inquiries and Observations* (2d ed., rev. and enl. by the author; Philadelphia: J. Conrad & Co., 1805), III, 3–66.

46 *Ibid.,* 57.

47 Rush to James Rush, May 10th, 1810, *Letters of Benjamin Rush,* II, 1048–1049; Rush to James Rush, June 8th, 1810, *ibid.,* II, 1052; Rush to John Redman Coxe, September 5, 1810, *ibid.,* II, 1058–1060.

48 Rush, *Medical Inquiries and Observations upon the Diseases of the Mind,* with an introduction by Dr. S. Bernard Wortis ("The History of Medicine Series Issued under the Auspices of the Library of The New York Academy of Medicine, No. 15"; New York: Published under the auspices of the Library of the New York Academy of Medicine by Hafner Publishing Company, 1962), pp. 24–25. This edition is a facsimile of the original first edition, published in 1812.

49 Rush to Ashton Alexander, December 21, 1795, *Letters of Benjamin Rush,* II, 766–767; Richard H. Shryock, "The Beginnings: From Colonial Days to the Foundation of the American Psychiatric Association," *One Hundred Years of American Psychiatry* (New York: Published for the American Psychiatric Association by the Columbia University Press, c1944), p. 12.

50 Rush, *Medical Inquiries . . . upon the Diseases of the Mind,* 4th ed., pp. 46, 246–247.

51 *Ibid.,* pp. 173, 191.

52 *Ibid.,* pp. 142–143.

53 Dain and Carlson, *Bulletin of the History of Medicine,* XXXIII (September-October, 1959), 455–460; see also "The Insane and Their Treatment Past and Present," *National Quarterly Review,* VII (September, 1863), 213. Kraepelin held that this belief arose because "stupid or mentally deficient patients . . . seemed passively to endure whatever was inflicted upon them" (Kraepelin, p. 12).

54 Albert Deutsch, *The Mentally Ill in America; a History of Their Care and Treatment from Colonial Times* (2d ed., rev. and enlarged; New York: Columbia University Press, c1949), p. 85; Goodman, p. 265; Fay, Jay Wharton, *American Psychology before William James* (New Brunswick, N. J.: Rutgers University Press, 1939), p. 72; James Hendrie Lloyd, "Benjamin Rush and His Critics," *Annals of Medical History*, new series, II (September, 1930), 472–473; Fritz Wittels, "The Contribution of Benjamin Rush to Psychiatry," *Bulletin of the History of Medicine*, XX (July, 1946), 162.

55 Shryock, "The Beginnings," *One Hundred Years of American Psychiatry*, p. 13; Clarence P. Oberndorf, *A History of Psychoanalysis in America* (New York: Grune & Stratton, 1953), p. 18.

56 Rush, *Medical Inquiries . . . upon the Diseases of the Mind*, facsimile of 1812 ed., p. 343.

57 Eric T. Carlson, "The Medical Psychology of Benjamin Rush," Unpublished paper, New York, 1962, pp. 21–25.

58 Rush, *Medical Inquiries . . . upon the Diseases of the Mind*, 4th ed., pp. 262, 355–357.

59 *Medical Inquiries and Observations upon the Diseases of the Mind.*

60 In 1788 a visiting Frenchman noted with approval the care given to the insane at the Pennsylvania Hospital, especially by Dr. Rush; similar French asylums seemed "atrocious" by comparison (J. P. Brissot de Warville, *New Travels in the United States of America, Performed in 1788*, trans. from the French [London: J. S. Jordan, 1792], pp. 211–213. The Rev. Manasseh Cutler visited the Pennsylvania Hospital in 1787 and described the condition of the "maniacs" as follows: "Some of them have beds; most of them clean straw. Some of them were extremely fierce and raving, nearly or quite naked; some singing and dancing; some in despair; some were dumb and would not open their mouths; others incessantly talking. . . . This would have been a melancholy scene indeed, had it not been that there was every possible relief afforded them in the power of man. Everything about them, notwithstanding the labor and trouble it must have required, was neat and clean." Although partly underground strong rooms were used as cells, and heating and ventilating arrangements were primitive, Cutler found the total effect to be "pleasing evidence of what humanity and benevolence can do." (William Parker Cutler and Julia Perkins Cutler, *Life, Journals, and Correspondence of Rev. Manasseh Cutler* (Cincinnati: Robert Clarke & Co., 1888), I, 280–281.

61 In the opinion of F. B. Sanborn, editor of *Memoirs of Pliny Earle, M.D., with Extracts from His Diary and Letters (1830–1892) and Selections from His Professional Writings (1839–1891)* ([Boston: Damrell & Upham, 1898], p. 155), Rush's theories on the treatment of insanity greatly influenced American medical thought as late as 1840. This is not true for the majority of American psychiatrists (including Earle) in 1840, but is probably valid for the average medical practitioners (see Chapters III–IV, VI). For a recent evaluation of Rush's influence see Farr, *American Journal of Psychiatry, 1844–1944*, pp. 3–15. Farr writes that Rush's admirers "were legion, including, *e.g.*, practically all of the medical profession in South Carolina" (p. 14). See also similar remarks by Rush's latest and best biographer (Goodman, pp. 128, 130, 141–142).

62 Goodman, p. 132. See also James E. Gibson, "Benjamin Rush's Apprenticed Students," *Transactions and Studies of the College of Physicians of Philadelphia*, 4th series, XIV (December, 1946), 127–132.

63 Eaton, pp. 30, 57–69. A New Englander, George Parkman, was the first American, so far as I can determine, who was trained by Pinel and his successor, J. E. D. Esquirol, in Paris (Oliver Wendell Holmes, *The Benefactors of the Medical School of Harvard University; with a Biographical Sketch of the Late Dr. George Parkman* [Boston: Ticknor, Reed and

Fields, 1850], pp. 19–24). Parkman, of course, became a strong advocate of their system of moral management (George Parkman, *Management of Lunatics with Illustrations of Insanity* [Boston: Printed by John Elliot, 1817], pp. 15–21 ff.) and owned a small private asylum in Massachusetts. In all likelihood Rush's many southern students accepted his approach to mental illness; some southern physicians, at any rate, did attempt reforms. The Friends' Asylum at Frankford, Pa., which practiced moral treatment, received visitors from the South who wanted to introduce the new methods in their states (Manuscript Diary of the Superintendent of the Friends' Asylum, Frankford, Pa., May 21, 1822; March 25, 1823; hereafter cited as Friends' Asylum, Superintendent's Diary). The second superintendent of the Eastern Kentucky Lunatic Asylum also tried to implement the Friends' system (Deutsch, pp. 107–108). These attempts at reform in the South seemed to have failed, according to several articles in the *Boston Medical and Surgical Journal:* "Insanity in Kentucky," XXIV (April 21, 1841), 165–171; "Kentucky Lunatic Asylum," XXVI (March 9, 1842), 80–81; W., "Insane Hospitals in the United States," XVIII (June 22, 1838), 309–313.

64 See Section 7 of Chapter I.

65 Friends' Asylum, Superintendent's Diary, for example, contains references to visits from hundreds of asylum physicians, trustees, superintendents, and other interested physicians and laymen, foreign and American. The same was true of the Hartford Retreat and McLean Asylum, both of which were known in Europe and throughout the United States. Psychiatrists Thomas S. Kirkbride and Pliny Earle served as resident physicians at the Friends' Asylum; Samuel B. Woodward was Todd's associate before he went to head the State Lunatic Hospital at Worcester, Mass.; Todd's successor at the Retreat, the brilliant Thomas G. Lee, who died at an early age in 1836, had been Todd's protege; and Amariah Brigham, founder of the *American Journal of Insanity*, and John S. Butler, later the superintendent of the Boston Lunatic Hospital and the Hartford Retreat, were influenced in their early careers by Todd.

66 One student recorded 396 pages of notes from Rush's lectures; 60 concerned mental illness (Farr, *American Journal of Psychiatry, 1844–1944*, p. 11). Russell (p. 59) concludes on the basis of another student's diary that only two lectures given at Columbia Medical College in the late 1790's may have discussed mental illness. The student, Alexander Anderson, discussed his thesis on chronic mania with his professors, Drs. Bard, Hosack, and Mitchill.

67 See: Anderson, *An Inaugural Dissertation on Chronic Mania;* Cutbush, *An Inaugural Dissertation on Insanity;* Beck, *An Inaugural Dissertation on Insanity;* Ashton Alexander, *An Inaugural Dissertation on the Influence of One Disease, in the Cure of Others* (Philadelphia: Printed by Alexander M'Kenzie, 1795); John C. Otto, *An Inaugural Essay on Epilepsy* (Philadelphia: Printed by Lang and Ustick, 1796); Joseph Parrish, *An Inaugural Dissertation on the Influence of the Passions upon the Body, in the Production and Cure of Diseases* (Philadelphia: Printed by Kimber, Conrad, and Co., 1805); Henry Rose, *An Inaugural Dissertation on the Effects of the Passions upon the Body* (Philadelphia: Printed by William W. Woodward, 1794); Thomas Middleton Stuart, *An Inaugural Essay on Genius and Its Diseases* (New York: Printed by Collins and Co., 1819). A list and survey of theses on psychiatric subjects accepted at the College of Physicians and Surgeons and Columbia College between 1796 and 1840 is found in Paul Stolley, "Psychiatry in New York State (1770–1820)," an unpublished paper written under the supervision of Dr. Eric T. Carlson at the Payne Whitney Psychiatric Clinic (Dept. of Psychiatry, Cornell University Medical College), Summer, 1959 (pp. 7–30).

68 Review of *Medical Inquiries and Observations upon the Diseases of the Mind*, by Benjamin Rush, *Medical Repository*, new series, I, No. 2 (1813), 146–147, 155–156.

69 George Hayward, *Some Observations on Dr. Rush's Work, on "The Diseases of the Mind,"* *with Remarks on the Nature and Treatment of Insanity* [Extracted from the *New England Journal of Medicine and Surgery*] (Boston: n.p., 1818), pp. 3, 16, 12, 3–4.

70 Charles Lawrence, *History of the Philadelphia Almshouses and Hospitals* . . . (Philadelphia: The Author, 1905), p. 57.

71 John Vaughan, "Remarkable Cases of Madness; Communicated by Dr. John Vaughan of Wilmington (State of Delaware), to Dr. Mitchill," *Medical Repository,* V, No. 4 (1802), 409. Vaughan said that he got the idea of applying cold in this case from a piece by Dr. Brown (of Bath [England?]) in the *Medical Repository.* (See G. G. Brown, "The Efficacy of Cold in Madness," *Medical Repository,* IV, No. 2 [1801], 209–210.)

72 Samuel Brown, M. D., of New Orleans, "An Account of Two Cases of Convulsions, Alternating with Temporary Insanity, Relieved by Violent Pressure over the Stomach," *Medical Repository,* 2d hexade, V (August, September, and October, 1807), 145–147; Vine Utley, "An Historical Essay on Epileptic Convulsions, Exemplified by a Case, Successfully Treated by Dr. Vine Utley, of New-London, Connecticut," *Medical Repository,* New Series, I, No. 4 (1813), 344–350. More enlightened views were sometimes expressed by leading physicians; see Review of *An Inaugural Dissertation on Insanity* . . . , *American Medical and Philosophical Register,* II (January, 1812), 349–352, a favorable review of Beck's summary of current psychiatric thought and advocacy of moral management, and a later article by Beck himself: Theodric Romeyn Beck, "An Account of Some of the Lunatic Asylums in the United States," *New-York Medical and Physical Journal,* VII (April, May, and June, 1828), 186–206. Stolley's paper also includes surveys of the medical journals of New York State and transactions of the medical societies of New York State on the subject of mental illness (pp. 31–44).

73 Some of these works available before 1824 were Rush, *Medical Inquiries . . . the Diseases of the Mind;* Pinel, *A Theatise on Insanity;* Trotter, *A View of the Nervous Temperament;* Beck, *An Inaugural Dissertation on Insanity;* Cox, *Practical Observations on Insanity;* John Haslam, *Considerations on the Moral Management of Insane Persons* (London: Printed for R. Hunter, 1817); John Ferriar, *Medical Histories and Reflections* (1st American ed.; 4 vols. in 1; Philadelphia: Thomas Dobson, 1816).

74 Dain and Carlson, *Bulletin of the History of Medicine,* XXXIII (September-October, 1959), 455–457.

75 William Frederick Norwood, *Medical Education in the United States before the Civil War* (Philadelphia: University of Pennsylvania Press, 1944), pp. 9, 29–56.

76 As late as 1874, Dr. George Chandler, superintendent of the State Lunatic Hospital at Worcester, Massachusetts, noted that the rural population generally had homes and conveniences for taking care of their insane and therefore sent fewer patients to the hospital than city-dwellers (State Lunatic Hospital at Worcester, *Annual Report,* 15th, 1847, p. 31).

77 Friends' Asylum, Superintendent's Diary, February 19, 1821; November 30, 1821.

78 Russell (p. 178) writes: "The governors of the New York Hospital did not intend to adhere to the proposal made by Thomas Eddy [a lay founder] that the practice at the Rural Retreat [Bloomingdale Asylum] should be confined 'almost exclusively to a course of moral treatment.'" See also Morton's description of the use of medical means at the Pennsylvania Hospital (pp. 125–126).

79 This was true as well of Dr. William Handy, superintendent of the New York Hospital from 1817 to 1818, who virtually rejected blood-letting and terror in favor of moral treatment for the insane (Russell, pp. 100–101). Parkman, as has been noted above, was trained by Pinel and Esquirol and espoused their ideas, but he never worked in the corporate, quasi-public mental hospitals, such as the McLean Asylum or the Hartford Retreat, that led the field.

80 Eaton, pp. 147–148; Charles Whitney Page, "Dr. Eli Todd and the Hartford Retreat," *AJI*, LXIX (April, 1913), 761–785. See also Leonard K. Eaton, "Eli Todd and the Hartford Retreat," *New England Quarterly*, XXVI (December, 1953), 435–453.

81 Rufus Wyman, *A Discourse on Mental Philosophy as Connected with Mental Disease,* Delivered before the Massachusetts Medical Society, June 2, 1830 (Boston: From the Office of the *Daily Advertiser, 1830*), p. 17. The only other published writings of Wyman were the annual reports of the McLean Asylum. For material about him see: Eaton, *New England Hospitals;* Morrill Wyman, Jr., *A Brief Record of the Lives and Writings of Dr. Rufus Wyman (1778–1842) and His Son, Dr. Morrill Wyman (1812–1903)* (Cambridge: Privately Printed, 1913); Eric T. Carlson and May F. Chale, "Dr. Rufus Wyman of the McLean Asylum," *American Journal of Psychiatry*, CXVI (May, 1960), pp. 1034–1037.

82 Rufus Wyman, p. 24.

Chapter 2

1 Rufus Wyman, [Report upon the State of the Asylum, during the First Triennial Term, Including also the Quarter Year Commencing October 1st, 1818] in *Address of the Trustees of Massachusetts General Hospital, to the Subscribers and the Public* (n.p.: [1822]), pp. 24–25.

2 [George Parkman], *Insanity;* Appendix to a Book, . . . Entitled, "Management of Lunatics, with Illustrations of Insanity, by Geo. Parkman, M. D. . . ." ([Boston?]: n.p., 1818), p. 11.

3 "Retreat for the Insane," *Christian Spectator,* VI (April, 1824), 219.

4 Franklin wrote many articles upon medical subjects, some of which were quite creditable in terms of the medical knowledge of his day. See Theodore Diller, *Franklin's Contribution to Medicine, Being a Collection of Letters Written by Benjamin Franklin, Bearing on the Science and Art of Medicine and Exhibiting His Social and Professional Intercourse with Various Physicians of Europe and America* (Brooklyn: A. T. Huntington, 1912), and William Pepper, *The Medical Side of Benjamin Franklin* (Philadelphia: William J. Campbell, 1911). As far as I can determine, Franklin was the earliest American experimenter with the use of electricity (electric shock) to treat paralyzed patients. Some years before 1757, he applied two wet-cell batteries to the limbs of these patients. He commented on the temporary success of his treatments: "And how far the apparent temporary advantage might arise from the exercise in the patients [*sic*] journey, and coming daily to my house, or from the spirits given by the hope of success, enabling them to exert more strength in moving their limbs, I will not pretend to say" (Benjamin Franklin, *Benjamin Franklin's Experiments; a New Edition of Franklin's Experiments and Observations on Electricity*, edited, with a critical and historical introduction, by I. Bernard Cohen [Cambridge, Mass.: Harvard University Press, 1941], pp. 346–347).

5 It is probable that Quaker Thomas Scattergood, who had visited the Retreat at York in January, 1797 (Thomas Scattergood, *Memoirs of Thomas Scattergood* . . . , compiled by William Evans and Thomas Evans [London: Charles Gilpin, 1845], p. 382), made the original proposal for the Friends' Asylum in 1810. Thomas Eddy, a Quaker merchant, led the founding of Bloomingdale Asylum in 1821 (Thomas Eddy, "Proposals for Improving the Care of the Insane, 1815," in *Some American Pioneers in Social Welfare; Select Documents with Editorial Notes*, ed. Edith Abbott ("The University of Chicago Social Service Series"; Chicago: University of Chicago Press, 1937), pp. 59–65.

6 *Meeting House and Counting House; the Quaker Merchants of Colonial Philadelphia,*

1682–1763 (Chapel Hill: Published for the Institute of Early American History and Culture at Williamsburg, Virginia, by the University of North Carolina Press), p. 9.

7 There are many entries concerning this subject in the Friends' Asylum, Superintendent's Diary. Daniel H. Tuke noted that historians of the York Retreat mistakenly claimed that non-restraint had been introduced there. He declared, "It never was . . . a dogma . . . of the Retreat that under no circumstances whatever is it justifiable to resort to mechanical means of restraint" (Tuke, p. 29).

8 See Friends' Asylum, Superintendent's Diary, Feb. 3, 1819; Feb. 8, 1819; Jan. 22, 1824, for reports of such visits, two of which were considered successful.

9 *Ibid.*, Feb. 8, 1819.

10 *Ibid.*, Sept. 8, 1819.

11 *Ibid.*, Oct. 15, 1819 ff.

12 *Ibid.*, May 24, 1819.

13 *Ibid.*, Dec. 4, 1820. For a discussion of this controversy see Norman Dain and Eric T. Carlson, "Milieu Therapy in the Nineteenth Century; Patient Care at the Friends' Asylum, Frankford, Pennsylvania, 1817–1861," *Journal of Nervous and Mental Disease,* CXXXI (October, 1960), 284–285.

14 Russell, p. 178. According to Dr. John W. Francis, a friend of Eddy, the latter changed his mind a few years before his death and came to recognize that "the proper administration of medicinal agents, was favourable to the treatment of insanity; nay, ofttimes indispensable" (Samuel Lorenzo Knapp, *The Life of Thomas Eddy; Comprising an Extensive Correspondence with Many of the Most Distinguished Philosophers and Philanthropists of This and Other Countries* [New York: Conner & Cooke, 1834], pp. 28–29).

15 It is also well known that Pinel left much of the direction of moral therapy at Bicêtre to Pussin, the asylum's lay superintendent (Evelyn A. Woods and Eric T. Carlson, "The Psychiatry of Philippe Pinel," *Bulletin of the History of Medicine,* XXXV [January-February, 1961], 23n). The governors of the Bloomingdale Asylum did not at first consider moral treatment the same as medical care and therefore gave its direction to laymen (Russell, pp. 178–179).

16 The first superintendent of the Friends' Asylum was aware of the limitations imposed upon the institution because only Quakers were accepted as patients. In 1821 he proposed that non-Quakers be admitted and that such a change would enable the inmates to be classified on the basis of type of illness, according to the best practice of European asylums. He also thought that the additional funds from non-Quaker patients would enable the admittance of Quakers unable to pay even the lowest rates ($2.00 per week) and help the Asylum to meet its expenses (Friends' Asylum, Superintendent's Diary, Feb. 19, 1821; Nov. 30, 1821; Dec. 16, 1821). For a more detailed discussion of this problem see Dain and Carlson, *Journal of Nervous and Mental Disease,* CXXXI (October, 1960), 280, 285–286.

17 For a perceptive analysis of Rush and some of his close friends' outlook toward disease see Daniel J. Boorstin, *The Lost World of Thomas Jefferson* (New York: Henry Holt and Company, c1948), pp. 50–53.

18 Jefferson to Rush, September 23, 1800, in Thomas Jefferson, *Works,* collected and edited by Paul Leicester Ford (New York: G. P. Putnam's Sons, 1905), IX, 146–147. Benjamin Smith Barton, the famous American botanist, said that the Lord never meant all mental and physical diseases to be cured (Boorstin, p. 52).

19 It does not seem likely that his son's illness promoted Rush's initial interest in mental patients. Rush's son John apparently suffered his first emotional disturbance in 1802, then suffered a breakdown in 1808 which eventually led to his confinement in Pennsylvania Hospital. Benjamin Rush gained exclusive charge of "maniacal patients" in 1787

and asked for improved care of them in 1789. His son's later illness probably gave him a deep personal interest in insanity, but there is no evidence that John Rush showed signs of mental disorder in 1787, when he was ten years old. See "Appendix 3. The Children of Benjamin and Julia Rush," in *The Autobiography of Benjamin Rush*, pp. 369–371.

20 Jefferson to Rush, Jan. 16, 1811, in Jefferson, *Works*, XI, 165–166.

21 There is an ambiguous exchange of letters between Jefferson's Secretary of the Treasury, Albert Gallatin, and the managers of the Pennsylvania Hospital about supporting insane seamen at the Federal government's expense. According to Gallatin, Jefferson directed that mentally ill seamen should not be kept at government expense as permanent residents at the hospital. When, however, Rush wrote to the managers of the hospital that these patients should not be discharged, the matter apparently was dropped. The issues involved are too complicated and the information too scanty to draw any conclusions about Jefferson's approach. Although the government might have been afraid that some seamen were malingering, lack of money in the seamen's medical insurance fund may have been the key factor. See Morton, pp. 229–231; Eaton, *New England Hospitals*, p. 102; and Milton Terris, "An Early System of Compulsory Health Insurance in the United States, 1798–1884," *Bulletin of the History of Medicine*, XV (May, 1944), 437.

22 Jefferson wrote to Rush (Jan. 16, 1811), "Although much of a skeptic in the practice of medicine, I read with pleasure its ingenious theories" (Jefferson, *Works*, XI, 166). What Jefferson distrusted was not the "facts . . . [but] only their extension by theory" (Jefferson to Rush, Aug. 17, 1811, in *ibid.*, 212).

23 Jefferson wrote about "respected names [in medicine], such as Stahl, Boerhaave, Sydenham, Hoffman, Cullen, and our own good Dr. Rush, whose depletive and mercurial systems have formed a school, or perhaps revived that which arose on Harvey's discovery of the circulation of the blood" (Thomas Jefferson, *The Complete Jefferson, Containing His Major Writings, Published and Unpublished, Except His Letters*, ed. Saul K. Padover [New York: Duell, Sloan & Pearce, Inc., c1943], p. 1091). See also *ibid.*, p. 1087.

24 John Adams, *Statesman and Friend; Correspondence of John Adams with Benjamin Waterhouse, 1742–1822*, ed. Worthington Chauncey Ford (Boston: Little, Brown, and Company, 1927), p. 91.

25 See Perry Miller, *The New England Mind: the Seventeenth Century* (Cambridge, Massachusetts: Harvard University Press, 1954), pp. 257 ff., and John Herman Randall, *The Making of the Modern Mind* (rev. ed.; Boston: Houghton Mifflin Company, c1940), p. 159.

26 Eaton, *New England Hospitals*, pp. 34 ff.

27 William Tudor, Jun., *A Discourse Delivered before the Humane Society At their Anniversary, May, 1817*, Published at the Request of the Society (Boston: Printed by John Eliot, 1817), p. 15.

28 Eaton, *New England Hospitals*, p. 72.

29 Russell, p. 178.

30 Eaton, *New England Hospitals*, pp. 125–126. See also references to mental illness in European magazine articles reproduced for American readers: "Lunatic Asylum in Lancashire," *Atheneum*, III (June 15, 1818), 216–219; "Extracts from a Lawyer's Port-Folio," *Atheneum*, IV (October 15, 1818), 68–74; "Hypochondriacs—Nerves—Blue Devils," *Atheneum*, IX (September 1, 1821), 443–445, and (September 15, 1821), 479–482; "Dr. Burrows and Others on Insanity," *Museum of Foreign Literature, Science, and Art*, XIV (April, 1829), 359–367.

31 Quoted in Eaton, *New England Hospitals*, p. 70. A Roman Catholic priest seemed to believe people were still suffering from demoniac possession. Father Stephen T. Badin, a missionary in Kentucky, wrote in 1804 about the effects of Protestant revivalism there: "The Baptists, &c., are now attacked with a malady of nerves, called Jirking, which is

very unnatural, so that the physicians cannot account for the violent fits which take place at the meeting houses, &c. They appear to me to bear a strong resemblance to the possession of Devils" (Quoted in Sister Mary Ramona Mattingly, *The Catholic Church on the Kentucky Frontier (1785–1812)* ["Catholic University of America, Studies in American Church History, Vol. XXV"; Washington, D. C.: Catholic University of America, 1936], p. 192).

32 Thomas Robbins, *The Design and Tendency of Christianity to Diminish the Miseries and Increase the Happiness of Mankind; an Address Delivered at the Retreat for the Insane, in Hartford, at the Dedication of that Institution . . . April 1, 1824* (Hartford: Printed by Goodwin & Co., 1824), pp. 3, 14.

33 John Wesley, *Primitive Physic; or, An Easy and Natural Method of Curing Most Diseases* (14th ed., corrected and much enl.; Philadelphia: Printed by Joseph Crukshank, 1770), pp. iii–iv, 41, 49, 53–54. Some physicians as well as laymen and clergymen believed that disease derived from Adam's fall and that man was thereafter never in his right mind. See, for example, John Stearns, M.D., *Philosophy of Mind* . . . (New York: William Osborn, 1840), pp. 4–5; Miller, pp. 183–185, 188, 259; and Stow Persons, *American Minds: A History of Ideas* (New York: Henry Holt and Company, c1958), pp. 21–22.

34 Clark Brown, *Human Life Not Always Desirable; Sermon Delivered at Richmond, N. H., November 17, 1813, at the Funeral of Mr. Solomon Atherton, AET. 73* (Keene [N. H.]: Printed by John Prentiss, 1814), pp. 9–10.

35 Eaton, *New England Hospitals*, pp. 69–71.

36 Hugh P. Greeley, "Early Wisconsin Medical History," *Wisconsin Medical Journal*, XX (April, 1922), 564.

37 William Buchan, *Domestic Medicine; or, The Family Physician* . . . (Edinburgh: Printed by Balfour, Auld, and Smellie, 1769), pp. 508–509, 515–516, 520.

38 *Ibid.*, pp. 515, 517.

39 An example is Wallis, pp. 432–433, 437–438. Such writers failed to emphasize that violence, even among maniacal patients, is not a constant but an occasional occurrence.

40 Buchan (1769 ed.), pp. 516, 508, 518–520.

41 *Ibid.*, p. 508. Wallis (p. 434) expressed similar attitudes: "All species and degrees of madness which are hereditary, or which grow up with people from their early youth, are incurable; and so, *for the most part*, are all maniacal cases that are above a year's standing, originate they from whatever source they may."

42 Buchan (1769 ed.), p. 518. This idea that other illnesses would drive away insanity was common among physicians (see *Encyclopaedia Britannica*, XI, 283).

43 Buchan (1769 ed.), pp. 520–522.

44 *Ibid.*, pp. 519–520. For a similar view see Harper, pp. 60–61.

45 Buchan (1769 ed.), pp. 519–520. Wallis, for example, did not agree: "A mistaken humanity often prevents the friends of unfortunate insane people from putting them under the care of strangers, and sending them from home" (Wallis, p. 438).

46 See, for example, John Elliot, *The Medical Pocket-Book* . . . (Philadelphia: Robert Bell, 1784), pp. 40–41, 46.

47 Lester S. King, *The Medical World of the Eighteenth Century* (Chicago: The University of Chicago Press, 1958), p. 34. For a partisan but still generally fair description of Wesley's views on medicine, see A. Wesley Hill, *John Wesley among the Physicians; a Study of Eighteenth-Century Medicine* (London: The Epworth Press, 1958).

48 Wesley, p. ix, iii–iv, 53–54.

49 Sir Walter Scott made a special study of insanity in order to depict it faithfully in his books ([Amariah Brigham], "Insanity—Illustrated by Histories of Distinguished Men, and by the Writings of Poets and Novelists," *AJI*, I (July 1844), 27.

50 Robert E. Spiller and Others (eds.), *Literary History of the United States* (New York: The Macmillan Company, 1948), I, 125.

51 Charles Brockden Brown, *Wieland; or, The Transformation, together with the Memoirs of Carwin the Biloquist,* a Fragment, edited with an introduction by Fred Lewis Pottee (New York: Hafner Publishing Co., 1958 [first published in 1798]); Charles Brockden Brown, *Edgar Huntly; or, Memoirs of a Sleepwalker,* edited with an introduction by David Lee Clark (New York: Macmillan Company, 1928 [first published in 1799]).

52 [Charles R. Maturin], *Melmoth the Wanderer, a Tale,* by the Author of "Bertram," &c. (4 vols.; Edinburgh: Printed for Archibald Constable and Company, 1820); James Hogg, *The Private Memoirs and Confessions of a Justified Sinner,* with an introduction by André Gide (New York: Grove Press, Inc., 1959 [first published in 1824]); Sir Walter Scott, *The Bride of Lammermoor* ("The Waverly Novels," Vol. IV; Abbotsford ed.; Philadelphia: J. B. Lippincott & Co., 1856).

53 Brown, *Wieland,* p. 173.

54 Hogg, pp. 82–83.

55 Maturin, I, 139.

56 Brown, *Wieland.* The case was reported in the *New-York Weekly Magazine,* II (July 20–27, 1796), 20, 28. Brown was friendly with New York physicians and probably consulted with them about insanity before he wrote *Wieland* (see his introduction to *Wieland,* p. 3; L. R. Wiley, *The Sources and Influence of the Novels of Charles Brockden Brown* [New York: Vantage Press, c1950], pp. 98–99; Harry R. Warfel, *Charles Brockden Brown, American Gothic Novelist* (Gainesville: University of Florida Press, 1949), pp. 97–100, 104.

57 Maturin, I, 113–129 ff. In other books two mad "heroes" die without regaining their senses, and in Maturin a sane man becomes deranged, or at least obsessed "with a species of insanity," while searching for the person responsible for having placed him in an asylum (Scott; Brown, *Edgar Huntly;* Maturin, I, 143).

58 Brown, *Wieland,* p. 202.

59 *Ibid.;* Hogg, pp. 229–230.

60 Scott, pp. 180–184; Albert S. G. Canning, *Sir Walter Scott Studied in Eight Novels* (London: T. Fischer Unwin, 1910), p. 122.

61 Hogg; Brown, *Wieland.* See also Scott's treatment of characters Madge Wildfire *(Heart of Mid Lothian),* Clara Mowbray *(St. Ronan's Will),* and Norma *(The Pirate)* for clear presentations of the doctrine of predisposing causes of insanity. For an analysis of these characters by a nineteenth-century psychiatrist see [Brigham], *AJI,* I (July, 1844), 43–46.

62 Quoted in N. L. Bowditch, *A History of the Massachusetts General Hospital* (Boston: Printed by John Wilson and Son, 1851), p. 44.

63 State Lunatic Hospital at Worcester, *Annual Report,* 7th, 1839, p. 4.

64 Quoted in Morton, p. 169.

65 "An Account of a Murder Committed by Mr. J————— Y—————, upon His Family, in December, A.D. 1781," *New-York Weekly Magazine,* II (July 27, 1796), 28.

66 Newspaper clipping, dated Aug. 12, 1804, enclosed in Benjamin Rush's MS notebook, "Facts & Documents on Moral Derangement as Exemplified Chiefly in Murder, Including Newspaper but *Not* Containing Judges' Opini," Ridgway Branch, Library Company of Philadelphia, p. 26.

67 Article quoted from the [Nashville] *Clarion* in the *New York Commercial Advertiser,* June 8, 1818, p. 2, col. 4.

68 Newspaper clipping, dated Mar. 27, 1804, in Rush's notebook, "Facts & Documents on Moral Derangement . . . ," p. 26.

69 Francis Tiffany, a biographer of Dorothea Dix, contended that a new and only slightly

less objectionable concept replaced the idea of diabolical possession. "Insanity was pure mental and moral, not physical, perversion. It was the outbreak of the animal, violent, filthy, blasphemous, and murderous elements of the fallen human *soul,* elements which had culpably been permitted to get the upper hand of the higher attributes." Thus the mentally ill were supposed to be tigers and jackals impervious to reason and therefore not truly human beings. Only cages, chains, clubs, and starvation could subdue them. For these reasons the insane were feared, despaired of, and considered repugnant (*Life of Dorothea Lynde Dix* [Boston: Houghton Mifflin and Company, 1892], pp. 57–58). This estimate of popular attitudes, though somewhat overdrawn and too all-inclusive, seems to be supported by the available evidence.

70 Francis Wharton, *A Treatise on Mental Unsoundness Embracing a General View of Psychological Law* ([3d ed.]; Philadelphia: Kay & Brother, 1873), I, 162–172.

71 *The Trial and Life and Confessions of John F. Van Patten, Who Was Indicted, Tried, and Convicted of the Murder of Mrs. Maria Schermerhorn, on the 4th of October Last and Sentenced to be Executed on the 25th February, 1825* (New York: n.p., 1825), p. 10.

72 Newspaper clipping, dated Mar. 27, 1804, in Rush's notebook, "Facts & Documents on Moral Derangement . . . ," p. 26. It is interesting that the author of the article was baffled by the fact that the murderer was in comfortable economic circumstances. A similar thought was expressed by the writer in the *New-York Weekly Magazine,* July 27, 1796, p. 28. This attitude contrasts with that of physicians interested in insanity, who assumed that the poor were less prone to this illness than the rich.

73 *Report of the Trial of Jason Fairbanks, on an Indictment for the Murder of Miss Elizabeth Fales at the Supreme Court, Holden at Dedham . . . on Thursday the 6th, and Friday the 7th Days of August, 1801* (2d ed.; Boston: Printed by Russell and Cutler, 1801), pp. 49–50.

74 *Ibid.,* pp. 84–86.

75 "Diana Sellick's Case," *New-York City-Hall Recorder,* I (December, 1816), 185–191.

76 "John Ball's Case," *New-York City-Hall Recorder,* II (June, 1817), 85–86.

77 *The Trial and Life and Confessions of John F. Van Patten . . . ,* pp. 7–8.

78 "Lawrence Pienovi's Case," *New-York City-Hall Recorder,* III (July-August, 1818), 124–126.

79 *Ibid.,* 126; John Locke, *An Essay Concerning Human Understanding,* collated and annotated, with prolegomena, biographical, critical, and historical, by Alexander Campbell Fraser (New York: Dover Publications, 1959), I, 344–345, 348–349.

80 For a detailed discussion of this question see Chapter 3, Section 5.

81 Rush, *Medical Inquiries . . . upon the Diseases of the Mind,* 4th ed., pp. 355–364; Rush, "Influence of Physical Causes upon the Moral Faculty," *The Selected Writings of Benjamin Rush,* pp. 181–211.

82 Eaton, *New England Hospitals,* pp. 47–48.

83 For example, Dr. Mason F. Cogswell, who helped to establish a school for deaf mutes so that his deaf daughter might be taught religion, was a founder of the Hartford Retreat; others gave money to the Retreat for similar reasons (*ibid.,* p. 70).

84 Morton, p. 153; Lawrence, p. 57.

85 For a more complete discussion of this problem see Dain and Carlson, *Bulletin of the History of Medicine,* XXXIII (September-October, 1959), 460–465.

86 In 1822 Wyman asserted that the public still had a great deal to learn about insanity: It was a curable disease whose treatment took more than a few weeks or months; both medical and moral management were important and must be applied in a special hospital; if at home, the patient had to be carefully watched; amusements, games, various types of light work, reading, writing, and music diverted their attention "from unpleas-

ant subjects of thought" and afforded "exercise of both body and mind"; a regulated life was of great benefit; the insane were not insensible to kind treatment, and whips and chains were "forever banished from every well regulated Asylum for the insane." (Rufus Wyman, in *Address to the Trustees of Massachusetts General Hospital*, pp. 27–28.) The public that Wyman spoke about consisted of the middle and upper classes.

Chapter 3

1 Derived from list of "Existing Institutions for the Mentally Ill in the United States with Date of Opening and Present Control," in Samuel W. Hamilton's "The History of American Mental Hospitals," *One Hundred Years of American Psychiatry*, pp. 153–166. Since very few asylums founded in the eighteenth and nineteenth centuries went out of existence, Hamilton's list is valid for this purpose.

2 It should be noted that in the South, as opposed to the rest of the country, laymen continued until the 1840's as superintendents of insane asylums. Even in the better asylums, where professional physicians were installed early as chiefs, moral treatment often lagged behind the North. See O. T. Powell, "A Sketch of Psychiatry in Southern States," *AJI*, LIV (July, 1897), 27–28; Henry M. Hurd (ed.), *The Institutional Care of the Insane in the United States and Canada*, by Henry M. Hurd, *et al.* (Baltimore: Johns Hopkins Press, 1916), II, 161, 458; III, 595.

3 In 1840, Amariah Brigham, a leading American psychiatrist, estimated that there were about 20,000 physicians in the United States (*An Inquiry Concerning the Diseases and Functions of the Brain, the Spinal Cord, and the Nerves* [New York: George Adlard, 1840], p. 17). In 1850 the census recorded 40,755 physicians in the United States (U. S., Bureau of the Census, *Historical Statistics of the United States, 1789–1945; a Supplement to the Statistical Abstract of the United States* [Washington: U. S. Government Printing Office, 1949], pp. 50, 42).

4 See Hurd, I, p. 76. There are also numerous letters from superintendents, protesting Gray's policies. At one point, Dr. John Curwen became so incensed at the cavalier treatment given to Isaac Ray by the *Journal* and at the tactics in general of its editors that he wrote: "I am seriously considering whether I shall continue my subscription as a means of assisting them in their crooked foolery" (Curwen to Thomas S. Kirkbride, July 31, 1860, Kirkbride MSS, Historical Library and Museum, Institute of the Pennsylvania Hospital, Philadelphia). Of course, even under Brigham's editorship, the *Journal* had certain biases. Brigham was a phrenologist, and the *Journal*, although allowing space to varying opinions, leaned toward a phrenological point of view from 1844 to Brigham's death in 1849, especially since he wrote many of the articles himself.

5 John M. Galt, *The Treatment of Insanity* (New York: Harper & Brothers, 1846), p. iv. Of course, Galt's remarks, made only two years after the Association and the *Journal* were founded, suggest that this unity already existed to some degree before 1844. In 1845 Dr. John Evans, who had visited many American mental institutions to gather information about the proper treatment of the insane, also remarked upon the similarity of opinion among psychiatrists (Indiana Hospital for the Insane, *Report*, 1845, p. 13).

6 A member of the Executive Council of Maine, then considering candidates for head of the new state asylum, remarked to Dr. George Chandler that he thought that some extended experience in the treatment of the insane was "*absolutely* necessary" for an asylum superintendent (A. C. Fletcher to Chandler, Chandler MSS, American Antiquarian Society, May 6, 1841). Dr. Charles H. Nichols told Dorothea Dix that "no man shd. be allowed

to superintend an institution for the insane who [had no] previous experience" (Nichols to Dix, August 18, 1858, Dix MSS, Houghton Library, Harvard University).

7 The Kirkbride MSS (Pennsylvania Hospital) and the Samuel B. Woodward MSS (American Antiquarian Society) include many such requests.

8 This situation resembled one in English geology. See Charles Coulston Gillispie, *Genesis and Geology; a Study in the Relation of Scientific Thought, Natural Theology, and Social Opinion in Great Britain, 1790–1850* (New York: Harper & Brothers, 1959, c1951).

9 Pliny Earle, "Beauty," 1841–42, Earle MSS, American Antiquarian Society.

10 Most psychiatrists were not much interested in politics; if they had any affiliation it would be to one of the two major parties, Whig or Democratic. Samuel B. Woodward, a strong advocate of temperance and prison reform, wrote in 1848 that he had not voted during the previous twenty years, but that he would break his custom in the presidential election of that year in order to prevent the election of a Democrat or a radical loco foco (Letter to editor, undated, Woodward MSS). However, Woodward's brother Charles and Amariah Brigham were both active Democrats and on that account were at a disadvantage as candidates for the chief of the Hartford Retreat (George Sumner to S. B. Woodward, April 17, 1840, Woodward MSS). Quaker Pliny Earle, though not an active abolitionist, opposed slavery on principle, and in 1838 attended abolitionist meetings of Quakers in London and Paris. He also became quite friendly with the Quaker Englishwoman Elizabeth Fry, whose prison reform efforts he heartily endorsed. (See *Memoirs of Pliny Earle, M.D.*, pp. 84–85, 104, 106.) Samuel Gridley Howe was greatly influenced by Woodward to wage his successful efforts to reform the treatment of idiots and to educate them (Harold Schwartz, *Samuel Gridley Howe: Social Reformer, 1801–1876* ["Harvard Historical Studies, Vol. LXVII"; Cambridge: Harvard University Press, 1956], p. 138). These efforts were supported by other psychiatrists as well. Almost all psychiatrists believed intemperance was related to insanity, and many agreed with proposals to establish inebriate asylums.

11 Samuel B. Woodward, "Article Advocating Establishment of an Inebriate Asylum" (1845?), p. 6, in his "Collected Writings," (typescript copy of original manuscripts, Worcester State Hospital), I. Most of the original manuscripts are in the American Antiquarian Society.

12 For an extended discussion of Locke's psychological theories see Richard I. Aaron, *John Locke* (2d ed.; Oxford: At the Clarendon Press, 1955).

13 Some psychiatrists offered sensationist explanations for why the insane often developed strong antagonisms to their friends and relatives. The head of the Illinois State Hospital for the Insane stressed disordered sense perception. In the majority of cases insanity "either entirely reverses or essentially changes the mind in its manner of receiving impressions. The light, so pleasurable to the healthy eye, becomes an unendurable irritant when thrown upon an inflamed surface. Those emotions that give pleasure to the healthy mind, are even more injurious when the mind is diseased, than is a flash of sunlight upon an inflamed retina." (Illinois State Hospital for the Insane, *Biennial Report*, 8th, 1861–62, in *Reports of the Illinois State Hospital for the Insane, 1847–1862* [Chicago: F. Fulton & Co., 1863], p. 359.)

14 See Chapter I, footnote 43.

15 Edwin G. Boring, *A History of Experimental Psychology* (2d ed.; New York: Appleton-Century-Crofts, Inc., c1950), pp. 193–194.

16 Thomas Cooper, "Outline of the Association of Ideas," in F. J. V. Broussais, *Irritation and Insanity . . .* , trans. Thomas Cooper (Columbia, S. C.: Printed by S. J. M'Morris, 1831), pp. 379, 391.

17 Dr. Samuel White, senior proprietor of the Hudson Lunatic Asylum, one of the founders of the Association of Medical Superintendents of American Institutions for the Insane, and a president of the New York State Medical Society, maintained, for example, that irritation was the basic cause of insanity. It excited the muscular coat of the arteries of the brain and thereby dilated the capillary vessels, increased the volume and velocity of the blood, and resulted in redness and pain. This was in contrast to Rush's theory that excess blood in the brain caused inflammation and therefore insanity. (Samuel White, *Address on Insanity,* Delivered before the New York State Medical Society, February 5th, 1844 [Albany: Printed by J. Munsell, 1844], p. 5.)

18 Boring, p. 207; W. B. Pillsbury, *The History of Psychology* (New York: W. W. Norton & Company, c1929), p. 129.

19 For a brief discussion of the Scottish "common sense" philosophy and its influence on the development of psychology and philosophy, see Boring, pp. 203–209. See also Gladys Bryson, *Man and Society; the Scottish Inquiry of the Eighteenth Century* (Princeton, N. J.: Princeton University Press, 1945), and a more recent study, S. A. Grave, *The Scottish Philosophy of Common Sense* (Oxford: At the Clarendon Press, 1960).

20 Eric T. Carlson, "The Influence of Phrenology on Early American Psychiatric Thought," *American Journal of Psychiatry,* CXV (December, 1958), 536. Brigham wrote, however, that he was not "confident that the organs can be ascertained by external examination" (Brigham to Earle, 14 Mar. 1844 or 45, Earle MSS). Woodward and Ray shared Brigham's reservations about the popular phrenologists' faith in craniology. For a discussion of phrenology in the United States see John D. Davies, *Phrenology: Fad and Science; a 19th-Century Crusade* ("Yale Historical Publications, Miscellany 62"; New Haven: Yale University Press, 1955).

21 Boring, p. 53.

22 Amariah Brigham, *Observations On the Influence of Religion upon the Health and Physical Welfare of Mankind* (Boston: Marsh, Capen & Lyon, 1835), pp. xiii–xix.

23 Isaac Ray, "Moral Aspects of Phrenology," Perry Miller (ed.), *The Transcendentalists, an Anthology* (Cambridge, Mass.: Harvard University Press, 1950), pp. 76–77.

24 Edward Jarvis, *Tendency of Misdirected Education and the Unbalanced Mind to Produce Insanity* (Extract from *Barnard's Journal of Education* for March, 1858) ([Hartford]: n.p., 1858), pp. 598–599.

25 Isaac Ray, "Hints to the Medical Witness in Questions of Insanity," *AJI,* VIII (July, 1851), 56; Samuel B. Woodward, "Improvements in the Practice of Medicine during the Last Year" (1840?), pp. 4-5, in his "Collected Writings," II.

26 Quoted in Nathan Allen, *An Essay on the Connection of Mental Philosophy with Medicine;* Inaugural Thesis for the Degree of Doctor of Medicine, Pennsylvania Medical College (Philadelphia: Adam Waldie, 1841), p. 31.

27 One psychiatrist remarked about the influence of philosophy upon psychiatry: "Metaphysical researches to the neglect of corporeal phenomena, have greatly retarded the pathology of Insanity" (White, p. 8).

28 See Maine Insane Hospital, *Annual Report,* 1850 (i.e., 1849/50), p. 31; 1854, pp. 24–25; *The Vermont Asylum for the Insane; Its Annals for Fifty Years* (Brattleboro: Printed by Hildreth & Fales, 1887), pp. 48–49; Friends' Asylum, *Annual Report,* 20th, 1837, p. 9. (Citations to the Friends' Asylum *Annual Reports* refer to the date the reports were published rather than to the years covered.) Incomplete knowledge about reflexes also led Brigham and others to believe that bodily changes such as congestion of the uterus or intestines might cause mental illness by means of the unconscious reflexes. Disorder in organs other than the brain might affect the brain through the action of automatic reflex actions over which the person concerned had no control. See Mark D. Altschule, with the

Collaboration of Evelyn Russ, *Roots of Modern Psychiatry; Essays in the History of Psychiatry* (New York: Grune & Stratton, 1957), pp. 64–65.

29 Pliny Earle, "Researches in Reference to the Causes, Duration, Termination, and Moral Treatment of Insanity," *American Journal of the Medical Sciences*, XXII (August, 1838), 351; Amariah Brigham, *Observations on the Influence of Religion upon the Health and Physical Welfare of Mankind*, p. 274; [Amariah Brigham], "Definition of Insanity—Nature of the Disease," *AJI*, I (October, 1844), 99–101; John P. Gray, "The Dependence of Insanity on Physical Disease," *AJI*, XXVII (April, 1871), 385; State Lunatic Hospital at Worcester, *Annual Report* [by S. B. Woodward], 7th, 1839, p. 66; Gregory Zilboorg, in Collaboration with George W. Henry, *A History of Medical Psychology* (New York: W. W. Norton & Company, c1941), p. 467. Zilboorg comments that this theory was "the almost unconscious but deliberate re-establishment of the old medieval point of view which on purely theological grounds insisted that all illnesses, including mental illness, must be physical. Thus the most scientific and most rationalistic system of psychiatric thought . . . unawares reasserted a principle which had been combatted by medicine for several centuries." Isaac Ray discussed the effect of this belief on the acceptance of new scientific discoveries (*Mental Hygiene* [Boston: Ticknor and Fields, 1863], pp. 1–3).

30 *Memoirs of Pliny Earle, M. D.*, p. 281. Earle also apparently believed those who claimed to have contact with supernatural forces. A friend wrote to him: "From the whole tenor of your letter, I perceive that you incline to the spiritual acceptation of some of these phenomena [i.e., table rappings, ability to read sealed letters, etc.]. I think all minds cultivated in the Quaker faith [Earle was a Quaker] are more inclined to admit such an interpretation than the rationalistic and philosophic multitude." (E. R. Arnold to P. Earle, Aug. 15, 1853, Earle MSS.)

31 Brigham, *Remarks on the Influence of Mental Cultivation and Mental Excitement upon Health* (3d ed.; Philadelphia: Lea & Blanchard, 1845), p. 47; [Brigham], *AJI*, I (October, 1844), 97. I cannot agree with Alden H. Bunker that Brigham did not believe that the "basis" of insanity (its pathology) was always "physical" or somatic (Alden Henry Bunker, "American Psychiatric Literature during the Past One Hundred Years," *One Hundred Years of American Psychiatry*, p. 199).

32 Brigham, *Remarks on the Influence of Mental Cultivation and Mental Excitement upon Health*, p. 47.

33 Gray, *AJI*, XXVII (April, 1871), 389–390. In general Gray took a position similar to that generally adopted by clergymen and educators (usually the same persons), who insisted that science must serve the interests of religion (Arthur Alphonse Ekirch, Jr., *The Idea of Progress in America, 1815–1860* [New York: Peter Smith, 1951], pp. 120–126).

34 "Mental Derangement," *Boston Medical Intelligencer*, V (October 16, 1827), 352. (Review of *Des causes morales et physiques des maladies mentales, et des quelques autres affections nerveuses, &c.*, par F. Voisin . . . [and] *Observations on the Causes, Symptoms, and Treatment of Derangement of the Mind, Founded on an Extensive Moral and Physical Practice in the Treatment of Lunatics*, by Paul Slade Knight, M. D.). For a discussion of the controversy referred to by the reviewer see Owsei Temkin, "Basic Science, Medicine, and the Romantic Era," *Bulletin of the History of Medicine*, XXXVII (March-April, 1963), 97–129.

35 Shryock, "The Beginnings," *One Hundred Years of American Psychiatry*, p. 11.

36 Pliny Earle, "On the Curability of Insanity," *American Journal of the Medical Sciences*, new series, V (April, 1843), 345–346.

37 Friends' Asylum, *Annual Report*, 20th, 1837, p. 9. See also *Vermont Asylum for the Insane, Its Annals*, pp. 48–49. In regard to the origin of popular pessimism about insanity Pinel took an opposite position. He wrote: "Derangement of the understanding is gen-

erally considered as an effect of an organic lesion of the brain, consequently as incurable" (*A Treatise on Insanity*, p. 3).

38 Ray, *Mental Hygiene*, pp. 1–3, 6, 7–8.

39 Ackerknect, p. 30.

40 James C. Prichard, *Treatise on Insanity and Other Disorders Affecting the Mind* (London: Sherwood, Gilbert, and Piper, 1835), p. 235.

41 *Ibid.*, p. 236.

42 New York State Lunatic Asylum at Utica, *Annual Report*, 1st, 1843, p. 51. See also, for example: State Lunatic Hospital at Taunton, Mass., *Annual Report*, 1st, 1854, p. 35; Maine Insane Hospital, *Annual Report* [by I. Ray], 3d, 1842, p. 25; Hartford Retreat, *Annual Report* [by J. Butler], 32d, 1855/56, pp. 22–23; State Lunatic Hospital at Worcester, *Annual Report* [by Trustees], 22d, 1854, p. 7; Pennsylvania Hospital for the Insane, *Annual Report* [by T. Kirkbride], 1842, p. 31.

43 H. R. Buttolph, "Modern Asylums, and Their Adaptation to the Treatment of the Insane," *AJI*, III (April, 1847), 375.

44 McLean Asylum for the Insane, *Annual Report*, 1843, pp. 43–44; Bell to Dix, 4 May 1843, Dix MSS. As Bell's remarks show, a consequence of the increased emphasis on moral treatment was the depreciation of the role of medicine. Curwen told Kirkbride that Ray seemed to take a "very superficial view" of the true usefulness of medicines. By undervaluing medicine, Ray was forgetting about the strong reciprocal influences of mind and body (Curwen to Kirkbride, June 22, 1857, Kirkbride MSS). R. J. Patterson, chief of the Indiana Hospital for the Insane, however, quoted Ray approvingly on this point (Indiana Hospital for the Insane, *Annual Report*, 1850, pp. 19–20). Woodward had earlier maintained his belief in the use of medicine despite possible accusations that he denied the value of moral treatment. He affirmed his conviction that kindness, indulgence, and inculcation of self-respect and self-control were indispensable auxiliaries to medical treatment in all instances. He thought, however, that medical means should be used in all early cases of insanity to subdue the excitement and enable moral influences to take effect. (State Lunatic Hospital at Worcester, *Annual Report*, 4th, 1836, pp. 49–50.)

45 Bell to Dix, 4 May 1843, Dix MSS.

46 Clarence P. Oberndorf, discussing precursors of Freud in America, writes that "the effects of suppression, which may merge imperceptibly into Freud's concept of repression, in causing physical disturbances in the body" is the real subject of Brigham's book, *Remarks on the Influence of Mental Cultivation and Mental Excitement upon Health*. "In this work," Oberndorf continues, "Brigham seeks to prove that dyspepsia is due to a disturbed mind that in turn caused a disordered stomach, that it is psychosomatic. Therefore, the cure must rest in the restoration of peace of mind" (Oberndorf, pp. 19–20). Brigham was not unique in his opinion, for many American psychiatrists and physicians in general practice also believed that mental problems could cause physical disease and vice versa. One modern writer notes that in England early in the nineteenth century psychosomatic medicine expanded enormously, but "lacking roots in physiologic observation it soon atrophied" (Altschule, p. 8).

47 Pinel, *A Treatise on Insanity*, p. 5.

48 John Charles Bucknill, "The Pathology of Insanity," *AJI*, XIV (October, 1857), 175.

49 *Ibid.*, XIV (July, 1858), 35–36; (October, 1858), 175.

50 Robley Dunglison, *Human Physiology* (5th ed.; Philadelphia: Lea and Blanchard, 1844), I, 271.

51 Allen, p. 21.

52 S. Annan, "Observations on Functional and Organic Diseases," *AJI*, XIII (April, 1857), 308; New York State Lunatic Asylum at Utica, *Annual Report*, 1st, 1843, p. 50. The so-

matic view of functional disorder was fairly widespread. It was advocated even by a physician practicing on the periphery of medicine, Dr. Thomas L. Nichols, a famous water cure specialist and phrenologist, who wrote: "Diseases are . . . divided into functional and organic. They are called organic, when some injury to, or alteration of the organ is perceptible; and functional, when it is not. Where there is organic disease, there must always be functional; where there is functional, there must be organic disease somewhere, though not necessarily in the part which appears to be affected. It may be in the nervous centers connected with it." (*Esoteric Anthropology* [Cincinnati: Valentine Nicholson & Co., 1853], pp. 263–264.)

53 Isaac Ray, *A Treatise on the Medical Jurisprudence of Insanity* (Boston: Charles C. Little and James Brown, 1838), pp. 136–139; "Proceedings of the Eighth Annual Meeting of the Association of Medical Superintendents of American Institutions for the Insane," *AJI*, X (July, 1853), 79 (remarks by L. V. Bell); Brigham, *An Inquiry Concerning the Diseases and Functions of the Brain*, pp. 231–232; Brigham, *Remarks on the Influence of Mental Cultivation and Mental Excitement upon Health*, p. 88.

54 New York State Lunatic Asylum at Utica, *Annual Report*, 1st, 1843, p. 50; Friends' Asylum, *Annual Report*, 42d, 1859, p. 10; Annan, *AJI*, XIII (April, 1857), 308.

55 Earle, *American Journal of the Medical Sciences*, XXII (August, 1838), 351.

56 Bloomingdale Asylum, *Annual Report*, 1850, p. 39.

57 The confusion that sometimes prevailed in the arguments favoring non-medical means of cure was evident in an article by Ray, who was usually clear-headed. He suggested that non-medical treatment was not synonymous with a non-somatic pathology. Since in many non-psychiatric chronic disorders, "proper diet and exercise, change of air and scene, useful and agreeable occupation of the mind" were more potent remedies than medicine, he asked if they would not operate as well "upon that disorder which mainly affects the material organ of the mind itself?" Up to this point Ray agreed with the accepted opinion that the brain is the material organ of the mind, that all insanity must involve some disorder of the brain, and that non-medical means indirectly could repair the damage to the brain and cure insanity. In his concluding remarks, however, he shifted his position and spoke of his remedies as not affecting the brain, but the mind: "In the treatment of insanity, therefore, it is no departure from the ordinary principles of therapeutics, to give to those means *which act directly upon the mind*, the preference over such as are applied directly to the corporeal system" (Quoted in Indiana Hospital for the Insane, *Annual Report*, 1850, p. 20. My italics, N. D.).

58 Earle, "Recoveries" [1850?], Earle MSS.

59 [Amariah Brigham], Review of *Traité complèt de l'hypochondrie*, by J. L. Bracht, *AJI*, I (January, 1845), 280; "Trial for Murder—Mysterious Disclosures," *AJI*, IV (April, 1848), 344 (testimony of A. Brigham at Johnson trial).

60 Indiana Hospital for the Insane, *Annual Report*, 1848, p. 17, quoted from [Brigham], *AJI*, I (October, 1844), 97.

61 Ray, *A Treatise on the Medical Jurisprudence of Insanity*, p. 142.

62 Prichard, pp. 4–5.

63 David Brion Davis, *Homicide in American Fiction, 1798–1860; a Study in Social Values* (Ithaca, New York: Cornell University Press, c1957), pp. 74–75.

64 Ray, *Treatise on the Medical Jurisprudence of Insanity*, pp. 168 ff; Isaac Ray, "An Examination of the Objections to the Doctrine of Moral Insanity," *AJI*, XVIII (October, 1861), 112.

65 Hurd (I, 28) and Gregory Zilboorg ("Legal Aspects of Psychiatry," *One Hundred Years of American Psychiatry*, pp. 550–558) give the impression that Ray stood virtually alone in his advocacy of moral insanity. Zilboorg acknowledges that a few psychiatrists and some

courts saw merit in the concept, but he subsequently claims that in 1861 Ray "still stood alone" (p. 561). My research indicates that, on the contrary, many leading psychiatrists agreed with Ray.

66 New York State Lunatic Asylum at Utica, *Annual Report* [by A. Brigham], 1st, 1843, p. 32; 4th, 1846, p. 56; 6th, 1849, p. 43; McLean Asylum for the Insane, *Annual Report* [by L. V. Bell], 1843, pp. 21–22, 46–47, 49 ff.; Hartford Retreat, *Annual Report* [by A. Brigham], 18th, 1841/42, p. 21; State Lunatic Hospital at Worcester, *Annual Report* [by S. B. Woodward], 11th, 1843, pp. 43–44; Dr. Benedict, "Moral Insanity," *Boston Medical and Surgical Journal*, XLIV (May 7, 1851), 285; Francis Wharton, *A Monograph on Mental Unsoundness* (Philadelphia: Kay and Brother, 1855), pp. 165–169. At the 1863 meeting of the superintendents' association, Nichols and Tyler accepted the concept of moral insanity and Chipley acknowledged that he had formerly believed in it ("Annual Meeting of the Association of Medical Superintendents of American Institutions for the Insane," *AJI*, XX [July, 1863], 63, 68, 83–84). John Curwen, Kirkbride's assistant and later superintendent of the State Hospital for the Insane at Harrisburg, Pennsylvania, was said to be a "strong believer in the doctrine of moral insanity" (Review of *Address Delivered before the Medical Society of the State of Pennsylvania at Its Annual Session, June, 1869*, by John Curwen, *AJI*, XXVI [January, 1870], 369–370). See also letter from A. V. Williams, assistant physician at Bloomingdale Asylum, to Kirkbride, August 3, 1852, Kirkbride MSS.

67 Charles Evans and R. R. Porter, "Reports of Cases of Insanity, Treated at the Friends' Asylum, near Frankford, with Remarks," *American Journal of the Medical Sciences*, XIX (November, 1836), 99–108; Evans and Porter, "Reports of Cases of Insanity, Treated at the Friends' Asylum near Frankford," *American Journal of the Medical Sciences*, XX (May, 1837), 61–77. Very early in its history the Asylum's superintendents had at times been puzzled by a form of mental illness that was later called moral insanity (Friends' Asylum, Superintendent's Diary, December 9, 1820; January 6, 1822). Dr. Worthington, long-time head of the Friends' Asylum, rejected the concept of moral insanity in 1857 (*Annual Report*, 40th, 1857, p. 10), but in 1849 the Philadelphia *Public Ledger* reported him as saying that he believed that a certain former inmate suffered from it (March 14, 1849, p. 1, col. 7).

68 [Brigham] *AJI*, I (October, 1844), 107–108.

69 *Ibid.*, p. 108.

70 Williams to Kirkbride, Aug. 3, 1852, Kirkbride MSS.

71 See M. B. Sampson, *Rationale of Crime and Its Appropriate Treatment; Being a Treatise on Criminal Jurisprudence Considered in Relation to Cerebral Organization*, from the 2d London ed., with notes and illustrations by E. W. Farnham (New York: D. Appleton & Company, 1846), pp. 14–18.

72 Samuel B. Woodward, "Moral Insanity," *Boston Medical and Surgical Journal*, XVIII (March 28, 1838), 126 (excerpt from his annual report).

73 State Lunatic Hospital at Taunton, *Annual Report*, 6th, 1859, p. 13.

74 *Trial of Charles B. Huntington for Forgery; Principal Defense: Insanity*, Prepared for Publication by the Defendant's Counsel, from Full Stenographic Notes Taken by Messrs. Roberts & Warburton, Law Reporters (New York: John S. Voorhies, Law Bookseller and Publisher, 1857), p. 248. At the same trial, Dr. Chandler R. Gilman, professor of Medical Jurisprudence at the College of Physicians and Surgeons, also testified that moral insanity was a true mental disease and even wrote a pamphlet about it (*A Medico-Legal Examination of the Case of Charles B. Huntington, with Remarks on Moral Insanity and on the Legal Test of Insanity* [New York: Baker & Goodwin, 1857]). Authorities on medical jurisprudence who recognized moral insanity were also cited at the trial: Wharton and

Stillés's *Medical Jurisprudence;* T. R. Beck's *Medical Jurisprudence;* and Ray's *Treatise on the Medical Jurisprudence of Insanity (Trial of Charles Huntington,* pp. 34 ff.). In a Cincinnati murder trial, Dr. L. M. Lawson, a professor at Cincinnati Medical College, also indicated his belief in moral insanity *(Trial of Mrs. Margaret Howard, for the Murder of Miss Mary Ellen Smith, Her Husband's Paramour, in Cincinnati, on the 2nd of Feb. Last* [Cincinnati: n.p., 1850], p. 45). Dr. Joseph Mather Smith, professor of Theory and Practice of Physic, and Clinical Medicine at the College of Physicians and Surgeons, also accepted moral insanity *(A Discourse on the Influence of Disease on the Intellectual and Moral Powers,* Delivered as an Introductory Lecture at the College of Physicians and Surgeons, in the City of New York, October 30th, 1848 [New York: Daniel Adee, 1848], pp. 18–20).

75 [John P. Gray], "Moral Insanity," *AJI,* XIV (April, 1858), 321.

76 *Ibid.,* 311–314. See also John P. Gray, "Homicide in Insanity," *AJI,* XIV (October, 1857), 144–145.

77 For the views of Gray and his colleagues on this point, see "Annual Meeting of the Association of Medical Superintendents of American Institutions for the Insane," *AJI,* XX (July, 1863), 63–106.

78 Pennsylvania Hospital for the Insane, *Annual Report,* 1856, pp. 8–10.

79 State Lunatic Hospital at Taunton, *Annual Report,* 6th, 1859, pp. 12–13.

80 Awl to Kirkbride, Oct. 25, 1849, Kirkbride MSS.

81 Samuel B. Woodward, "Moral Insanity," *Boston Medical and Surgical Journal,* XXX (April 17, 1844), 228 (excerpt from his annual report).

82 "Annual Meeting of the Association of Medical Superintendents of American Institutions for the Insane," *AJI,* XX (July, 1863), 63–106.

83 *Ibid.,* 68, 98–99.

84 *Ibid., passim;* see also Zilboorg, "Legal Aspects of Psychiatry," *One Hundred Years of American Psychiatry,* p. 552. Gray, for example, asserted that drunkenness was not a disease but a vice, which was "not in law an excuse for crime, and [did] not release from responsibility" those who commit anti-social acts under the influence of drink (Quoted in "Reports of American Asylums," *AJI,* XVI [July, 1859], 111).

85 "Annual Meeting of the Association of Medical Superintendents of American Institutions for the Insane," *AJI,* XX (July, 1863), 82.

86 Ray, *AJI,* XVIII (October, 1861), 112–138.

87 *Ibid.,* 136–137; Ray, "Moral Insanity," in his *Contributions to Mental Pathology* (Boston: Little, Brown, and Company, 1873), pp. 97–98. For the views of a psychiatrist who did relate moral insanity to phrenology, see Dr. J. Draper, *Insanity in Vermont, 1835 to 1885;* from the *Transactions* of the State Medical Society (Montpelier, Vt.: Argus and Patriot Book and Job Printing House, 1886), pp. 8–9.

88 Ray, *AJI,* XVIII (October, 1861), 120–121.

89 Grave, p. 242. See also Wilson Smith, *Professors & Public Ethics; Studies of Northern Moral Philosophers before the Civil War* (Ithaca, New York: Published for the American Historical Association [by] Cornell University Press, c1956), p. 37. Smith writes: ". . . The Scottish philosophy was interpreted as one of intentions and purity."

90 In an anonymous book review, probably written by Gray, there is another example of psychiatry interpreted in light of religious beliefs. Discussing suicide, the reviewer wrote: "No one, unless he is prepared to follow the teachings of materialism to their results in the denial of moral freedom and responsibility, will [deny that] underlying and supporting all influences which temperament, organic disease, and the contagion through depraved mental states may afford, is irreligion. It cannot be gainsayed that sin, in its broad sense, is the primary cause of suicide. . . . the maniacal delirium in which it is sometimes

committed is nearly always the direct consequence of a breach of physiological laws, in the sinful indulgence of the appetites or passions" ("Bertrand on Suicide" [unsigned review of *Traité du suicide considéré dans ses rapports avec la philosophie, la théologie, la médecine, et la jurisprudence*, par *Louis Bertrand*], *AJI*, XIV [October, 1857], 209.) The more common psychiatric view of suicide was expressed by Henry M. Harlow, superintendent of the Maine Insane Asylum, who avoided discussing the role of sin and testified that "suicide [was] rarely committed by sane men" ([H. M. Harlow], "Homicide in which the Plea of Insanity was Interposed," *AJI*, XIII [January, 1857], 254, [Brown trial]).

91 "In Court of Appeals, State of Kentucky, Smith vs. Commonwealth," *AJI*, XXIII (July, 1800), 19.

92 See "Proceedings of the Fifteenth Annual Meeting of the Association of Medical Superintendents of American Institutions for the Insane," *AJI*, XVII (July, 1860), 45–52; "Reports of American Asylums," *AJI*, XVII (April, 1861), 449.

93 Israel Zwerling and Milton Rosenbaum, "Alcoholic Addiction and Personality (Nonpsychotic Conditions)," *American Handbook of Psychiatry*, ed. Silvano Arieti (New York: Basic Books, 1959), I, 624.

94 "Proceedings of the Fifteenth Annual Meeting of the Association of Medical Superintendents of American Institutions for the Insane," *AJI*, XVII (July, 1860), 49–51.

95 See his "Article Advocating Establishment of an Inebriate Asylum," in his "Collected Writings," I.

96 Earle, "Mind and Body," 1858, Earle MSS.

Chapter 4

1 See Pliny Earle, "On the Causes of Insanity . . . ," *AJI*, IV (January, 1848), 185.

2 Vincent Nowlis, "The Concept of Mood," in Seymour M. Farber, Roger H. L. Wilson (eds.), *Conflict and Creativity, Part Two of Control of the Mind, a Symposium* (New York: McGraw-Hill, c1963), pp. 75–76. The second statement is quoted by Nowlis from K. Lashley, "The Problem of Serial Order in Behavior," in L. A. Jeffress (ed.), *Cerebral Mechanisms in Behavior* (New York: John Wiley & Sons, Inc., 1951).

3 Friends' Asylum, *Annual Report*, 37th, 1854, pp. 19–20. See also Hartford Retreat, *Annual Report*, 18th, 1841/42, pp. 16–17; 22d, 1845/46, p. 25; Indiana Hospital for the Insane, *Annual Report*, 1849, p. 15.

4 Friends' Asylum, *Annual Report*, 37th, 1854, pp. 19–20; State Lunatic Hospital at Taunton, *Annual Report*, 8th, 1861, pp. 11–12; Hartford Retreat, *Annual Report*, 23d, 1846/47, p. 24; Pennsylvania Hospital for the Insane, *Annual Report*, 1842, p. 17.

5 Gray, *AJI*, XXVII (April, 1871), 380–381; Gray, "Insanity and Its Relations to Medicine," *AJI*, XXV (October, 1868), 145–171; Gray, "Thoughts on the Causation of Insanity," *AJI*, XXIX (October, 1872), 264–283. These post-1865 articles are cited because they express Gray's somatic orientation more clearly and in more detail and are more accessible than his earlier writings on the subject.

6 "American Psychiatric Literature during the Past One Hundred Years," *One Hundred Years of American Psychiatry*, p. 207.

7 Even after the Civil War Gray's position met opposition. In 1872 H. B. Wilbur wrote that leading psychiatrists from Pinel up to that time believed that the causes of insanity were often moral. Gray and a few others stood alone in denying that moral causes produced insanity ("Materialism in Its Relations to the Causes, Conditions, and Treatment of Insanity," *Journal of Psychological Medicine*, VI [January, 1872], 35). The somatic approach to etiology gained support with the growth of neurology after the

Civil War, but even then superintendents of mental hospitals did not adhere to a strictly somatic theory of insanity as uniformly as neurologists did.

8 Carlson, *American Journal of Psychiatry*, CXV (December, 1958), 537; see also Samuel B. Woodward, "Errors of Education" (1840?), p. 5, in his "Collected Writings," III.

9 Woodward wrote: "All sin comes from the propensities of animal nature. These are implanted in our minds for wise and important purposes, and when rightly directed and controlled promote our happiness. Disease comes almost universally from the violation of the organic laws of our frame, by excesses which in various ways expose us, and from a total ignorance with which we pass through life, of the nature of our constitutions and the dangers to which we expose ourselves. The appetites, the passions, and the propensities of man are subjects of education and should be early attended to, or they will be likely to fall into courses dangerous in their tendency. There is nothing so easy as the formation of bad habits; nothing more difficult than the eradication of them" ("Errors of Education," p. 2, in his *Collected Writings*, III).

10 *Ibid.*, pp. 37–38.

11 Edward Jarvis, "On the Supposed Increase of Insanity," *AJI*, VIII (April, 1852), 343–344; Friends' Asylum, *Annual Report*, 28th, 1845, p. 22.

12 See, for example: *Vermont Asylum for the Insane, Its Annals . . .* , p. 53; State Lunatic Hospital at Worcester, *Annual Report*, 17th, 1849, pp. 49–52.

13 [Edward Jarvis], *The Causes and Prevention of Idiocy* (Boston: Coolidge & Wiley, 1848), pp. 13–15.

14 Jarvis, *AJI*, VIII (April, 1852), 353–354.

15 *Ibid.*, 355–364. See also Samuel Gridley Howe's review of Jarvis' *What Shall We Do with the Insane?* (Howe, "Insanity in Massachusetts," *North American Review*, LVI [January, 1843], 173) and [Amariah Brigham], "Insanity and Insane Hospitals," *North American Review*, XLIV (January, 1837), 118–119. Butler cited the remarks of Professor Buillarger at the Salpêtrière, to the effect that the number of insane persons was in direct proportion to the degree of liberty enjoyed by the population (Hartford Retreat, *Annual Report*, 22d, 1845/46, p. 31).

16 Jarvis, *AJI*, VIII (April, 1852), 349–350; [Amariah Brigham], "Exemption of the Cherokee Indians and Africans from Insanity," *AJI*, I (January, 1845), 287–288. See also Indiana Hospital for the Insane, *Annual Report*, 1849, p. 15, and McLean Asylum for the Insane, *Annual Report*, 39th, 1856, pp. 20–22. Contrary opinion and evidence did exist, but American psychiatrists seemed to ignore it. Peter Ludwig Panum, reporting on an epidemic of measles on the Faroe Islands, noted that "since it has been proved that the frequency of mental diseases is generally in direct proportion to civilization and the social collisions accompanying it," it was surprising to find that the proportion of mental illness on the Faroes was greater than that of almost any civilized metropolis. See his "Iagttagelser, anstillede under Maeslinge-Epidemien paa Faeroerne i Aaret 1846 (Observations Made during the Epidemic of Measles on the Faroe Islands in the Year 1846)," trans. Mrs. A. S. Hatcher (*Medical Classics*, III [May 1939], 837–838).

17 Jarvis, *AJI*, VIII (April, 1852), 333–335; Kings County Lunatic Asylum, Flatbush, L. I., *Annual Report*, 1857/58, p. 6; Hartford Retreat, *Annual Report*, 22d, 1845/46, p. 24; J. H. Worthington, "On a Form of Insanity for Which the Name of Congestive Mania Has Been Proposed," *AJI*, XVII (October, 1860), 113.

18 Jarvis, *AJI*, VIII (April, 1852), 348–349; Worthington, *AJI*, XVII (October, 1860), 113; McLean Asylum for the Insane, *Annual Report*, 39th, 1856, p. 22; Maine Insane Hospital, *Annual Report*, 1851 (i.e., 1850/51), p. 53; Hartford Retreat, *Annual Report*, 17th, 1840/41, p. 19; Indiana Hospital for the Insane, *Annual Report*, 1849, p. 15.

19 McLean Asylum for the Insane, *Annual Report*, 39th, 1856, p. 22; Brigham, *Observations*

on the Influence of Religion upon the Health and Physical Welfare of Mankind, p. 275; George Rosen, "Social Stress and Mental Disease from the Eighteenth Century to the Present: Some Origins of Social Psychiatry," *Milbank Memorial Fund Quarterly,* XXXVII (January, 1959), 18.

20 Pennsylvania Hospital for the Insane, *Annual Report,* 1853, pp. 30–32; O. M. Langdon of the Longview Asylum, Cincinnati, did not believe that Americans were more susceptible to insanity than foreigners (Longview Asylum, *Annual Report,* 1861, pp. 13–14).

21 Quoted in New York State Lunatic Asylum at Utica, *Annual Report,* 14th, 1856, pp. 20, 19.

22 Indiana Hospital for the Insane, *Annual Report,* 1854, p. 19.

23 Stanford Chaillé, "Insane Asylum of the State of Louisiana, at Jackson," *New Orleans Medical and Surgical Journal,* XV (January, 1858), 115–116. There was also a difference of opinion about the greater violence of patients in the north and therefore the need for more heroic therapeutics for them than for southern patients. Thomas Cooper, for example, in contrast to other writers, claimed that people in southern climates required stronger medication than those up north (see his note in Broussais, p. vi).

24 "Reports of American Asylums," *AJI,* XVI (October, 1859), 218. State Lunatic Hospital at Taunton, *Annual Report,* 6th, 1859, pp. 39–40. Kirkbride remarked that farmers were least likely to become insane, for they furnished the smallest proportion of patients to Pennsylvania Hospital (Pennsylvania Hospital for the Insane, *Annual Report,* 1845, pp. 16–17; 1856, p. 17). Ray disagreed. He believed that intermarriage was a more important factor than occupation or place of residence and cited a statistical report by Jarvis that showed that insanity was as frequent in old rural areas as in urban communities, if not more so (Ray, *Mental Hygiene,* pp. 41–43).

25 *Vermont Asylum for the Insane, Its Annals . . . ,* p. 53. Harvey Peit, head of the New York Institution for the Instruction of the Deaf and Dumb, wrote: "It has been remarked of the Deaf and Dumb that they have frequently a purity and religious fervor of expression, as if they were kept in a better state by remaining ignorant of a large portion of the wicked and mean things that fly from tongue to tongue in common society" (quoted in *New York Tribune,* March 18, 1846, p. 1, col. 1).

26 When one of the teacher-companions at the Pennsylvania Hospital visited a mental institution in her native Scotland she was surprised to find that the superintendent did not think dancing parties too exciting for patients and that he handed a snuffbox to several of them (quoted in Gertrude Stout, "Mixed Interests," [Typed manuscript of paper delivered before the Section on Medical History], pt. 2, pp. 5–6, Kirkbride MSS).

27 Shyrock, "The Beginnings," *One Hundred Years of American Psychiatry,* p. 25.

28 Illinois State Hospital for the Insane, *Biennial Report,* 5th, 1855–56, in *Reports of the Illinois State Hospital . . . ,* pp. 213–215.

29 Jarvis, *AJI,* VIII (April, 1852), 363.

30 New York State Lunatic Asylum at Utica, *Annual Report,* 6th, 1848, p. 38.

31 "The Study of Mind," *AJI,* XVII (January, 1861), 247–249. See also Butler Hospital, *Annual Report,* 1859, p. 12.

32 Hartford Retreat, *Annual Report,* 24th, 1847/48, pp. 16–17; Pennsylvania Hospital for the Insane, *Annual Report,* 1856, p. 17. Dr. Bates of the Maine Insane Hospital thought that confinement and sedentary habits gave workers in manufacturing towns a decided predisposition to insanity (Maine Insane Hospital, *Annual Report,* 6th, 1845, p. 44). Woodward also believed that sedentary work was detrimental to mental health. He commented that men who had been engaged in hard outdoor labor often had been out of work for some time before they showed signs of insanity (State Lunatic Hospital at Worcester, *Annual Report,* 9th, 1841, pp. 49–50).

33 Brigham, for one, did not agree that stupid persons never became insane (*AJI*, I [July, 1844], 19).

34 Pliny Earle, "The Poetry of Insanity," *AJI*, I (January, 1845), 197–204 ff. See also [Brigham], *AJI*, I (July, 1844), 19.

35 State Lunatic Hospital at Worcester, *Annual Report*, 9th, 1841, p. 50; 5th, 1837, pp. 45–46. See also remarks by Woodward's successor, in *ibid.*, 15th, 1847, p. 42.

36 State Lunatic Hospital at Taunton, *Annual Report*, 5th, 1858, p. 26.

37 Ray, *Mental Hygiene*, pp. 228 ff. He thought, for example, that general paralysis was a product of civilization and that with civilization insanity became hereditary in families (Butler Hospital for the Insane, Providence, R. I., *Annual Report*, 1858, pp. 17–19).

38 Brigham, *Remarks on the Influence of Mental Cultivation and Mental Excitement upon Health*, p. 190.

39 Butler Hospital, *Annual Report*, 1856, pp. 24–27.

40 *Ibid.*, pp. 28–29. For a similar view see New York State Lunatic Asylum at Utica, *Annual Report*, 16th, 1858, p. 28. Patterson thought that spirit rapping and transcendentalism caused insanity. By "rejecting the inspired authority of scripture, and regarding the human family as ignorant of their relations to God, and their condition in eternity, [transcendentalists] teach that man, by some *mysterious, unintelligible* process, after a long series of ages, may possibly arrive at some definite truth. Who can wonder that minds involved in such error should seek to find some *surer, quicker* means of knowledge?" If such people did not look to the Bible they became adherents of wizards and table rapping. At Indiana Hospital and elsewhere he knew of none becoming insane from belief in table rappings who had "an intelligent acquaintance with the bible [*sic*]" (Indiana Hospital for the Insane, *Annual Report*, 1852, pp. 36–38). Patterson did not explain why so many eminent educators and theologians among the transcendentalists did not go mad.

41 Butler Hospital, *Annual Report*, 1856, p. 29.

42 Illinois State Hospital for the Insane, *Biennial Report*, 5th, 1855–56, in *Reports of the Illinois State Hospital . . .*, pp. 201–202. See also "Reports of American Asylums," *AJI*, XVI (July, 1859), 105.

43 Butler Hospital, *Annual Report*, 1856, pp. 27–29.

44 Ray cited as an example the spread of convulsive chorea among students during the Great Awakening in the eighteenth century (*ibid.*, 1859, pp. 14–16, 23–24).

45 *Ibid.*, p. 18. Brigham took a similar view in his "Insanity and Insane Hospitals," *North American Review*, XLIV (January, 1837), 119.

46 Butler Hospital, *Annual Report*, 1859, pp. 23–24.

47 Brigham, *North American Review*, XLIV (January, 1837), 119; Bell to Dix, 29 Dec. 1848, Dix MSS.

48 Hartford Retreat, *Annual Report*, 24th, 1847/48, pp. 17–18; 36th, 1859/60, pp. 15–17.

49 George Cook, "Mental Hygiene," *AJI*, XV (January, 1859), 275, 277, 279–281.

50 Woodward, "Errors of Education," pp. 2–8, 33–34 in his "Collected Writings," III; Woodward, "Management of Children" (1838–40), pp. 1–2, 18, 27, in *ibid.* The emphasis upon moral education was common among educators, who sought to insure the maintenance of republican institutions by developing good people, a result not necessarily obtained by purely intellectual training (Merle Curti, *The Social Ideas of American Educators*, with New Chapter on the Last Twenty-Fve Years; Vol. X of *Report of the American Historical Association Commission on the Social Studies* [Paterson, N. J.: Littlefield, Adams & Co., 1959], p. 59).

51 Carlson, *American Journal of Psychiatry*, CXV (December, 1958), 536.

52 Brigham, *Remarks on the Influence of Mental Cultivation and Mental Excitement upon Health*, p. 98. See also Albert Deutsch, "The History of Mental Hygiene," *One Hundred Years of American Psychiatry*, pp. 327–328.

53 See Butler Hospital, *Annual Report*, 1860, pp. 17–18; McLean Asylum, *Annual Report*, 39th, 1856, pp. 22–24; New York State Lunatic Asylum at Utica, *Annual Report*, 1st, 1843, pp. 26, 29; Maine Insane Hospital, *Annual Report*, 1854, pp. 26–27.

54 Brigham, *Remarks on the Influence of Mental Cultivation and Mental Excitement upon Health*, p. 92.

55 In a footnote in his *Remarks on the Influence of Mental Cultivation and Mental Excitement upon Health* (pp. 164–165), Brigham seemed to approve of education for the lower classes.

56 Kirkbride noted that the public should be informed that anyone could become insane under proper conditions. The best and the worst people succumbed, and wealth did not ensure mental health any more than physical health (Pennsylvania Hospital for the Insane, *Annual Report*, 1858, pp. 36–37). The upper classes believed that the poor were peculiarly subject to many illnesses. In New York City, for example, wealthy laymen as well as physicians thought that cholera primarily infected the sinful and poor, because the latter were degraded, vicious, and dirty. The wealthy believed that they themselves might be seriously endangered only after cholera remained in an area for an extended time. (Charles Rosenberg, "The Cholera Epidemic of 1832 in New York City," *Bulletin of the History of Medicine*, XXXIII [January-February, 1959], 40–41, 45.)

57 See "Reports of American Asylums," *AJI*, XVI (October, 1859), 218.

58 Massachusetts, Commission on Lunacy, 1854, *Report on Insanity and Idiocy in Massachusetts*, by the Commission on Lunacy, under Resolve of the Legislature of 1854 (Boston: William White, Printer to the State, 1855), pp. 188–189.

59 *Ibid.*, pp. 45, 52–55.

60 Quoted in "Reports of American Asylums," *AJI*, XVI (October, 1859), 230–231. It seems that Bell took a somewhat similar view in stressing the essential role that the level of patients' education played in their restoration to mental health. See article from *New Hampshire Patriot* in *Extracts from Newspapers and Periodicals in Relation to the Condition of the Insane in New Hampshire, Previous to the Erection of the N. H. Asylum for the Insane* ([Concord, N. H.]: Asylum Press, 1890), p. 98. Since Bell at this time was involved deeply in the campaign to establish an asylum in New Hampshire, it is probable that this article was written by him, especially since it is signed "B." Bell also wrote a report for the legislature of New Hampshire about the insane.

61 Maryland Hospital for the Insane, *Report*, 1846–49, p. 7; Massachusetts, Commission on Lunacy, 1854, p. 56.

62 Butler Hospital, *Annual Report*, 1860, p. 21; State Lunatic Hospital at Taunton, *Annual Report*, 5th, 1858, pp. 29–30.

63 [Bell?] *Extracts from Newspapers and Periodicals . . . New Hampshire*, p. 98.

64 Woodward, "Errors of Education," pp. 34, 37–39, in his "Collected Writings," III. Ray believed that people were born with different powers to recognize right and wrong and to "pursue the one and avoid the other." They were therefore not equally responsible for their acts (*Mental Hygiene*, pp. 61–63).

65 [Amariah Brigham], Review of *Life Among Lunatics*, by J. B. Derby, Author of *Scenes in a Mad-House, etc.*, *AJI*, IV (July, 1847), 81–82. For a similar approach see State Lunatic Hospital at Taunton, *Annual Report*, [by Dr. Choate], 6th, 1859, p. 19.

66 State Lunatic Hospital at Worcester, *Annual Report*, 22nd, 1854, pp. 10–11. Choate also noted that foreigners were outnumbering native Americans in the Taunton Hospital (State Lunatic Hospital at Taunton, *Annual Report*, 1st, 1854, p. 32).

67 State Lunatic Hospital at Worcester, *Annual Report,* 26th, 1858, pp. 9–10, 20.

68 Illinois State Hospital for the Insane, *Biennial Report,* 4th, 1853–54, p. 159.

69 [Bell?], in *Extracts from Newspapers and Periodicals . . . New Hampshire,* p. 99.

70 State Lunatic Hospital at Taunton, *Annual Report,* 5th, 1858, p. 27; "Reports of American Asylums," *AJI,* XVII (April, 1861), 445–446.

71 "Reports of American Asylums," *AJI,* XVI (July, 1859), 106. Ten years earlier, when the need for a new mental hospital in Massachusetts was being discussed in that state, Bell told Kirkbride that he favored the construction of a separate asylum for the Irish (Bell to Kirkbride, 23 Jan. 1849, Kirkbride MSS). A new asylum was finally built, the State Lunatic Hospital at Taunton, but not officially as a segregated hospital.

72 Massachusetts, Commission on Lunacy, 1854, pp. 147–150, 154. See also Jarvis to Governor John D. Andrews, 11th Feb. 1861, Andrews MSS, Massachusetts Historical Society.

73 Massachusetts, Commission on Lunacy, 1854, p. 100.

74 Ray, *North American Review,* LXXXII (January, 1856), 83–84, 95–96.

75 Massachusetts, Commission on Lunacy, 1854, pp. 59–62; "Proceedings of the Twelfth Annual Meeting of the Association of Medical Superintendents of American Institutions for the Insane," *AJI,* XIV (July, 1857), 102–103; M. H. Ranney, "On Insane Foreigners," *AJI,* VII (July, 1850), 54–55.

76 State Lunatic Hospital at Taunton, *Annual Report,* 1st, 1854, p. 33; see also Ranney, 54–55.

77 State Lunatic Hospital at Worcester, *Annual Report,* 15th, 1847, p. 33.

78 Maine Insane Hospital, *Annual Report,* 14th, 1852 (i.e., 1851–52), p. 19; see also Ray, *North American Review,* LXXXII (January, 1856), 87.

79 "Proceedings of the Twelfth Annual Meeting . . . ," *AJI,* XIV (July, 1857), 103.

80 *Ibid.,* 102–103.

81 State Lunatic Hospital at Taunton, *Annual Report,* 6th, 1859, p. 15.

82 State Lunatic Hospital at Worcester, *Annual Report,* 15th, 1847, p. 33.

83 "Proceedings of the Twelfth Annual Meeting . . . ," *AJI,* XIV (July, 1857), 103. Dr. Nichols of Bloomingdale Asylum mentioned three Irish homicidal maniacs who were restored to sanity (*ibid.*).

84 Ranney, 56–57.

85 Butler Hospital, *Annual Report,* 1849, pp. 30–32; Ray, *North American Review,* LXXXII (January, 1856), 87.

86 Butler Hospital, *Annual Report,* 1849, pp. 30–32; Ray, *North American Review,* LXXXII (January, 1856), 95–96.

87 State Lunatic Hospital at Worcester, *Annual Report,* 15th, 1847, p. 33; Ranney, *AJI,* VII (July, 1850), 57.

88 [Amariah Brigham], "Number of the Insane and Idiotic, with Brief Notices of the Lunatic Asylums in the United States," *AJI,* I (July, 1844), 80–81; Edward Jarvis, "Insanity among the Colored Population of the Free States," *AJI,* VIII (January, 1852), 268–270. The *AJI* reproduced a letter to the editors of the *New-York Observer* which claimed that according to the 1840 census, *"every fourteenth colored person in the State of Maine is an idiot or lunatic."* The author attributed this supposed fact to the social condition of the free Negro in the North ("Startling Facts from the Census," *AJI,* VIII [October, 1851], 153–155).

89 Edward Jarvis, "Insanity among the Coloured Population of the Free States," *American Journal of the Medical Sciences,* new series, VII (January, 1844), 74; see also "Dr. Dunglison's Statistics of Insanity in the United States," *AJI,* XVII (July, 1860), 111.

90 Jarvis, *American Journal of the Medical Sciences,* new series, VII (January, 1844), 74; Edward Jarvis, "Statistics of Insanity in the United States," *Boston Medical and Surgical*

Journal, XXVII (September 21, 1842), 119–121; Edward Jarvis, "Statistics of Insanity in the United States," *ibid.,* XXVII (November 30, 1842), 281–282.

91 Jarvis, *AJI,* VIII (January, 1852), 268–270. Jarvis pointed out that the number of Negroes who were listed as insane in some towns exceeded the total number of Negroes who lived there. This was true in nine towns in Maine, twelve in Michigan, one in Iowa, ten in Illinois, five in Indiana, seven in Massachusetts, thirty-seven in Ohio, one in Connecticut, three in Vermont, sixteen in New York, and nine in New Hampshire (Howe, *North American Review,* LVI [January, 1843], 172n–173n). See also Edward Jarvis, J. Wingate Thornton, and Wm. Brigham, "The Sixth Census of the United States; Memorial to the Honorable the Senate and House of Representatives in Congress Assembled," *Merchants' Magazine,* XII (February, 1845), 132–135, and Jarvis, *American Journal of the Medical Sciences,* new series, VII (January, 1844), 75–83.

92 *Ibid.,* 74–75.

93 "Reflections on the Census of 1840," *Southern Literary Messenger,* IX (June, 1843), 351; C. B. Hayden, "On the Distribution of Insanity in the U. States," *Southern Literary Messenger,* X (March, 1844), 180.

94 "The Vital Statistics of Negroes in the United States," *DeBow's Review,* XXI (October, 1856), 405–410. Using census figures for insanity and other ailments to defend slavery did not stop with the 1840 returns. In 1855 a pamphleteer said that the census of 1850 showed "that the Negro race is much more subject to these afflictions than the white. . . . yet . . . as a slave the negro is almost exempt from them all—not only is he far less afflicted than the free negro, but even less than his master" (B. F. Stringfellow, *Information for the People; Two Tracts for the Times; The One Entitled "Negro-Slavery, No Evil:"* by B. F. Stringfellow of Missouri . . . [Boston: Alfred Mudge and Son, Printers, 1855], p. 11).

95 Quoted in Chaillé, *New Orleans Medical and Surgical Journal,* XV (January, 1858), 108–109.

96 *Ibid.,* 109.

97 "Mr. Calhoun to Mr. Pakenham," Department of State, Washington, April 18th, 1844, in John C. Calhoun, *Works,* ed. Richard K. Crallé (New York: D. Appleton and Company, 1857), V, 337–338.

98 Jarvis to Dix, 25 May 1844, Dix MSS.

99 John Quincy Adams, *Memoirs of John Quincy Adams, Comprising Portions of His Diary from 1795 to 1848,* ed. Charles Francis Adams (Philadelphia: Lippincott, 1877), XII, 61–62, 36; see also U. S., *Congressional Globe,* 28th Cong., 1st Sess., 1844, XIII, 323.

100 Quoted in Robert Williams Wood, M.D., *Memorial of Edward Jarvis, M.D.* (Boston: T. R. Marvin & Son, Printers, 1885), pp. 11–12; Jarvis, *AJI,* VIII (January, 1852), 281. For further discussion of the political aspects of the census controversy see William Stanton, *The Leopard's Spots; Scientific Attitudes toward Race in America, 1815–59* (Chicago: University of Chicago Press, 1960), pp. 58–65, and Albert Deutsch, "The First U. S. Census of the Insane (1840), and Its Use as Pro-Slavery Propaganda," *Bulletin of the History of Medicine,* XV (May, 1944), 469–482.

101 *New York Tribune,* February 1, 1844, p. [4], col. 1–2; February 24, 1844, p. [2], col. 3.

102 See Stanton, pp. 54–81, and William Sumner Jenkins, *Pro-Slavery Thought in the Old South* (Chapel Hill: The University of North Carolina Press, 1935), pp. 242–284.

103 Indiana Hospital for the Insane, *Annual Report,* 1854, pp. 36–37. Nichols thought that segregation by race, as suggested by another psychiatrist, Dr. Stribling, was worth considering (Nichols to Dix, January 1, 1853, Dix MSS).

104 Galt to Woodward, undated letter, Woodward MSS.

105 American Freedman's Inquiry Commission MSS, Houghton Library, Harvard University. Cited hereafter as American Freedmen's Inq. Comm. MSS.

106 Ray to Samuel Gridley Howe, 24 Aug. 1863; J. B. Chapin to Howe, Sept. 7, 1863, American Freedmen's Inq. Comm. MSS.

107 Jarvis told Howe not to rely on the abstract of the 1850 U. S. census for statistics on rates of mortality; its distinction between insane and idiots was also unreliable (Jarvis to Howe, Aug. 21, 1863, American Freedmen's Inq. Comm. MSS).

108 Kirkbride to Howe, Aug. 23, 1863, American Freedmen's Inq. Comm. MSS.

109 Geo. L. Chapman to Howe, Columbus, O., Sept. 21, 1863; R. I. Patterson to Howe, 28 Aug. 1863; Curwen to Howe, Aug. 24, 1863, American Freedmen's Inq. Comm. MSS.

110 Butler to Howe, Sept. 9, 1863; Worthington to Howe, 24 Aug. 1863, American Freedmen's Inq. Comm. MSS.

111 Earle, *AJI*, IV (January, 1848), 186.

112 Pennsylvania Hospital for the Insane, *Annual Report*, 1841, p. 40.

113 [Amariah Brigham], "Insanity and Insane Hospitals," *North American Review*, XLIV (January, 1837), 118; Butler gave similar advice in Hartford Retreat, *Annual Report*, 22d, 1845/46, pp. 22–23.

114 New York State Lunatic Asylum at Utica, *Annual Report*, 6th, 1848, pp. 36–37; see also "Reports of American Asylums," *AJI*, XVI (July, 1859), 100–101; "Reports of American Asylums," *AJI*, XVI (October, 1859), 239–240.

115 Maine Insane Hospital, *Annual Report*, 6th, 1845, pp. 41–42; Butler Hospital, *Annual Report*, 1860, p. 14.

116 State Lunatic Hospital at Worcester, *Annual Report*, 5th, 1837, p. 48.

117 Friends' Asylum, *Annual Report*, 47th, 1864, p. 12; 42d, 1859, p. 10.

118 Illinois State Hospital for the Insane, *Biennial Report*, 5th, 1855–56, in *Reports of the Illinois State Hospital . . .* , pp. 200–201.

119 Brigham, *An Inquiry Concerning the Diseases and Functions of the Brain*, p. 288; Hartford Retreat, *Annual Report*, 18th, 1841/42, p. 17; New York State Lunatic Asylum at Utica, *Annual Report*, 6th, 1848, p. 36; [Brigham], "Sleep, Its Importance in Preventing Insanity," *AJI*, I (April, 1845), 319–320.

120 New York State Lunatic Asylum at Utica, *Annual Report*, 12th, 1854, p. 26.

121 Pennsylvania Hospital for the Insane, *Annual Report*, 1858, p. 36.

122 "Reports of American Asylums," *AJI*, XVI (October, 1859), 239–240.

123 "Reports of American Asylums," *AJI*, XVI (July, 1859), 101. Harlow also thought that insanity was an inherited disease; by this he meant that the inherited brain structure was susceptible to disease (Maine Insane Hospital, *Annual Report*, 1854, pp. 25–26). See also remarks of Dr. J. Workman, superintendent of the Toronto Asylum, quoted in "Reports of American Asylums," *AJI*, XVII (January, 1861), 314; and Friends' Asylum, *Annual Report*, 45th, 1862, pp. 14–15.

124 Isaac Ray, "Hereditary Insanity," *North American Review*, CIX (July, 1869), 14–16.

125 Earle, *AJI*, IV (January, 1848), 192; see also Friends' Asylum, *Annual Report*, 44th, 1861, p. 11.

126 John C. Greene, *The Death of Adam; Evolution and Its Impact on Western Thought* (Ames, Iowa: The Iowa State University Press, c1959), p. 224.

127 Ray, "Causes of Insanity," in his *Contributions to Mental Pathology*, pp. 39–45. See also Friends' Asylum, *Annual Report*, 47th, 1864, p. 13.

128 For a modern study of the relationship between the social outlook of scientists and their adherence to heredity or environment as the dominant factor in development, see Nicholas Pastore, *The Nature-Nurture Controversy*, with a foreword by Goodwin Watson (New York: King's Crown Press, Columbia University, 1949).

129 Ray, *Mental Hygiene,* pp. 22–23.

130 "Reports of American Asylums," *AJI,* XVII (April, 1861), 453; Butler Hospital, *Annual Report,* 1853, pp. 27–28. Workman of the Toronto Asylum wrote: "Insanity would die out if the sane avoided intermarrying with insane stock" ("Reports of American Asylums," AJI, XVII [January, 1861], 314). See also Pennsylvania Hospital for the Insane, *Annual Report,* 1858, pp. 36–37.

131 McLean Asylum for the Insane, *Annual Report,* 1843, pp. 41–42. See State Lunatic Hospital at Worcester, *Annual Report* [by G. Chandler], 20th, 1852, p. 47; remarks by Tyler, quoted in "Reports of American Asylums," *AJI,* XVI (April, 1860), 470; John M. Galt, "Fragments on Insanity," *AJI,* I (October, 1844), 123; New York State Lunatic Asylum at Utica, *Annual Report,* 1st, 1843, p. 52.

132 See quotation from a report by Joseph Workman in "Reports of American Asylums," AJI, XVII (January, 1861), 311–312; Friends' Asylum, *Annual Report,* 47th, 1864, p. 12. The editors of the *AJI* criticized Tyler for telling the public that hereditary insanity was as curable as other insanity; see "Reports of American Asylums," *AJI,* XVI (April, 1860), 470.

Chapter 5

1 Deutsch, *The Mentally Ill in America,* p. 132.

2 Deutsch, *The Mentally Ill in America,* pp. 189–190; Eaton quotes this evaluation approvingly (*New England Hospitals,* p. 147).

3 This account is largely a summary of an article on patient care at the Friends' Asylum from 1817 to 1861 (Dain and Carlson, *Journal of Nervous and Mental Disease,* CXXXI [October, 1961], 277–290). Since it excluded documentation, specific bibliographical references will be supplied here where necessary.

4 See Friends' Asylum, Superintendent's Diary, Oct. 28, 1817; Oct. 10, 1819; Friends' Asylum, *Annual Report,* 1st, 1818, p. 2. In an attempt to give individualized care to each patient Brigham requested friends to tell him everything that might shed light on the cause of the patient's disease or that might guide him in care and treatment. He also urged that the patient's best clothing be sent to the asylum for "Sunday" wear (New York State Lunatic Asylum at Utica, *Annual Report,* 2d, 1844, pp. 32–33). Ray and Kirkbride expressed similar views; they recognized the importance of good interpersonal relations in the asylum and the need for the physician to know his patients thoroughly (see Isaac Ray, "Ideal Characters of the Officers of a Hospital for the Insane," *AJI,* XXX [July, 1873], 67, and State Lunatic Hospital at Worcester, *Annual Report,* 7th, 1839, pp. 96–99). There was also discussion among psychiatrists about the need for tactful, intelligent, and resourceful attendants. For an analysis of the doctor-patient relationship in moral treatment, see Eric T. Carlson and Norman Dain, "The Psychotherapy That Was Moral Treatment," *American Journal of Psychiatry,* CXVII (December, 1960), 519–524.

5 One attendant who did not comply lost his job (Friends' Asylum, Superintendent's Diary, June 4, 1821). See also *ibid.,* Mar. 3, 1819.

6 *Ibid.,* Dec. 18, 1824; Apr. 10, 1825; Feb. 8, 1824; Feb. 26, 1827; Aug. 1, 1824; Aug. 2, 1825; Aug. 17, 1825; Aug. 19, 1827; Sept. 11, 1827; Dec. 29, 1824; Mar. 3, 1827; Oct. 14, 1833; Sept. 7, 1826.

7 *Ibid.,* Apr. 8, 1827; Dec. 26, 1824; Feb. 27, 1824; Apr. 12, 1824; Oct. 14, 1831; Sept. 26, 1817; Sept. 30, 1817; May 1, 1824; Oct. 9, 1823; Dec. 1, 1824; Oct. 14, 1823; Sept. 29, 1817; Mar. 2, 1827.

8 Friends' Asylum, *Annual Report,* 46th, 1863, pp. 4, 16–17; *ibid.,* 34th, 1851, p. 19. The

first ward included the quiet, curable, and convalescent; next came the noisy and excited but curable patients; quiet inmates deemed incurable made up the third class; the fourth ward housed the violent, unmanageable, hopeless cases.

9 *Ibid.*, 25th, 1842, p. 20; 28th, 1845, p. 18; 32d. 1849, pp. 17–18. All the reports during this period describe the activities of the patients, and the references given here are samples.

10 *Ibid.*, 22d, 1839, p. 14; Friends' Asylum, Superintendent's Diary, Oct. 21, 1854; Jan. 30, 1856; Friends' Asylum, *Annual Report*, 21st, 1838, pp. 10–12.

11 *Ibid.*, 22d, 1839, pp. 13–14; 21st, 1838, p. 12; 24th, 1841, p. 14; 28th, 1845, pp. 20–21; 29th, 1846, pp. 12–13; 32d, 1849, p. 18. In other asylums patients held annual fairs open to the public, published weekly newspapers, presented theatrical performances, and attended frequent lectures on a wide variety of topics.

12 *Ibid.*, 39th, 1856, p. 14; 36th, 1853, p. 18; 42d, 1859, p. 13.

13 See Pliny Earle, "Bloodletting in Mental Disorders," *AJI*, X (April, 1854), 287–405; J. H. Worthington, "On the Construction of Baths, and the Utility of Warm and Cold Bathing in the Treatment of Insanity," *AJI*, VII (January, 1851), 201–213.

14 Earle, "The Curability of Insanity, a Statistical Study," *AJI*, XLII (October, 1885), 179–209. Deutsch, for example, based his evaluation of asylum statistics on curability largely on Earle's article (*The Mentally Ill in America*, pp. 155–157).

15 Bockoven, *Journal of Nervous and Mental Disease*, CXXIV (September, 1956), 295–298.

16 Friends' Asylum, *Annual Report*, 2d, 1819, p. 3.

17 The idea that those ill for more than a year had poor chances of recovery was not new; see *Encyclopaedia Britannica*, XI, 283. The impression received from reading the annual reports of southern asylums is that the "cult of curability" was not widespread there. Conditions were so poor in most southern mental institutions that few patients ever recovered or were even viewed or treated therapeutically. For a brief discussion of this question see Powell, *AJI*, LIV (July, 1897), 26–28.

18 McLean Asylum for the Insane, *Annual Report*, 24th, 1841, p. 18.

19 [Amariah Brigham], "Statistics of Insanity," *AJI*, VI (October, 1849), 142–143.

20 [Amariah Brigham], "Institutions for the Insane in the United States," *AJI*, V (July, 1848), 57.

21 "Proceedings of the Tenth Annual Meeting of the Association of Medical Superintendents of American Institutions for the Insane," *AJI*, XII (July, 1855), 99.

22 Brigham to Earle, Feb. 27, 1845, Earle MSS.

23 "It is rather remarkable," he wrote, ". . . that no injury has been sustained by either patient or attendant" as a consequence of the increased freedom for the inmates and abolition of restraint (Insane Asylum of Louisiana, *Annual Report*, 1860, p. 7). Six years later the Board of Administration noted that reduced restraint and more freedom seemed to have a humanizing effect on the patients. "A little tact is usually more efficacious than either persuasion or force in the management of the insane" (*ibid.*, 1866, pp. 3–4).

24 "Proceedings of the Twelfth Annual Meeting of the Association of Medical Superintendents of American Institutions for the Insane," *AJI*, XIV (July, 1857), 76–77.

25 See Worthington's remarks in *ibid.*, p. 77. The proceedings of the superintendents' annual meetings reveal that some were even considering new methods of restraint ("Proceedings of the Eighth Annual Meeting of the Association of Medical Superintendents of American Institutions for the Insane," *AJI*, X [July, 1853], 77).

26 Isaac Ray, "Observations on the Principal Hospitals for the Insane, in Great Britain, France and Germany," *AIJ*, II (April, 1846), 343–349 (quotation taken from p. 347). See also Jarvis' comment about the common beliefs concerning American and British mental patients in his "On the Proper Functions of Private Institutions or Homes for the Insane," *AJI*, XVII (July, 1860), 25.

27 Butler Hospital, *Annual Report*, 1853, p. 29.

28 "Proceedings of the Twelfth Annual Meeting of the Association of Medical Superintendents of American Institutions for the Insane," *AJI*, XIV (July, 1857), 72 ff.; "Proceedings
of the Fourteenth Annual Meeting of the Association of Medical Superintendents of
American Institutions for the Insane," *AJI*, XVI (July, 1859), 65. In 1851 McFarland
thought that insanity presented "almost precisely the same aspects" from Louisiana to
Maine. This was not true in European communities "where the lines between different
grades of society have been closely drawn for ages, and where contiguous neighborhoods,
from different pursuits, have a distinct character" (quoted from New Hampshire Asylum
for the Insane, *Reports . . . June session 1851*, in "Reports of Hospitals for the Insane,"
AJI, IX [October, 1852], 200).

29 Jarvis to Earle, Dec. 1, 1860, Earle MSS. See also Jarvis, *AJI*, XVII (July, 1860), 25; he
notes the belief of some psychiatrists that the insane in the United States were more
excitable and unruly than those in Britain and needed more restraint.

30 Maine Insane Hospital, *Annual Report*, 7th, 1846, p. 42. Butler also attributed the great
success of non-restraint in England to "the stupidity of their patients" ("Proceedings of
the Tenth Annual Meeting of the Association of Medical Superintendents of American
Institutions for the Insane," *AJI*, XII [July, 1855], 90–91).

31 For an extended discussion of the non-restraint movement in the United States see
Deutsch, *The Mentally Ill in America*, Chapter XI.

32 See, for example, Illinois State Hospital for the Insane, Biennial Report, 6th, 1857–58, in
Reports of the Illinois State Hospital, pp. 261–262.

33 Quoted in Russell, p. 154. See also *Annals of the Vermont Asylum*, p. 125; Massachusetts,
Commission on Lunacy, 1854, pp. 149–150; and Ray, *North American Review*, LXXXII
(January, 1856), 95–96. Some indication of the pressure under which superintendents
sometimes were placed by wealthy patients was given by Kirkbride, writing in 1845 about
the need to build better accommodations for the insane in Pennsylvania Hospital. He
opposed extending the hospital to take care of more patients, for many of the patients
there already were well-to-do and should have intimate contact with the superintendent.
He proposed instead the improvement of existing facilities. The friends of some wealthy
patients wanted larger accommodations for them, and although Kirkbride doubted that
this would aid their recovery materially, he noted that it would bring into the hospital
patients then kept at home and add substantially to its income. It could thereby take in
more patients at a low rate or add to the number of patients supported by corporation
funds. (Pennsylvania Hospital for the Insane, *Annual Report*, 1845, pp. 13–14.) See also
[Bell?], in *Extracts from Newspapers and Periodicals . . . New Hampshire*, p. 99.

34 Quoted from a letter to Robert Cassie Waterston, in Waterston's *The Condition of the
Insane in Massachusetts* (Boston: James Munroe and Company, 1843), p. 22. One of the
inducements offered to Woodward to accept the superintendency of the Hartford Retreat
was its upper-class clientele. Rev. Thomas H. Gallaudet, chaplain of the Retreat, wrote
to Woodward: "Cannot you do more good to the cause in which you have been so successfully engaged *here* than where you are? I think so. The class of patients, you know,
are of a higher order, and would afford, I should think, a larger sphere of operation for
the exercise of skill and ingenuity, and for the accumulation of results that would benefit
mankind." (Gallaudet to Woodward, Feb. 21, 1840, Woodward MSS.) George Sumner, a
visiting physician at the Retreat, made the same kind of appeal (Sumner to Woodward,
Feb. 22, 1840, Woodward MSS), but Woodward remained at the State Lunatic Hospital
at Worcester, to which he was greatly attached.

35 Gerald N. Grob, "Samuel B. Woodward and the Practice of Psychiatry in Early Nineteenth-Century America," *Bulletin of the History of Medicine*, XXXVI (September-

October, 1962), 433–434; Dain and Carlson, *Journal of Nervous and Mental Disease,* CXXXI (October, 1960), 280, 286. Kirkbride also maintained that his charity patients were treated the same as other patients (Pennsylvania Hospital for the Insane, *Annual Report,* 1841, p. 20). (From 1751 to 1850 approximately 17 per cent of the insane treated at the Pennsylvania Hospital were subsidized or on the free list [*ibid.,* 1850, p. 40].) Kirkbride must have meant the same treatment as patients paying low rates, for there were different rates at the hospital and rich patients had special accommodations. Even the lowest rates were so high that John Curwen, superintendent of the State Lunatic Hospital at Harrisburg, Pennsylvania, wrote Kirkbride that when he told friends of the insane that the minimum rate at the Pennsylvania Hospital was five dollars a week they said that they could not afford it (Curwen to Kirkbride, May 1, 1861, Kirkbride MSS).

36 Massachusetts Commission on Lunacy, 1854, pp. 148–150; [Bell?], in *Extracts from News-papers and Periodicals . . . New Hampshire,* p. 98.

37 See Stanley T. Michael, "Social Attitudes, Socio-Economic Status and Psychiatric Symptoms," *Acta Psychiatrica et Neurologica Scandinavica,* XXXV, fasc. 4 (1960), 509–516.

38 McLean Asylum for the Insane, *Annual Report,* 22d, 1839, p. 13. See also Bell to Dix, 4 May 1843, Dix MSS; Ray to Dix, 20 Feb. 1843, Dix MSS.

39 [Isaac Ray?], "American Hospitals for the Insane," *North American Review,* LXXIX (July, 1854), 71, 75. Not all psychiatrists were sufficiently aware that poorly built institutions might endanger the practice of moral treatment. Woodward suggested that an asylum for lower-class patients could be built at the cost of $500 per patient (Woodward to Hugh Bell, Sept. 20, 1845, Woodward MSS), about half of what other psychiatrists thought necessary. Hurd (I, 14) contended that New Englanders were responsible for hospital organization in the United States in this period and that they were unduly economical, "which unquestionably hampered their [i.e., mental hospitals'] development."

40 See George Cook, *Remarks on the Care and Treatment of the Chronic Insane Poor* (Canandaigua, N. Y.: Milliken, Printer, Ontario County *Times Office,* 1867), p. 4.

41 Pennsylvania, Legislature, House of Representatives, *Report in Relation to an Asylum for the Insane Poor,* Read in the House of Representatives, March 11, 1839 (Harrisburg: Boas & Coplan, Printers, 1839), p. 12.

42 Woodward to [?], April 16, 1847, Woodward MSS. See also Buttolph to Kirkbride, Feb. 6, 1849, Kirkbride MSS.

43 George Chandler, "On the Proper Number of Patients for an Institution . . . ," [n.d.], Chandler MSS, American Antiquarian Society.

44 Stephen Collins, *Report on Pauper Insanity;* Presented to the City Council of Baltimore on March 28th, 1845, by Dr. Stephen Collins, Chairman of the Committee (Baltimore: Printed by James Lucas, 1845), p. 3.

45 McLean Asylum for the Insane, *Annual Report,* 28th, 1845, p. 15; Ray to Dix, Dec. 8, 1851, Dix MSS.

46 Hurd, III, 721–723; Powell, *AJI,* LIV (July, 1897), 26–28; Insane Asylum of Louisiana, *Annual Report,* 1859, p. 8; Chaillé, *New Orleans Medical and Surgical Journal,* XV (January, 1858), 103 ff.; W., "Insane Hospitals in the United States, in Operation in May, 1838," *Boston Medical and Surgical Journal,* XVIII (June 22, 1838), 313; "Insanity in Kentucky," *Boston Medical and Surgical Journal,* XXIV (April 21, 1841), 165–171; "Kentucky Lunatic Asylum," *Boston Medical and Surgical Journal,* XXVI (March 9, 1842), 80–81; Chipley to Kirkbride, Feb. 5, 1860, Kirkbride MSS.

47 Grob, *Bulletin of the History of Medicine,* XXXVI (September-October, 1962), 434.

48 Howe, *North American Review,* LVI (January, 1843), 187. In 1843 there were 130 paying patients; in December, 1841, 78 paupers were discharged for want of room and sent back to almshouses and jails (*ibid.,* 186). At that time Worcester did not serve the poor as a

matter of course. This is indicated by a letter asking if special provision could be made for the wife of a teamster who earned only $1.12 a day and who could not afford to have his wife confined at Worcester (A. R. Thompson to Woodward, [n.d.], Woodward MSS).

49 State Lunatic Hospital at Worcester, *Annual Report*, 22d, 1854, p. 11.

50 Schwartz, p. 188.

51 State Lunatic Hospital at Worcester, *Annual Report*, 21st, 1853, pp. 6–7; 22d, 1854, pp. 8, 10–12.

52 Grob, *Bulletin of the History of Medicine*, XXXVI (September-October, 1962), 439 ff.

53 State Lunatic Hospital at Worcester, *Annual Report*, 22d, 1854, p. 8.

54 *Ibid.*, p. 9.

55 [Ray?], "American Hospitals for the Insane," *North American Review*, LXXIX (July, 1854), 82.

56 Ray to Dix, 15 April 1854, Dix MSS.

57 McLean Asylum for the Insane, *Annual Report*, 38th, 1855, pp. 26–27.

58 Deutsch, *The Mentally Ill in America*, p. 155.

59 In the 1860's superintendents of newly founded asylums in the West had no time to become disillusioned about the possibility of "easy and speedy cure," even in cases of hereditary predisposition (Michigan Asylum for the Insane, *Biennial Report*, 1859–60, p. 36). These new hospitals still had to make strong efforts to justify their usefulness to state legislatures, and they could not afford to indulge in any pessimistic speculations. Despite incompleted buildings and imperfect classification of patients, as well as a host of other problems, the trustees of the Iowa Hospital for the Insane, at Mount Pleasant, for example, boasted that they had restored proportionately as many patients "as the most successful Institutions of its kind" (*Biennial Report*, 1st, 1861, p. 7).

60 Friends' Asylum, *Annual Report*, 27th, 1844, p. 14.

61 *Ibid.*, 34th, 1851, pp. 14–15.

62 Pliny Earle, *The Curability of Insanity*, Read before the New England Psychological Society, on Retiring from Office as Its President, December 14, 1876; and Published by That Society (Utica, N. Y.: Ellis H. Roberts & Co., Printers, 1877); see also Earle, *AJI*, XLII (October, 1885), 179–209.

63 Hartford Retreat, *Annual Report*, 51st, 1874/75, pp. 5–6; see also *ibid.*, 59th, 1882/83, p. 13.

64 Friends' Asylum, *Annual Report*, 60th, 1877, pp. 15–16, 12–13.

65 McLean Asylum for the Insane, *Annual Report*, 61st, 1878, pp. 36–37.

66 *Ibid.*, 65th, 1882, p. 36.

67 Hartford Retreat, *Annual Report*, 55th, 1878/79, pp. 24–25.

68 Clifford Whittingham Beers, *A Mind That Found Itself; an Autobiography* (5th ed., rev., reprinted with additions; Garden City, N. Y.: Doubleday & Company, Inc., 1960).

69 One superintendent suggested that the continued reliance upon moral methods resulted from an inability to discover specific medical remedies for mental illness (Butler Hospital, *Annual Report*, 1893, p. 18).

70 Friends' Asylum, *Annual Report*, 77th, 1894, p. 27.

71 Hartford Retreat, *Annual Report*, 67th, 1898/99, pp. 15–16.

72 *Ibid.*, 61st, 1884/85, p. 18.

73 Pennsylvania Hospital for the Insane, *Annual Report*, 1889/90, pp. 8–9; 1894/95, p. 12; 1893/94, p. 10.

74 Friends' Asylum, *Annual Report*, 87th, 1904, pp. 27–28; McLean Asylum for the Insane, *Annual Report*, 84th, 1901, pp. 179–181.

75 See review of *On the Construction, Organization and General Management of Hospitals for the Insane, with Some Remarks on Insanity and Its Treatment*, by Thomas S. Kirk-

bride, 2d ed. . . . *Journal of Nervous and Mental Disease*, VIII (April, 1881), 338–339; Editorial Department, "The Curability of Insanity," *Journal of Nervous and Mental Disease*, VII (January, 1880), 135; Isaac Ray, "Curability of Insanity," *Journal of Nervous and Mental Disease*, VI (October, 1879), 764.

76 See Friends' Asylum, *Annual Report*, 89th, 1906, pp. 28–31; Hartford Retreat, *Annual Report*, 61st, 1884/85, pp. 16–17.

77 Bockoven, *Journal of Nervous and Mental Disease*, CXXIV (August, 1956), 176.

78 Richard H. Shryock, *American Medical Research, Past and Present* ("The New York Academy of Medicine Committee on Medicine and the Changing Order, Monograph Studies"; New York: The Commonwealth Fund, 1947), pp. 30–31.

79 Deutsch, *The Mentally Ill in America*, pp. 273–274; Franklin G. Ebaugh, "The History of Psychiatric Education in the United States from 1844 to 1944," *American Journal of Psychiatry, 1844–1944*, p. 152.

80 An example of the better statistical compilations were those made by Jarvis in the *Report* of the Massachusetts Commission on Lunacy, 1854, which was one of the main sources for a recent statistical study of psychosis. See Herbert Goldhamer and Andrew W. Marshall, *Psychosis and Civilization: Two Studies in the Frequency of Mental Disease* (Glencoe, Ill.: Free Press, c1953).

81 Isaac Ray, "The Statistics of Insane Hospitals," *AJI*, VI (July, 1849), 23–52.

82 Shryock, *American Medical Research*, pp. 30–31.

83 Since Brigham thought it likely that all cases of insanity involved specific changes in the brain, these autopsies, in conjunction with a study of symptoms and of the effects of different kinds of treatment, seemed to have value. (*North American Review*, XLIV [January, 1837], 115–116; Brigham, *An Inquiry Concerning the Diseases and Functions of the Brain*, pp. 17–18.)

84 Thomas S. Kirkbride, *On the Organization and General Arrangement of Hospitals for the Insane, with some Remarks on Insanity and Its Treatment* (2d ed., rev.; Philadelphia: J. B. Lippincott & Co., 1880). The situation was not improved by the tendency of state appointing officers to treat asylum superintendencies and trustee positions as patronage plums. The result sometimes was the appointment of unqualified or undistinguished physicians with little interest in the development of psychiatry, much less in serious research.

85 Shryock, *American Medical Research*, pp. 34–35.

86 Ray to Earle, 18 Feb. 1872, Earle MSS.

87 Quoted in *Memoirs of Pliny Earle, M.D.*, p. 151.

88 Amariah Brigham, *A Letter from Doctor Brigham to David M. Reese, M.D., Author of Phrenology Known by Its Fruits* ([Hartford, Conn.]: n.p., 1836), pp. 9–10.

89 *Ibid.*, p. 2.

Chapter 6

1 "Reports of American Asylums," *AJI*, XVII (July, 1860), 85.

2 The frequency with which medical journals printed psychiatrists' reviews of books on mental illness indicates respect for their opinions.

3 The 1850 population census listed 40,755 physicians in the United States (U. S., Bureau of the Census, *Historical Statistics of the United States*, p. 50).

4 Ebaugh, "The History of Psychiatric Education in the United States from 1844 to 1944," *American Journal of Psychiatry, 1844–1944*, p. 151. According to Ebaugh, there was "a prevailing indifference" to psychiatry in all but a few American medical schools until the

1870's. See also: [Thomas S. Kirkbride?], Review of *Observations on the Admission of Medical Pupils to the Wards of Bethlem* [sic] *Hospital, for the Purpose of Studying Mental Diseases,* by John Webster, 3d ed., *American Journal of the Medical Sciences,* new series, V (April, 1843), 416–417 (signed T.S.K.); James Macdonald, "Puerperal Insanity," *AJI,* IV (October, 1847), 163; *Memoirs of Pliny Earle, M.D.,* pp. 189, 253. Earle's appointment in 1863 at the Berkshire Medical Institute marked the first time that mental diseases were "recognized as a necessary part of the study of medical science, though they had long been so considered" in Europe (*ibid.,* p. 253).

5 Eaton, *New England Hospitals,* p. 158.

6 Bunker, "American Psychiatry as a Specialty," *One Hundred Years of American Psychiatry,* p. 482.

7 Maine Insane Hospital, *Annual Report,* 7th, 1846, p. 39.

8 Pliny Earle, "Institutions for the Insane in Prussia, Austria, and Germany," *AJI,* IX (October, 1852), 126.

9 Although it is difficult to estimate how many persons read them, it is known that the reports of the important asylums were sometimes printed in thousands of copies for distribution to the medical and lay public in the United States and Europe. Woodward's reports averaged three thousand copies in each edition (Deutsch, *The Mentally Ill in America,* p. 195).

10 I searched the following medical journals, published from 1800 to 1865, for discussions of mental illness: *Boston Medical and Surgical Journal, Medical Repository, Philadelphia Journal of the Medical and Physical Sciences, North American Medical and Surgical Journal, Philadelphia Medical and Philosophical Journal, Boston Medical Intelligencer,* and *American Journal of the Medical Sciences.* Articles by physicians and psychiatrists were also printed in general periodicals like the *North American Review* and the *National Quarterly Review.*

11 S. V. C. Smith to Woodward, Aug. 15, 1840, Woodward MSS.

12 William H. Stokes, "On a Court of Medical Experts in Cases of Insanity," *AJI,* X (October, 1853), 114–115.

13 See Illinois State Hospital for the Insane, *Biennial Report,* 5th, 1855–56, in *Reports of the Illinois State Hospital . . . ,* p. 203. The commitment certificates of the Friends' Asylum from 1822 to 1857 indicate that methods of depletion remained popular with general practitioners throughout the period, although opium came into favor as a sedative in the thirties. Bates attributed the frequency with which most physicians resorted to the lance to their outmoded belief in the inflammatory nature of insanity (Maine Insane Hospital, *Annual Report,* 7th, 1846, pp. 39–40).

14 *Ibid.,* 3d, 1842, p. 25; Francis T. Stribling of the Western Lunatic Asylum of Virginia complained that he seldom received a patient who had not been well-bled, blistered, and purged (Helen E. Marshall, *Dorothea Dix, Forgotten Samaritan* [Chapel Hill: University of North Carolina Press, 1937], p. 74). The most extensive attack upon bloodletting came from Earle in 1854 in an article that gathered together the arguments of physicians for and against this practice in cases of insanity (Earle, "Bloodletting in Mental Disorders," *AJI,* X [April, 1854], 287–405).

15 John R. Allen, "On the Treatment of Insanity," *AJI,* VI (January, 1850), 274–276. (From the *Transylvania Medical Journal.*)

16 Commitment Certificates, Friends' Asylum; see also Earle, "Psychologic Medicine: Its Importance as Part of the Medical Curriculum," *AJI,* XXIV (January, 1868), 278–279.

17 Quoted in Henry Burnell Shafer, *The American Medical Profession, 1783 to 1850* (New York: Columbia University Press, 1936), pp. 122–123.

18 R. R. Porter, "Reports of Cases of Insanity, Treated at Friends' Asylum, near Frankford," *American Journal of the Medical Sciences*, XX (August, 1837), 351. The doctoral dissertations of two University of Pennsylvania medical students indicated their belief in the late 1820's that a psychological approach was primary in treating some forms of insanity. "All the medicines in the Materia Medica," wrote Jacob S. Zorns, "are generally found, per se, insufficient to cure hypochondriasis, but by resorting to well conducted stratagems, through the medium of the mind, cures are frequently affected" ("Influence of the Passions on the Human System" [unpublished M.D. inaugural thesis, University of Pennsylvania, 1827], p. 44). William N. Johnson, writing on "The Remedial Agency of Musick in Mental Disease," remarked that the ultimate action of music "is purely a mental operation and as such can only produce effects which must be ascribed to the mind, mysteriously connected with and operating upon the body" ([unpublished M.D. inaugural thesis, University of Pennsylvania, 1829], p. 18).

19 Friends' Asylum, *Annual Report*, 46th, 1862, p. 8.

20 A partial list of the trial records upon which this section is based is given in the bibliography.

21 Stokes, *AJI*, X (October, 1853), 113–114.

22 Woodward deplored this situation, which resulted in unfair trials and inhumane verdicts ("Medical Jurisprudence" [1848], p. 18, in his "Collected Writings," II).

23 This was the Freeman trial, which is related in *The Trial of William Freeman, for the Murder of John G. Van Nest, Including the Evidence and the Arguments of Counsel, with the Decision of the Supreme Court Granting a New Trial, and an Account of the Death of the Prisoner, and of the Post-Mortem Examination of His Body by Amariah Brigham, M.D., and Others*, Reported by Benjamin F. Hall (Auburn: Miller & Co., 1848).

24 *Report of the Trial of Abner Rogers, Jr., Indicted for the Murder of Charles Lincoln, Jr., Late Warden of the Massachusetts State Prison;* before the Supreme Judicial Court of Massachusetts, Holden at Boston, on Tuesday, January 30, 1844, by George Tyler Bigelow and George Bemis, Esqrs., Counsel for the Defendant (Boston: Charles C. Little and James Brown, 1844).

25 *Ibid.*, pp. 30–33.

26 *The Trial of Agostinho Rabello for the Murder of Ferris Beardsley, at New-Preston, Conn., April 27, 1835; with Some Particulars in Relation to the Life of Rabello* (Litchfield: Printed for Birdsey Gibs, 1835), p. 38.

27 "Homicidal Insanity, Court of Oyer and Terminer, City of New York, before Judge Edmonds and Aldermen Henry and Seaman; M. C. Paterson, Esq., District Attorney, May 21, 1845—Case of Murder [Trial of Andrew Kleim for Murder of Catherine Hanlin, December 23, 1844]," *AJI*, II (January, 1846), 260.

28 "Law Cases Bearing on the Subject of Insanity; Trial of Adeline Phelps, Alias Bass, for the Murder of Her Father, Elihu Phelps," *AJI*, XI (July, 1854), 68.

29 *Life and Trial of Dr. Abner Baker, Jr. (a Monomaniac) Who Was Executed October 3, 1845, for the Alleged Murder of His Brother-in-Law, Daniel Bates; Including Letters and Petitions in Favor of a Pardon, and Narrative of the Circumstance Attending His Execution, etc. etc.*, by C. W. Crozier; Trial and Evidence by A. R. M'Kee (Louisville, Ky.: Prentice and Weissinger, Printers, 1846), pp. 20–23.

30 E. P. W. Packard, *Marital Power Exemplified in Mrs. Packard's Trial, and Self-Defence from the Charge of Insanity; or, Three Years' Imprisonment for Religious Belief . . .* (Hartford: Case, Lockwood & Company, 1866), p. 21.

31 *The Trial of William Freeman*, pp. 68–71, 79–80.

32 In dividing the doctors who knew little about mental illness into two broad categories, some violence is done to reality, for such a division is only approximately valid. Yet the

evidence of the trial records seems to warrant such a distinction, if not maintained too rigidly.

33 *The Trial of William Freeman*, pp. 46–47 ff.; G., "Trial of Capt. John Windsor for the Murder of His Wife, before the Court of Oyer and Terminer Held at Georgetown, Delaware, June 25th, 1851, before His Honor, Chief Justice Booth; Harrington and Wooten, Associates," *AJI*, VIII (January, 1852), 238–239.

34 New York *Evening Post*, December 30, 1856, p. 2, col. 2. This case is also described in "Homicide and Insanity; the Case of John W. Layman," *AJI*, XIV (January, 1858), 240–248.

35 *The Trial of Agostinho Rabello*, pp. 13–15; see also "Criminal Lunacy; Case of John Hadcock," *AJI*, XI (April, 1855), 372. In the Hadcock case, however, the physician believed the defendant was feigning insanity; on the basis of the evidence, the editors of the *AJI* did not agree (*ibid.*, 380–381).

36 See *The Trial of William Freeman*, pp. 353–368.

37 Of course, one cannot always assume that a professor had up-to-date psychiatric knowledge. It is hard to believe, for example, that a professor testifying at the Freeman trial had read the latest works on the subject when he defined insanity as a state in which a person "is essentially a dreaming man awake" (*ibid.*, p. 355). The implication is that the insane invariably receive false impressions which they do not recognize and live perpetually in a world of hallucinations. By the 1840's this definition was considered totally inadequate by most authorities.

38 *Ibid.*, pp. 49–50. In another trial a physician judged insanity on the basis of deportment and demeanor; see the account of the Hinchman trial in the Philadelphia *Public Ledger*, March 28, 1849, p. 1, col. 6.

39 Since insanity was often insidious in its onset. Brigham wrote, the physician should know the early signs. They should also be aware that many persons were subject to the disease from hereditary predisposition, previous attacks, "long continued menorrhagia or other diseases, from repelled eruptions, and extreme nervous susceptibility and be able to advise such and warn them in time, of impending danger." Physicians could also prevent puerperal insanity by quieting the fears of timid women and by offering advice to expectant mothers and their husbands and friends. (New York State Lunatic Asylum at Utica, *Annual Report*, 6th, 1848, pp. 45–46).

40 Allan addressed remarks similar to Brigham's to Western physicians, who, he believed, were not well-informed about psychiatry. He also discussed methods of treatment and advised physicians how to handle insane patients. He particularly urged early treatment, which was apparently not common in the West. (Allan, *AJI*, VI [January, 1850], 263–283.)

41 See the evaluation by Shryock, *The Development of Modern Medicine*, pp. 263–264.

42 Nichols, pp. 351–353.

43 Grace Adams and Edward Hutter, *The Mad Forties* (New York: Harper & Brothers, c1942), pp. 45–49.

44 Nichols, pp. 354–355. As early as 1809, Valentine Seaman, who later became a prominent New York practitioner, noted in his M.D. dissertation on the mineral waters of Saratoga that the waters were used in cases of "*hypochondriasis* and other *nervous affections*, arising from the indolence and luxury of a city life." The waters, he believed, had less value than the amusing scenes, simple food, and constant exercise associated with the cure (*A Dissertation on the Mineral Waters of Saratoga, Including an Account of the Waters of Ballston* [2d ed., enl.; New-York: Printed and sold by Collins & Perkins, 1809], pp.100–101).

45 See, for example, "Mental Exercise as a Cure of Insanity," *Water-Cure Journal and*

Herald of Reforms, VII (March, 1849), 72–74 (from *Moral and Intellectual Science*) and Nelson Sizer, "Death of Dr. Brigham," *ibid.,* VIII (November, 1849), 154.

46 Joel Shew, *The Hydropathic Family Physician, a Ready Prescriber and Hygienic Adviser . . .* (New York: Fowler and Wells, 1854), pp. 235–243; "Vermont Asylum for the Insane," *Water-Cure Journal,* VII (January, 1849), 14; J. A. Spear, "Insanity and Delirium Tremens," *ibid.,* XI (May, 1851), 118–119; R. T. Trall, "Physiological Development," *ibid.,* XV (December, 1853), 3–4; Shew, *Tobacco,* pp. 39–47; Adams and Hutter, p. 38.

47 Sylvester Graham, *Lectures on the Science of Human Life* (New York: Fowler & Wells, 1858), pp. 222–223, 227–229 ff.

48 Samuel Thomson, *The Thomsonian Materia Medica; or, Botanic Family Physician* (13th ed.; Albany: J. Munsell, 1841), pp. 810–811.

49 Horton Howard, *An Improved System of Botanic Medicine . . .* (new ed.; Cincinnati: Kost, Bigger & Hart, 1854), pp. 111–114.

50 Shryock, *The Development of Modern Medicine,* p. 263; Madge E. Pickard and R. Carlyle Buley, *The Midwest Pioneer; His Ills, Cures, & Doctors* (New York: Henry Schuman, 1946), pp. 208–209.

51 *Stedman's Medical Dictionary,* p. 657.

52 George E. Shipman, *The Homoeopathic Family Guide, for the Use of Twenty-Five Principal Remedies in the Treatment of the More Simple Forms of Disease* (2d ed.; Chicago: C. S. Halsey, 1865), p. 58.

53 J. Kost, *Domestic Medicine; a Treatise on the Practice of Medicine, Adapted to the Reformed System, Comprising a Materia Medica* (Cincinnati: J. W. Sewell, 1859), pp. 176–178.

54 John C. Peters, *A Treatise on Nervous Derangements and Mental Disorders, Based upon Th. J. Rückert's "Clinical Experience in Homoeopathy"* (New York: William Radde, 1854), pp. i–xvii.

55 Orson S. Fowler, *Physiology, Animal and Mental: Applied to the Preservation and Restoration of Health of Body, and Power of Mind* (6th ed.; New York: Fowler and Wells, 1854), pp. 306–307; William C. Rogers, "The Hartford Retreat for the Insane," *American Phrenological Journal,* XVIII (July, 1853), 43–44.

56 Orson S. Fowler, *Self-Culture, and Perfection of Character, Including Management of Youth* (New York: Fowler and Wells, 1847), pp. 42–43.

57 Fowler, *Physiology, Animal and Mental,* p. 307.

58 Orson F. Fowler, "Hereditary Descent . . . ," *American Phrenological Journal,* V (November, 1843), 502–503.

59 Fowler, *Physiology, Animal and Mental,* pp. 306–307; Rogers, *American Phrenological Journal,* XVIII (July, 1853), 43–44; "New Publications," *American Phrenological Journal,* XII ([November?], 1850), 360.

60 For discussions of the treatment of diseases of the brain see Fowler, *Physiology, Animal and Mental,* p. 307; D.M.R., "Chronic Disease of the Brain," *American Phrenological Journal and Miscellany,* II (July 1, 1840), 457–458; and also Joseph R. Buchanan, *Outlines of Lectures on the Neurological System of Anthropology, as Discovered, Demonstrated, and Taught in 1841 and 1842* (Cincinnati: Printed at the Office of *Buchanan's Journal of Man,* 1854), pp. 239–242. Buchanan was not a thoroughgoing phrenologist, for he tried to reconcile magnetism with Gall's system. (See *Buchanan's Journal of Man.*) Magnetism, or mesmerism, had strong ties to phrenology, plus a strain of mysticism. Its advocates claimed it could calm troubled minds and cure epilepsy, hysteria, hypochondriasis, catalepsy, toothache, *tic doloureux,* headache, and other pains and swellings. See Rev. Jacob Baker, *Human Magnetism: Its Origin, Progress, Philosophy and Curative Qualities, with Instructions for Its Application* (Worcester, Mass.: Jacob Baker and M. D. Phillips,

[1843], preface and pp. 17–18; John B. Newman, M.D., *Fascination; or, The Philosophy of Charming, Illustrating the Principles of Life in Connection with Spirit and Matter* (New York: Fowler and Wells, 1848), pp. 172–176.

61 Maine Insane Hospital, *Annual Report*, 3d, 1842, pp. 7–8. The superintendent of the Indiana Hospital for the Insane listed unorthodox medical fads as responsible for the insanity of a few patients (*Annual Report*, 1849, p. 14; 1851, p. 23; 1852, p. 32).

Chapter 7

1 This group does not include religious organs, which are discussed in Chapter 8. For a list of journals in which articles on mental illness were found, see the bibliography.

2 These included journals like the *Westminster Review, Edinburgh Review, London Quarterly, Psychological Journal,* and *Journal of Psychological Medicine and Mental Pathology.*

3 Isaac Ray, *Address Delivered on the Occasion of Laying the Corner Stone of the State Hospital for the Insane, at Danville, Penn'a. . . . August 26th, 1869* (Harrisburg: Theo. F. Scheffer, Printer, 1869), pp. 10–12.

4 Tiffany, p. 59.

5 *Ibid.,* pp. 71–72.

6 Marshall, p. vii, and *passim.*

7 Deutsch, *The Mentally Ill in America,* pp. 164, 186; Gladys Brooks, *Three Wise Virgins* (New York: E. P. Dutton & Co., 1957), pp. 28–44 ff.

8 Earle, *Memoirs of Pliny Earle, M.D.,* pp. 306–309.

9 Bockoven, *Journal of Nervous and Mental Disease,* CXXIV (August, 1956), 186–187.

10 Deutsch, *The Mentally Ill in America,* p. 184.

11 Tiffany, p. 94.

12 In addition to most well-known American psychiatrists, she cited such foreign authorities as Willis, Pinel, Esquirol, Heinroth, Conolly, Ellis, Browne, Halliday, Barrow, Veitch, Falret, and Jacobi.

13 Dorothea L. Dix, *Memorial Soliciting an Appropriation for the State Hospital for the Insane, at Lexington; and also Urging the Necessity for Establishing a New Hospital in the Green River Country* (Frankfort, Ky.: A. G. Hodges, State Printer, 1846), p. 4; Dorothea L. Dix, "Memorial of Miss Dix, to the Honorable the Senate and House of Representatives of the State of Illinois," *Reports of the Illinois State Hospital . . . ,* p. 9; Dorothea L. Dix, *Memorial Soliciting a State Hospital for the Insane, Submitted to the Legislature of New Jersey, January 23, 1845* (2d ed.; Trenton: n.p., 1845), p. 37; Dorothea L. Dix, "Memorial to the Honorable the Legislative Assembly of the Province of Nova Scotia and Its Dependencies," in Hurd, I, 482–497.

14 Dorothea L. Dix, *Memorial Soliciting Enlarged and Improved Accommodations for the Insane of the State of Tennessee, by the Establishment of a New Hospital* (Nashville: B. R. M'Kennie, Printer, *Whig and Politician* Office, 1847), p. 5.

15 Dorothea L. Dix, *Memorial Soliciting a State Hospital for the Insane,* Submitted to the Legislature of Pennsylvania, February 3, 1845 (Philadelphia: Isaac Ashmead, Printer, 1845), p. 4.

16 Dorothea L. Dix, *Memorial of D. L. Dix, Praying a Grant of Land for the Relief and Support of the Indigent Curable and Incurable Insane in the United States,* June 27, 1848, Referred to a Select Committee, and Ordered to Be Printed, and 5,000 Additional Copies Printed for the Use of the Senate, 30th Cong., 1st Sess., 1848, Miscellaneous No. 150 [Washington: Tippin & Streeter, Printers, 1848], p. 27.

17 Dorothea L. Dix, *Memorial to the Honorable the Legislature of the State of New-York* (Albany: n.p., 1844), p. 55; Howe, *North American Review,* LVI (January, 1843), 171–173; Dix, *Memorial . . . Pennsylvania,* p. 5.

18 Dix, *Memorial . . . Lexington,* p. 4; Dix, "Memorial . . . Nova Scotia," in Hurd, I, 488–492.

19 Dix, *Memorial . . . United States,* p. 4.

20 Dorothea L. Dix, *Memorial [to the Legislature of Massachusetts Protesting against the Confinement of Insane Persons and Idiots in Almshouses and Prisons]* (Boston: Printed by Munroe & Francis, 1843), pp. 12, 25, 31; Dix, "Memorial . . . Nova Scotia," in Hurd, I, 484, 488, 494–497; Dix, *Memorial . . . Lexington,* p. 4; Dix, *Memorial . . . Tennessee,* pp. 12–13; Dorothea L. Dix, *Memorial Soliciting a State Hospital for the Insane,* Submitted to the Legislature of Alabama, November 15, 1849 (Montgomery: Book and Job Office of the *Advertiser and Gazette,* 1849), p. 7.

21 Dix, *Memorial . . . New-York,* p. 5; see also Dix, *Memorial . . . Tennessee,* pp. 10–13.

22 Dix, *Memorial . . . United States,* p. 24.

23 Dix, *Memorial . . . New-York,* p. 56.

24 Maine Insane Hospital, *Annual Report,* 19th, 1859, p. 20; Kirkbride to Dix, Aug. 18, 1852; Dix to Kirkbride, June, 1847; Curwen to Kirkbride, Sept. 21, 1853; T. H. H. Smith to Kirkbride, May 19, 1853, all in Kirkbride MSS.

25 Tiffany (p. 244) quotes a letter from Daniel Hack Tuke, August, 1888, to this effect.

26 Nichols to Kirkbride, Aug. 15, 1858, Kirkbride MSS; Nichols to Dix, Aug. 18, 1858, Dix MSS.

27 Marshall, pp. 196, 236, 239–240; Deutsch, *The Mentally Ill in America,* p. 183.

28 See the following letters in the Dix MSS: Nichols to Dix, Nov. 27, 1851; Ray to Dix, 20 Feb. 1843; Awl to Dix, Apr. 4, 1845; Bell to Dix, 29 Dec. 1848; Jarvis to Dix, 25 May 1844. See also Kirkbride to Dix, Mar. 17, 1852, Kirkbride MSS.

29 Kirkbride to Dix, May 30, 1849, Dix MSS; Kirkbride to Dix, May 30, 1851, Kirkbride MSS.

30 Bell to Dr. G. Peters, 18 Aug. 1849, Dix MSS.

31 Tiffany, p. 159.

32 Woodward to Mann, January[?] 26, 1840, Woodward MSS. See also Mann to Woodward, Feb. 29, 1840, Mann MSS, Massachusetts Historical Society.

33 Ray, *Address Delivered . . . at Danville, Penn'a.,* p. 9.

34 Mann to Woodward, Nov. 27, 1840, Mann MSS.

35 Mary Peabody Mann, *Life of Horace Mann* (Centennial ed. in facsimile; Washington, D. C.: National Education Association of the United States, 1937), p. 231. Mann loved and respected Woodward; Eli Todd, superintendent of the Hartford Retreat, was also close to Mann, who wrote that Todd was "a man one wished to embrace if he only met him in the street" (*ibid.,* p. 47).

36 See above, Chapter 4, Section 4.

37 Mann to George Combe, Feb. 11, 1839, Mann MSS. (Combe was a leading British phrenologist.) Mann did not believe that actions could be pinpointed as having moral or physical bases. Motives depended on innate propensity, education, association, external conditions, and a thousand other things, which, if measurable, would reveal the reasons for human actions. To ensure honorable actions man must be properly trained to follow natural physical laws; this was the only safeguard against evil. (Mann to Miss Peabody, 1833?; to Lydia B. Mann, Nov. 9, 1838; to S. B. Woodward, July 9, 1843, all in Mann MSS.)

38 Schwartz, pp. 98–102.

39 *Ibid.,* p. 140; Samuel Gridley Howe, *Report Made to the Legislature of Massachusetts, upon Idiocy* (Boston: Printed from the State Edition by Coolidge & Wiley, 1848), pp. 4, 78–92; Howe, *North American Review,* LVI (January, 1843), 172–174.

40 Schwartz, pp. 138–147.

41 Howe, *North American Review*, LVI (January, 1843), 189–191.

42 F. B. Sanborn, *Dr. S. G. Howe* (New York: Funk & Wagnalls, 1891), pp. 297–300.

43 *Appleton's Cyclopaedia of American Biography*, ed. James Grant Fiske and John Fiske (New York: D. Appleton and Company, 1888), I, 168.

44 Harris Elwood Starr, "Barnard, Henry," *Dictionary of American Biography*, ed. Allen Johnson & Dumas Malone, published under the auspices of the American Council of Learned Societies (New York: Charles Scribner's Sons, 1943), I, 622.

45 Henry Barnard, *Tribute to Gallaudet; a Discourse in Commemoration of the Life, Character and Services of the Rev. Thomas H. Gallaudet, LL.D., Delivered before the Citizens of Hartford, Jan. 7th, 1852* . . . (Hartford: Brockett & Hutchinson, 1852), pp. 41–43.

46 *Ibid.*, 32d Cong., 1st Sess., 1852, XXI, Appendix, 472. See also: Albert G. Brown, *Speech of Albert G. Brown, of Mississippi, on the President's Veto Message, and in Defense of the Bill Making a Grant of Land to the Several States for the Benefit of the Indigent Insane*, Delivered in the Senate of the United States, May 17, 1854 (Washington: Printed by John T. and Lem. Towers, 1854), p. 3; John M. Clayton, *Speech of Hon. John M. Clayton, of Delaware, on the Veto Message of the President, on the Bill for the Benefit of the Indigent Insane;* in the Senate of the United States, June 15, 1854 (Washington: Printed at the *Congressional Globe* Office, 1854), p. 22.

47 Clement C. Clay, Jr., *President's Veto Message, Speech of Mr. C. C. Clay, Jr., of Alabama, on the President's Veto Message, Rejecting the Indigent Insane Bill and against Giving Away the Public Lands*, Delivered in the Senate of the United States, June 20, 1854 (Washington: Printed by John and Lem. Towers, 1854), pp. 3–4. Senator Clay thought that his constituents had the erroneous impression that the bill would help them to finish building an insane asylum that had been started under Miss Dix's pressure but could not be completed because of a lack of money. See also remarks of Senator Davis of Mississippi, in U. S., *Congressional Globe*, 31st Cong., 2d Sess., 1851, XX, 508.

48 See, for example: U. S., *Congressional Globe*, 31st Cong., 1st Sess., 1850, XIX, Part 2, 2005–2008; *ibid.*, 31st Cong., 2d Sess., 1851, XX, 506–511; *ibid.*, 32d Cong., 2d Sess., 1853, XXII, 1091–1095.

49 This section is a summary of impressions gained by reading Miss Dix's memorials to the various states; they will not be cited individually. A complete list of those consulted is given in the bibliography under "Memorials of Dorothea L. Dix." More direct evidence of the attitudes of state legislators can be found in reports of various committees concerning the founding of mental hospitals. See Pennsylvania, Legislature, House of Representatives, *Report in Relation to an Asylum for the Insane Poor*, pp. 4–5 ff.

50 Marshall, pp. 104 ff.; Tiffany, p. 110.

51 In 1834 a New Hampshire state representative had opposed the establishment of an asylum because he considered insanity usually incurable and "had heard frightful stories of the abuses, and bad treatment of the insane, at some private institutions" (*Portsmouth Journal*, May 12, 1836, reprinted in *Extracts from Newspapers and Periodicals . . . New Hampshire*, p. 17). This was a common belief.

52 Marshall, pp. 104, 108.

53 Tiffany, pp. 145, 149. See also the letters from Lieber to Dix in the Dix MSS.

54 Tiffany, p. 75; Marshall, pp. 61–62, 95, 154.

55 Quoted in David Donald, *Charles Sumner and the Coming of the Civil War* (New York: Knopf, 1960), p. 316. In 1856 Sumner, an anti-slavery leader, was beaten in the United States Senate by Preston Brooks, a pro-slavery Representative from South Carolina.

56 "Editor's Introduction," in Isaac Ray, *A Treatise on the Medical Jurisprudence of In-*

sanity, ed. Winfred Overholser ("The John Harvard Library"; Cambridge, Mass.: The Belknap Press of Harvard University Press, 1962), pp. xv–xvi.

57 Obituary of Hon. Silas Wright, *AJI*, IV (October, 1847), 183.

58 *The Diary of Philip Hone, 1828–1851*, edited, with an introduction, by Bayard Tuckerman (New York: Dodd, Mead and Company, 1910), I, 3–4, 171, 96.

59 Eaton, *New England Hospitals*, p. 158.

60 Sedgwick to Woodward, Feb. 26, 1839, Woodward MSS; L. P. Brockett, M.D., to Earle, June 14, 1858, Earle MSS.

61 Captain Basil Hall, *Travels in North America, in the Years 1827 and 1828* (3d ed.; Edinburgh: Printed for Robert Cadell, Edinburgh, and Simpkin and Marshall, London, 1830), II, 191–197. Eaton, in *New England Hospitals*, calls Hall's work "classic" (p. 242).

62 Edward S. Abdy, *Journal of a Residence and Tour in the United States of North America, from April, 1833, to October, 1834* (London: John Murray, 1835), I, 98. Charles Dickens, who also did not like the United States, visited the Boston Lunatic Asylum and was favorably impressed with the moral treatment practiced there (*American Notes and Pictures from Italy* [London: Oxford University Press, 1957], pp. 45–48).

63 Woodward to Bancroft, March 31, 1842; Woodward MSS; Egbert C. Smyth, *Sketch of the Rev. Seth Sweetser, D.D.* (Boston: Alfred Mudge & Son, Printers, 1878), p. 17; Woodward to Sweetser, Dec. 22, 1843, Woodward MSS.

64 Catharine Maria Sedgwick, *Life and Letters of Catharine M. Sedgwick*, ed. Mary E. Dewey (New York: Harper & Brothers, 1871), pp. 29, 185–186, 200–201; *Clarence; or, A Tale of Our Own Times* (Philadelphia: Carey & Lea, 1830), I, 55 ff. Gladys Brooks' *Three Wise Virgins* called attention to Miss Sedgwick's interest in insanity (pp. 158–159, 188–189, 193).

65 Sedgwick to Woodward, Feb. 26, 1839, Woodward MSS.

66 I have not made a special study of popular fiction for the 1825–1865 period. In writing this section I have relied heavily on Davis' *Homicide in American Fiction, 1789–1860*, which contains several sections on insanity.

67 Oliver Wendell Holmes, *The Psychiatric Novels of Oliver Wendell Holmes;* Abridgement, Introduction, and Psychiatric Annotations by Clarence P. Oberndorf (2d ed., rev. and enl.; New York: Columbia University Press, 1946) contains an analysis of Holmes' novels by a modern psychiatrist.

68 Holmes served, along with Jarvis and others, on a committee of the Massachusetts Medical Society to investigate the 1840 census figures on the number of insane, deaf, dumb, and blind among the Negro population of Massachusetts (Oliver Wendell Holmes, *et al.*, to Woodward, June 24, 1844, Woodward MSS).

69 Davis, pp. 117–143.

70 American Temperance Society, *Annual Report*, 4th, 1831, p. 2; Appendix, pp. 64–66, in American Temperance Society, *Permanent Temperance Documents of the American Temperance Society* (Boston: Seth Bliss and Perkins Marvin and Co., 1835), I.

71 For discussion of this controversy see Prison Discipline Society, Boston, *Report*, 23d, 1848, pp. 51–61. Some of the reports of the Society discussed insanity and the need for asylums for the insane poor and cited from various asylum reports; see *ibid.*, 25th, 1850, pp. 71–87.

72 [Frederick A. Packard], *An Inquiry into the Alleged Tendency of the Separation of Convicts, One from the Other, to Produce Disease and Derangement*, by a Citizen of Philadelphia (Philadelphia: E. C. & J. Biddle, 1849), pp. 82, 91–101, 144–145. Packard was secretary of the committee that issued *An Appeal to the People of Pennsylvania on the Subject of an Asylum for the Insane Poor of the Commonwealth* (Philadelphia: Printed for the Committee, 1838).

73 Samuel G. Howe, *An Essay on Separate and Congregate Systems of Prison Discipline;*

Being a Report Made to the Boston Prison Discipline Society (Boston: William D. Ticknor and Company, 1846), pp. xi, 72–77. Francis Lieber also wrote extensively in favor of the Philadelphia plan and denied that isolation was conducive to insanity. See his *A Popular Essay on Subjects of Penal Law, and on Uninterrupted Solitary Confinement at Labor* . . . (Philadelphia: Published by Order of the Society, 1838), pp. 71–72.

Chapter 8

1 Material on mental illness was found in these religious journals: *Biblical Repertory and Princeton Review, Christian Journal and Literary Register, Christian Spectator, Church Review and Ecclesiastical Register, Friends' Review, New Englander,* and *Universalist Union.*

2 Waterston, *passim.*

3 Pittsburgh: Printed by Geo. Parkin & Co., 1851.

4 In Maryland asylums Catholic nuns sometimes acted as psychiatric nurses.

5 Amariah Brigham, "Religious Services in Lunatic Asylums—Duties of the Chaplain," *AJI,* II (October, 1845), 121–123; Ray, *AJI,* II (April, 1846), 377–383. Superintendents found the subject so embarrassing that they hesitated to discuss it publicly. A discussion at their 1860 meeting was omitted from the published proceedings, and in 1869 some objected to reopening the subject. Several superintendents expressed misgivings about having chaplains in asylums. See "Proceedings of the Association of Medical Superintendents [23d]," *AJI,* XXVI (October, 1869), 150–160.

6 See Louisiana Insane Asylum, *Annual Report,* 1860, pp. 15–16.

7 Barnard, p. 43. See also Heman Humphrey, *The Life and Labors of the Rev. T. H. Gallaudet, LL.D.* (New York: Robert Carter & Brothers, 1857), pp. 339, 350–371. Gallaudet's successor at the Retreat, the Rev. Horace Hooker, was also sympathetic to the Retreat's aims and methods (Hartford Retreat, *Annual Report,* 30th, 1854, p. 37).

8 Hartford Retreat, *Annual Report,* 18th, 1841/42, p. 35; see also Barnard, pp. 36–41. Gallaudet, although assiduous in his labors on behalf of the sick and handicapped, was not without social prejudices toward them if they were poor (see Gallaudet to Woodward, Feb. 21, 1840, Woodward MSS, quoted above, Chapter 5, footnote 34).

9 Brigham to Earle, May 27, 1846, Earle MSS. Brigham did not approve of this situation. He told Earle: "I fear if such a practice becomes popular & is forced upon other institutions, trouble will arise from it." (Perhaps this practice was forced upon Brigham when he was head of the Retreat from 1840 to 1842.) Woodward also believed that an asylum chaplain should be under the control of the superintendent. (Woodward to the Rev. Jeremiah Day, Nov. 15, 1838, Woodward MSS, Yale University. All other references to Woodward MSS refer to the collection at the American Antiquarian Society.)

10 See a letter from W. S. Chipley to Kirkbride, Feb. 21, 1866, and an enclosure, a letter from Rev. _____, who asked Kirkbride about placing his mother in the Pennsylvania Hospital for the Insane (Feb. 21, 1866). (Names of patients or their relatives have not been used unless they appear in published material.)

11 Wayland to Woodward, Aug. 8, 1841; Wayland to Woodward, [n.d.], Woodward MSS.

12 Francis Wayland, *The Elements of Intellectual Philosophy* (Boston: Phillips, Sampson and Company, 1855), pp. 20–22, 17–18.

13 I am indebted to Wilson Smith's *Professors & Public Ethics* for its bibliographical suggestions and list of moral philosophers.

14 Mark Hopkins, *Lectures on Moral Science; Delivered before the Lowell Institute, Boston* (Boston: Gould and Lincoln, 1870), pp. 80, 99; Noah Porter, *The Elements of Intellectual*

Science: a Manual for Schools and Colleges, Abridged from "The Human Intellect" (New York: Charles Scribner's Sons, 1884), p. 294. In the following works moral philosophers analyze the mind but do not discuss insanity: Jaspar Adams, *Elements of Moral Philosophy* (New York: Wiley and Putnam, 1837); Laurens Persens Hickok, *Empirical Psychology; or, The Human Mind as Given in Consciousness* (New York: Ivison & Phinney, 1857); Laurens Persens Hickok, *A System of Moral Science* (3d ed.; New York: Ivison & Phinney, 1858); Asa Mahan, *Abstract of a Course of Lectures on Moral Philosophy* (Oberlin, O.: Printed by James Steele, 1840).

15 See *The American Almanac and Repository of Useful Knowledge, for the Year 1843*, XIV, 170–173; *ibid., for the Year 1845*, XVI, 156–159, which contains excerpts from a memorial sent to Congress by the American Statistical Association in protest against the errors in the 1840 census.

16 Thomas C. Upham, *Outlines of Imperfect and Disordered Mental Action* ("Family Library, No. 100"; New York: Harper & Brothers, 1840), pp. 42, 124.

17 *Ibid.*, pp. 28–29; see also W. Smith, pp. 36–40.

18 Upham, pp. 357–358.

19 "Modern Spiritualism," *Church Review and Ecclesiastical Register*, VIII (July 1855), 171, 175–176; Nathan L. Rice, *Modern Spiritualism: What Are We to Think of It?* [Philadelphia: Presbyterian Board of Publications, n.d.], p. 15.

20 Joseph H. Jones, *Man, Moral and Physical; or The Influence of Health and Disease on Religious Experience* (2d ed.; Philadelphia: James S. Claxton, 1865), pp. 139–141.

21 See the discussion of religious insanity in Chapter 4, Section 3.

22 Brigham, *AJI*, II (October, 1845), 121.

23 Brigham, *Observations on the Influence of Religion upon the Health and Physical Welfare of Mankind.*

24 Eric T. Carlson, "Amariah Brigham: I. Life and Works," *American Journal of Psychiatry*, CXII (April, 1956), 833. See also David M. Reese, *Phrenology Known by Its Fruits* (New York: Howe and Bates, 1836), a critique of Brigham's book, and Brigham's answering pamphlet, *A Letter from Doctor Brigham to David M. Reese, M. D.* . . . Another critical review of Brigham's book is "Influence of Religion upon the Health," *Christian Spectator*, 3d series, VIII (March 1836), 51–80. For a defense of Brigham in a secular journal, see: Review of *Phrenology Known by Its Fruits* . . . , by David Meredith Reese, M.D., *Knickerbocker*, VIII (November, 1836), 615–617.

25 Lyman Beecher, *Autobiography, Correspondence, Etc.*, ed. Charles Beecher (New York: Harper & Brothers, 1864), pp. 46–47. See also Otis Ainsworth Skinner, *Letters to Rev. B. Stow, R. H. Neale and R. W. Cushman, on Modern Revivals* (Boston: Abel Tompkins, 1842), pp. 106, 136–138, 141–144.

26 [Frederick A. Packard], "The Relations of Religion to What Are Called Diseases of the Mind," *Biblical Repertory and Princeton Review*, XXII (January, 1850), 7; Jones, pp. 127–130.

27 Rev. Archibald Alexander, *Thoughts on Religious Experience* (Philadelphia: Presbyterian Board of Publications, c1844), p. 105.

28 Jones, pp. 127–138, 141–144; "Religious Melancholy," *Biblical Repertory and Princeton Review*, XVI (July, 1844), 361–367, 371–372, 374.

29 Harold I. Donnelly, "Packard, Frederick Adolphus," *Dictionary of American Biography*, XIV, 127; [Packard], *Biblical Repertory and Princeton Review*, XXII (January, 1850), 27, 34–35.

30 "Influence of Religion upon the Health," *Christian Spectator*, 3d series, VIII (March, 1836), 52, 61.

31 Butler Hospital, *Annual Report*, 1859, pp. 15–16. See also Edward Jarvis, "Causes of Men-

tal Disease," *North American Review,* LXXXIX (October, 1859), 333–334, and the discussion of religious insanity in Chapter 4, Section 3.

32 Brigham, *Observations on the Influence of Religion upon the Health and Physical Welfare of Mankind,* p. 304.

33 *Ibid.,* pp. 304–305 ff.

34 A person alleging communication with the spirit world might be looked upon as sane and even as a marvelous being, when in fact he was suffering from mental illness. A minister who believed in the possibility of communing with spirits thought that spiritualism produced insanity when the spirits contacted were not benevolent but were agencies of the devil (William R. Gordon, *A Three-Fold Test of Modern Spiritualism* [New York: Charles Scribner, 1856], pp. 264–273). See also W. W. Capron, *Modern Spiritualism: Its Facts and Fanaticism, Its Consistencies and Contradictions . . .* (Boston: Bela Marsh, 1855), p. 377. One nineteenth-century critic of spiritualism gave a perceptive explanation of how it worked: The participants would sit "perfectly passive, in the firm conviction that some mysterious power would come upon them and move them to rise . . . , utter language, or to move in the dance." This belief was the "cause of producing the expected result, because the involuntary powers have a strong tendency to concur in the same state of action with the voluntary powers." The only evil of mediums, who were honest, was "indulging and strengthening the habit by practice, and then applying the results to the agency of spirits, by which many are rendered insane, some commit suicide" (John Bovee Dods, *Spirit Manifestations Examined and Explained . . .* [New York: De Witt & Davenport, c1854], p. 51).

35 Bishop Lavington, quoted in Brigham, *Observations on the Influence of Religion upon the Health and Physical Welfare of Mankind,* p. 195.

36 Skinner, pp. 129–134, 143–144. A modern analyst of the British Methodist Revival doubts that Whitefield's preaching produced mental illness in his audience, although such cases seemed to have occurred during Wesley's career (Sydney G. Dimond, *The Psychology of the Methodist Revival, an Empirical & Descriptive Study* [London: Oxford University Press, 1926], pp. 125–139).

37 Review of *Man, Moral and Physical . . . ,* by the Rev. Joseph H. Jones, D.D., *Biblical Repertory and Princeton Review,* XXXII (April, 1860), 319–320.

38 Rev. Robert Davidson, D.D., *History of the Presbyterian Church in the State of Kentucky; with a Preliminary Sketch of the Churches in the Valley of Virginia* (New York: Robert Carter, 1847), pp. 172, 184, 189.

39 Charles G. Finney, *Lectures on Revivals of Religion,* ed. William G. McLaughlin ("John Harvard Library"; Cambridge, Mass.: The Belknap Press of Harvard University Press, 1960), p. 11.

40 Charles G. Finney, *Memoirs* (New York: A. S. Barnes & Company, 1876), pp. 108–110.

41 "Influence of Religion upon the Health," *Christian Spectator,* 3d series, VIII (March, 1836), 76–77.

42 "Insanity and Crime," *New Englander,* XIV (February, 1856), 51 (Review of *Report of the Trial of Willard Clark . . . Sept. 17, 1855*).

43 In 1869 Joseph Workman, superintendent of the Provincial Lunatic Asylum of Toronto, Canada, noted that some insane persons exhibited surprising traits at odds with their previous character: "Not only is utterance given to ideas totally foreign to their prior mental habits and tendencies; but the language used is generally of a character so alien to all the past experience of the speakers, that we are utterly unable to account for its source, and are constrained to regard it as the product of morbid extemporization. He who moralizes on such mental manifestations from a mere meta-physical stand-point, will hardly avoid regarding them as indicative of a latent depravity, which, finding now

an opportune occasion for its evincement, throws aside the fetters of conventional re-
straint, and stalks forth as the undissembling exponent of a corrupt and sinful heart"
("Insanity of the Religious-Emotional Type, and Its Occasional Physical Relations," *AJI*,
XXVI [July, 1869], 33–34).

44 "Influence of Nervous Disorders upon Religious Experience," *Christian Spectator*, new
series, I (April, 1827), 186, 197; see also "Moral Insanity," *Biblical Repertory and Princeton Review*, XXIX (July, 1857), 349, 371; "Insanity and Crime," *New Englander*, XIV
(February, 1856), 49–50; Jones, pp. 150–151.

45 "The Increase of Crimes against Life," *New Englander*, II (July, 1844), 349.

46 [Packard], *Biblical Repertory and Princeton Review*, XXII (January, 1850), 40–41. In an
exceptional article, moral insanity is defended and is equated in part with religious
melancholia: "Religious Melancholy," *Biblical Repertory and Princeton Review*, XVI
(July, 1844), 356–357, 367.

47 "Moral Insanity," *Biblical Repertory and Princeton Review*, XXIX (July, 1857), 348–351,
349, 352.

48 *Ibid.*, 355–356, 370–372.

49 For a discussion of the role of original sin in evangelical religion, see Hilrie Shelton
Smith, *Changing Conceptions of Original Sin, a Study in American Theology since 1750*
(New York: Charles Scribner's Sons, 1955).

Chapter 9

1 This distrust of hospitals was common in the Midwest (Pickard and Buley, p. 145). The
superintendent of the Friends' Asylum described the case of a wealthy woman kept at
home for thirty years before being sent to the asylum (*Annual Report*, 37th, 1854, p. 10).
See also New York State Lunatic Asylum at Utica, *Annual Report*, 2d, 1844, p. 25; 15th,
1857, pp. 26–27; McLean Asylum for the Insane, *Annual Report*, 18th, 1835, p. 17;
S. Theobald, "Some Account of the Lunatic Asylum of Kentucky," *Transylvania Journal
of Medicine*, III (February, 1830), 88; Friends' Asylum, *Annual Report*, 24th, 1841, pp.
16–17; Maryland Hospital for the Insane, *Annual Report*, 1844, p. 6.

2 "Proceedings of the Fifteenth Annual Meeting of the Association of Medical Superintendents of American Institutions for the Insane," *AJI*, XVII (July, 1860), 38.

3 Pennsylvania Hospital for the Insane, *Annual Report*, 1845, p. 8. See also State Lunatic
Hospital at Worcester, *Annual Report*, 9th, 1841, p. 71; Hartford Retreat, *Annual Report*,
16th, 1839/40, pp. 5–6. Kirkbride's papers contain letters from people as far away as Iowa
who were interested in sending friends to the Pennsylvania Hospital because they knew
of others who had been cured there: A. A. Ramsay, M.D., to Kirkbride, Oct. 3, 1855;
————to Kirkbride, May 30, 1861.

4 McLean Asylum for the Insane, *Annual Report*, 24th, 1841, pp. 17–18; Bloomingdale
Asylum, *Annual Report*, 1852, p. 31. See also discussion of asylum statistics in Chapter V,
Section 1.

5 Maine Insane Hospital, *Annual Report*, 2d, 1841, pp. 39–40; Maryland Hospital for the
Insane, *Annual Report*, 1845, p. 7; Butler Hospital, *Annual Report*, 1854, pp. 14–18;
Hartford Retreat, *Annual Report*, 20th, 1843/44, pp. 10–11; 33d, 1856/57, p. 13; Friends'
Asylum, *Annual Report*, 34th, 1851, p. 13.

6 Hartford Retreat, *Annual Report*, 22d, 1845/46, pp. 14–15.

7 Pennsylvania Hospital for the Insane, *Annual Report*, 1854, p. 9; State Lunatic Hospital
at Taunton, *Annual Report*, 3d, 1856, p. 20; Butler Hospital, *Annual Report*, 1850, pp.
17–18.

8 *Ibid.*, 1850, p. 19.

9 Ray to Dix, 31 Aug. 1864, Dix MSS; see also Marshall, p. 187.

10 Isaac H. Hunt, *Astounding Disclosures! Three Years in a Madhouse, By a Victim, Written by Himself, a True Account of the Barbarous, Inhuman and Cruel Treatment of Isaac H. Hunt, in the Maine Insane Hospital* . . . (2d ed.; n.p.: Printed for Isaac H. Hunt, 1852), pp. 3–9.

11 Robert Fuller, *An Account of the Imprisonment and Sufferings of Robert Fuller of Cambridge, Who, While Peaceably and Quietly and Rationally in Possession of His Own House, Was Seized and Detained in the McLean Asylum* . . . (Boston: Printed for the Author, 1833), pp. 3–4, 29–30. For similar accounts see Lydia B. Denny, *Statement of Mrs. Lydia B. Denny, Wife of Reuben S. Denny, in Regard to Her Alleged Insanity* (n.p.: [1865?]); *The Vermont Asylum for the Insane; Its Annals for Fifty Years*, p. 98; Elizabeth T. Stone, *Exposing the Modern Secret Way of Persecuting Christians in Order to Hush the Voice of Truth* . . . (Boston: Printed for the Author, 1859).

12 Ray to Dix, 31 Aug. 1864, Dix MSS.

13 *The Hinchman Conspiracy Case, in Letters to the New York Home Journal, with an Abstract of the Evidence for the Defence, Furnishing a Complete Explanation of this Most Extraordinary Case*, by an American Citizen (Philadelphia: Stokes & Brother, 1849), pp. 34–35, 30, 24.

14 Clipping from the *Times Messenger*, Feb. 26, 1865, enclosed in Denny, *Statement of Mrs. Lydia B. Denny* (copy in Massachusetts Historical Society).

15 Samuel E. Sewall, *Petition to the Honorable Senate and House of Representatives of the Commonwealth of Massachusetts* (Boston: n.p., 1862), pp. 4–5.

16 Hartford Retreat, *Annual Report*, 29th, 1852/53, pp. 24–25; Russell, pp. 145–146; McLean Asylum for the Insane, *Annual Report*, 1839, p. 16.

17 Francis Wharton, *A Monograph on Mental Unsoundness*, pp. 43–45.

18 *The Trial of William Freeman*, p. 427.

19 New York State Lunatic Asylum at Utica, *Annual Report*, 4th, 1846, p. 57; [Luther V. Bell], "Insanity and Crime," *AJI*, VI (April, 1850), 318–321 (reprint of an article addressed to the mayor of Boston; the editors of the *AJI* say they "have the best authority for believing" that Bell wrote it).

20 *Life and Trial of Dr. Abner Baker, Jr.*, pp. 97–114; [Isaac Ray], Review of *Life and Trial of Dr. Abner Baker, Jr., AJI*, III (July, 1846), 27; Woodward, "Medical Jurisprudence," pp. 19–22, in his "Collected Writings," II.

21 *Albany Argus*, July 25, 1846, p. 215, col. 3; see also *Portland Transcript*, May 31, 1856, p. 59, col. 3; p. 61, col. 3; quotation from *Auburn Advertiser* in *New York Tribune*, July 28, 1846, p. 1, col. 9; *New York Herald*, May 5, 1856, p. 4, col. 1.

22 *New York Times*, December 20, 1856, p. 4, col. 1; December 29, p. 4, col. 2. Similar opinions were expressed by other New York papers (*Tribune*, December 20, 1856, p. 6, cols. 4–6; December 22, p. 7, cols. 5–6; *Herald*, December 20, 1856, p. 4, col. 5; *Evening Post*, December 31, 1856, p. 2, col. 1). Proceedings of the trial were published in these papers from December 17–31, 1856, and in full in *Trial of Charles B. Huntington for Forgery*.

23 [New York] *Evening Post*, December 31, 1856, p. 2, col. 1. A defense lawyer in another case said that clergymen, physicians, jurists, and writers were propagating the idea that public expediency required making an example of the partially insane who committed crimes. They claimed that since the insane could be controlled by fear of punishment, the contagiousness of insanity might be halted by an "occasional enforcement of the law upon some of their number." (*Report of the Trial of Abner Rogers, Jr.*, pp. 55–56.)

24 Reprint from the *Rochester Daily Advertiser* in the New York *Evening Post*, March 19,

1846, p. 1, col. 9; *New York Tribune*, March 20, 1846, p. 3, col. 1; and *The Trial of William Freeman*, pp. 63–64.

25 His attorneys won a new trial, which the judges refused to hold because Freeman was so demented. He died soon afterwards in prison. For a romanticized, popular account of the case see Earl Conrad's *Mr. Seward for the Defense* (New York: Rinehart & Company, c1956).

26 *The Trial of William Freeman*, pp. 373–374.

27 *Ibid.*, pp. 173, 132, 304–305, 320, 424, 441, 453.

28 Ibid., pp. 61–62; William H. Seward, *Works*, ed. George E. Baker (New York: Redfield, 1853), I, 417.

29 Quoted in the *New York Tribune*, July 28, 1846, p. 1, cols. 6–7. The *Advertiser* declared that the most impressive lesson to be drawn from "this tragic event" was that society had a duty "to see to the moral cultivation of the colored youth now being educated for good or evil in the midst of us." The *Tribune* expressed similar sentiments (March 24, 1846, p. 2, col. 3).

30 Quoted from the *Cayuga Tocsin* in the *Albany Argus*, July 25, 1846, p. 215, col. 3.

31 *The Parish Will Case Before the Surrogate of the City of New York; Medical Opinions upon the Mental Competency of Mr. Parish*, by John Watson, M.D., D. T. Brown, M.D., M. H. Ranney, M.D., Sir Henry Holland, Bart., M.D., F.R.S., Pliny Earle, M.D., Luther V. Bell, M.D., LL.D., I. Ray, M.D. (New York: John F. Trow, Printer, 1857).

32 New York (County), Surrogate's Court, *In the Matter of Proving the Last Will of Henry Parish, Deceased; Testimony and Exhibits* (New York: Wm. C. Bryant & Co., 1857), II, 61–65, 702; I, 517, 463, 530.

33 *Ibid.*, I, 577, 587. It is true that witnesses and jurors generally tended to be more willing to find insanity if murder was not involved, but not necessarily. In another will case, the jury declared a will valid even though the testator had claimed to have died and been resurrected and to have conducted his affairs on direct advice from the Deity. ("Law Cases Bearing on the Question of Insanity," *AJI*, X [October, 1853], 181–183.)

34 *Report of the Trial of Willard Clark, Indicted for the Murder of Richard W. Wight, before the Superior Court of Connecticut, Holden at New Haven, on Monday, September 17, 1855*, by Henry H. McFarland, Assisted by the Counsel for the State and Defense (New Haven: Thomas H. Pease, 1855), pp. 26–27.

35 *Ibid.*, pp. 28–37 ff. Similar testimony was given in the trial of Andrew Kleim for the senseless murder of a neighbor. His fellow workers noted that he had changed over the years and become "queer" and "strange." His employer said he sometimes acted like a "maniac." The jury acquitted him on grounds of insanity. Reports of his trial are given in the *New York Herald*, May 23, 1845, p. 2, cols. 5–6; May 24, p. 1, col. 6; May 25, p. 2, col. 4, and in *AJI*, II (January, 1846), 254–266.

36 *The Trial of Agostinho Rabello*, pp. 18, 24, 39; see also quotation from the Litchfield *Enquirer* in the *Connecticut Courant*, May 4, 1835, p. 2, col. 5.

37 *The Trial of Agostinho Rabello*, pp. 22–23, 16–17, 25–28.

38 This was the Hinchman case; see [Philadelphia] *Public Ledger*, 13 March 1849, p. 1, col. 5; 14 March, p. 1, col. 5; 21 March, p. 1, col. 7; 27 March, p. 1, col. 7.

39 Deutsch, in Chapter VIII of *The Mentally Ill in America*, seems to give the impression that the "cult of curability" permeated throughout the American population during the mid-nineteenth century.

Chapter 10

1 See Joint Commission on Mental Illness and Health, *Action for Mental Health*, chaps. 3–4, and Jum C. Nunnally, Jr., *Popular Conceptions of Mental Health, Their Development and Change* (New York: Holt, Rinehart and Winston, Inc., c1961).

2 *Ibid.*, p. 235.

3 See Joint Commission on Mental Illness and Health, *Action for Mental Health*, chap. 6, for a discussion of its recommendations.

SELECTED BIBLIOGRAPHY

PRIMARY SOURCES

Unpublished Material

American Freedmen's Inquiry Commission MSS, Houghton Library, Harvard University.
Brigham, Amariah. Notebooks, Osler Library, McGill University.
Coates, Samuel. Memorandum Book (1785–1825), Historical Library and Museum, Institute of the Pennsylvania Hospital, Philadelphia.
Chandler, George, MSS, American Antiquarian Society.
Dix, Dorothea L. Papers, 1836–39, in the Chamberlain Collection of Autographs, Boston Public Library.
———, MSS, Houghton Library, Harvard University.
Earle, Pliny, MSS, American Antiquarian Society.
Friends' Asylum. Commitment Certificates, Friends Hospital, Philadelphia.
———. Manuscript Diary of the Superintendent, 1817–1865, Friends Hospital, Philadelphia.
Johnson, William N. "The Remedial Agency of Musick in Mental Disease." Unpublished manuscript M.D. inaugural thesis, University of Pennsylvania, 1829.
Kirkbride, Thomas S., MSS, Historical Library and Museum, Institute of the Pennsylvania Hospital, Philadelphia.
Mann, Horace, MSS, Massachusetts Historical Society.
Rush, Benjamin, MSS, College of Physicians, Philadelphia.
———, MSS, Library Company of Philadelphia, Ridgway Branch.

Woodward, Samuel B. "Collected Writings." Typescript copy of original manuscripts, Worcester State Hospital, Medical Library, Worcester, Massachusetts. 3 vols. (Most of the original manuscripts are in the American Antiquarian Society.)

———, MSS, American Antiquarian Society. (All references in the text to Woodward MSS are to this collection unless otherwise indicated.)

———, MSS, Yale University Library.

Woodward, Samuel B. (grandson of the early pyschiatrist Dr. S. B. Woodward). "Notes on Some of My Ancestors," Scrapbooks, American Antiquarian Society. (Vol. I only has information about the first Dr. S. B. Woodward.)

Zorns, Jacob. "Influence of the Passions on the Human System." Unpublished manuscript M. D. inaugural thesis, University of Pennsylvania, 1827.

Reports of Mental Hospitals

The periodic official reports of mental hospitals were published in various forms and under various titles. Where these reports were issued regularly by the hospital itself, each report as a separate publication in a series, I have listed the name and place of the hospital and the inclusive years of the reports I examined. Where many reports were compiled into one volume I have cited the entire volume, with full bibliographic information. Unless otherwise indicated, the reports are annual. The names used are those in the reports examined; entry is under a standard name, usually the latest found; variant names for the years concerned are noted.

Bloomingdale Asylum (of New York Hospital), New York. 1821–1900. (Issued as part of the *Reports* of the New York Hospital.)

Butler Hospital for the Insane, Providence, Rhode Island. 1847–1900.

Friends' Asylum, Frankford, Pennsylvania. 1817–1900. (Official name: Asylum for the Relief of Persons Deprived of the Use of their Reason.)

Hartford Retreat, Hartford, Connecticut. 1824–1900 (some years missing). (Official name: Connecticut Retreat for the Insane.)

Illinois State Hospital for the Insane, Jacksonville. *Reports of the Illinois State Hospital for the Insane, 1847–1862.* Chicago: F. Fulton & Co., 1863. (Biennial.)

Indiana Hospital for the Insane, Indianapolis. 1845–1854. (Also known as Indiana Lunatic Asylum.)

Insane Asylum of Louisiana, Jackson. 1850–1865 (scattered issues). (Also known as Louisiana Insane Asylum.)

Iowa Hospital for the Insane, Mount Pleasant. 1861–1866. (Biennial.)

Kings County Lunatic Asylum, Flatbush, Long Island. 1856–1859.

Longview Asylum, Cincinnati, Ohio. 1861.

Lunatic Asylum of the State of Georgia, Milledgeville. 1843–1866 (scattered issues). (Also known as Lunatic, Idiot and Epileptic Asylum of the State of Georgia.)

McLean Asylum for the Insane (of Massachusetts General Hospital), Charlestown, Massachusetts. 1824–1907 (some years missing). (Until 1826 known as the "Asylum" to distinguish it from the "Hospital," i.e., Massachusetts General Hospital. Some reports issued as part of reports of the Massachusetts General Hospital.)

Maine Insane Hospital, Augusta. 1840–1900.

Maryland Hospital for the Insane, Baltimore. 1843–1865 (scattered issues).

Michigan Asylum for the Insane, Kalamazoo. 1855–1860. (Annual and biennial.)

New York State Lunatic Asylum at Utica. 1843–1865.

Ohio Lunatic Asylum, Columbus, Ohio. 1841. (Also known as Lunatic Asylum of Ohio.)

Pennsylvania Hospital for the Insane, Philadelphia. 1841–1905. (Previous to 1841 also called Pennsylvania Hospital. Department for the Insane.)

State Lunatic Hospital at Northampton, Massachusetts. 1856–1865. (Also known as North-ampton Lunatic Hospital.)

State Lunatic Hospital at Taunton, Massachusetts, 1855–1865.

State Lunatic Hospital at Worcester, Massachusetts. 1834–1865.

Tennessee Hospital for the Insane, near Nashville. 1853–1864. (Biennial.)

The Vermont Asylum for the Insane: Its Annals for Fifty Years. Brattleboro: Hildreth & Fales, 1887. (Located in Brattleboro.)

Western Kentucky Lunatic Asylum at Hopkinsville. 1856–1865. (Also known as Western Lunatic Asylum of the State of Kentucky.)

Memorials of Dorothea L. Dix

Memorial of D. L. Dix, Praying a Grant of Land for the Relief and Support of the Indigent Curable and Incurable Insane in the United States. June 27, 1848. Referred to a Select Committee, and Ordered to Be Printed, and 5,000 Additional Copies Printed for the Use of the Senate. 30th Cong., 1st Sess., Miscellaneous No. 150. [Washington: Tippin & Streeter, Printers, 1848].

Memorial of Miss D. L. Dix, to the Honorable the General Assembly in Behalf of the Insane of Maryland (Document C.) By the Senate, February 25th, 1852, Read and Ordered Printed. [Annapolis: n.p., 1852].

"Memorial of Miss Dix, to the Honorable the Senate and House of Representatives of the State of Illinois," in *Reports of the Illinois State Hospital for the Insane, 1847–1862* (Chicago: F. Fulton & Co., 1863), pp. 9–31.

Memorial Soliciting a State Hospital for the Insane. Submitted to the Legislature of Ala-bama, November 15, 1849. Montgomery: Book and Job Office of the *Advertiser and Gazette,* 1849.

Memorial Soliciting a State Hospital for the Insane. Submitted to the Legislature of New Jersey, January 23, 1845. Printed by Order of the Legislature of New Jersey. 2d ed. Trenton: n.p., 1845.

Memorial Soliciting a State Hospital for the Insane. Submitted to the Legislature of Penn-sylvania, February 3, 1845. Philadelphia: Isaac Ashmead, Printer, 1845.

Memorial Soliciting Adequate Appropriations for the Construction of a State Hospital for the Insane, in the State of Mississippi. Feb. 1850. Printed by the Order of the Legisla-ture. Jackson, Miss.: Fall & Marshall, 1850.

Memorial Soliciting an Appropriation for the State Hospital for the Insane, at Lexington; and also Urging the Necessity for Establishing a New Hospital in the Green River Country. Frankfort, Ky.: A. G. Hodges, State Printer, 1846.

Memorial Soliciting Enlarged and Improved Accommodations for the Insane of the State of Tennessee, by the Establishment of a New Hospital. Printed by Order of the General Assembly, November, 1847. Nashville: B. R. M'Kennie, Printer, *Whig and Politician* Office, 1847.

"Memorial to the Honorable the Legislative Assembly of the Province of Nova Scotia and Its Dependencies. Appendix of Journals of House of Assembly, Nova Scotia, 1850, No. 18," in Henry M. Hurd, (ed.), *The Institutional Care of the Insane in the United States and Canada,* by Henry M. Hurd, *et al.* (Baltimore: The Johns Hopkins Press, 1916), I, 482–497.

Memorial to the Honorable the Legislature of the State of New-York. Albany: n.p., 1844.

Memorial to the Legislature of Massachusetts [*Protesting against the Confinement of Insane*

Persons and Idiots in Almshouses and Prisons]. Boston: Printed by Munroe & Francis, 1843.

Reports, Verbatim Accounts, and
Reviews of Trials Involving Insanity

These entries are arranged alphabetically by the surname of the defendant or, in will cases, of the testator. An article reporting various cases is listed first.

"Law Cases Bearing on the Question of Insanity," *AJI*, X (October, 1853), 179–184.

Angell: Ray, Isaac, "The Angell Will Case," *AJI*, XX (October, 1863), 145–186.

Baker: Life and Trial of Dr. Abner Baker, Jr. (a Monomaniac) Who Was Executed October 3, 1845, for the Alleged Murder of His Brother-in-Law, Daniel Bates; Including Letters and Petitions in Favor of a Pardon, and Narrative of the Circumstances Attending His Execution, Etc. Etc. By C. W. Crozier. Trial and Evidence by A. R. M'Kee. Louisville, Ky.: Prentice and Weissinger, Printers, 1846.

[Ray, Isaac], Review of *Life and Trial of Dr. Abner Baker, Jr. . . .* , *AJI*, III (July, 1846), 26–35. (Signed: I.R.)

Ball: "John Ball's Case," *New-York City-Hall Recorder*, II (June, 1817), 85–86.

Blaisdell: Trial of John Blaisdell, on an Indictment for the Murder of John Wadleigh, at the Superior Court of Judicature, Holden at Exeter, September 1822. Reported by a Member of the Bar. Exeter [N. H.: n.p., 1822?].

Brown, Joseph I., Capt.: [Harlow, Henry M.] "Homicide in Which the Plea of Insanity was Interposed," *AJI*, XIII (January, 1857), 249–259. (Signed: H.M.H. Harlow, the superintendent of the Maine Insane Hospital, was a witness at Brown's trial, which took place in Maine, and I have assumed that he wrote the article.)

Bush: The Trial of Robert Bush for the Murder of Sally Bush, His Wife, Who Was Found Guilty and Sentenced to Be Hung at Springfield, Nov. 14, 1828—But Committed Suicide on the 12th. With Extracts from His Own Writings and the Last Words of Said Bush, Delivered to a Fellow Prisoner, a Few Hours before His Death. Springfield: n.p., 1828.

Clark, Stephen M.: Report of the Evidence, Arguments of Counsel, Charge and Sentence at the Trial of Stephen Merril Clark, for Arson, before the Supreme Judicial Court, February 15, 16 & 17, 1821. Salem [Mass.]: T. C. Cushing and W. Palfray, Jun., 1821.

Clark, Willard: Report of the Trial of Willard Clark, Indicted for the Murder of Richard W. Wight, before the Superior Court of Connecticut, Holden at New Haven, on Monday, September 17, 1855. By Henry H. McFarland, Assisted by the Counsel for the State and Defense. New Haven: Thomas H. Pease, 1855.

"Insanity and Crime," *New Englander*, XIV (February, 1856), 32–52. (Review of *Report of the Trial of Willard Clark . . .*)

"Trial of Willard Clark, Indicted for the Murder of Richard W. Wight, before the Superior Court of Connecticut, Held at New Haven, Sept. 17, 1855," *AJI*, XII (January, 1856), 212–237.

Clough: Trial, Sentence, Confession, and Execution of Joel Clough, Who Was Executed on the 26th July, for the Wilful Murder of Mrs. Mary Hamilton, at Bordentown, N. Jersey on the 6th of April, 1833. Also an Account of His Escape from Prison for a Few Days Previous to His Execution. New York: Christian Brown, n.d.

Corey: Report of the Trial of Daniel H. Corey, on an Indictment for the Murder of Mrs. Matilda Nash, at the Term of the Superior Court of Judicature, Holden at Keene, in the County of Cheshire, on the First Tuesday of October, A.D. 1829. By Joel Parker. Newport: French & Brown, 1830.

Darby: Review of *Proceedings in the Trial of Jeremiah Darby, for the Murder of His Wife, in the Circuit Court for Montgomery County, May 19, 1847.* Reported by J. J. Hutchinson, *AJI,* IV (October, 1847), 179.

Fairbanks: Report of the Trial of Jason Fairbanks, on an Indictment for the Murder of Miss Elizabeth Fales, at the Supreme Court at Dedham, . . . on Thursday the 6th, and Friday the 7th Days of August, 1801. 2d ed. Boston: Printed by Russell and Cutler, 1801.

Farrer: Quinn, J. J. "Homicidal Insanity.—The Case of Nancy Farrer," *AJI,* XII (April, 1856), 316–334. (From the *Western Lancet.*)

Freeman: The Freeman Trial; Presenting the Testimony Given in this Remarkable Case, with Comments by David Dimon, M.D., Auburn, N. Y. Auburn: Dennis Bro's. & Throne, 1871.

The Trial of William Freeman, for the Murder of John G. Van Nest, Including the Evidence and the Arguments of Counsel, with the Decision of the Supreme Court Granting a New Trial, and an Account of the Death of the Prisoner, and of the Post-Mortem Examination of His Body by Amariah Brigham, M. D., and Others. Reported by Benjamin F. Hall. Auburn: Derby, Miller & Co., 1848.

Freeth: "The Case of Freeth. Trial for Murder. Defense, Insanity," *AJI,* XV (January, 1859), 297–306.

Furbush: Ray, Isaac, "Trial of Furbush," *AJI,* IX (October, 1852), 151–166.

Griffin: "Medical Jurisprudence of Insanity: Trial of James C. Griffin, for the Murder of Erastus Coit. Plea of Insanity," *AJI,* III (January, 1847), 227–253.

Hadcock: "Criminal Lunacy—Case of John Hadcock," *AJI,* XI (April, 1855), 365–382.

Hammond: "Trial of George Hammond, Indicted for the Murder of Joshua Worley, before the Fayette Court, Held at Lexington, Ky., March 3, 1857," *AJI,* XVI (October, 1859), 168–184.

Hinchman: The Hinchman Conspiracy Case, in Letters to the New York Home Journal, with an Abstract of the Evidence for the Defence, Furnishing a Complete Explanation of This Most Extraordinary Case. By an American Citizen. Philadelphia: Stokes & Brother, 1849.

Speeches of Defendants' Counsel, and the Charge of Judge Burnside, in the case of Hinchman vs. Richie et al. Reported by Oliver Dyer and Dennis F. Murphy. Philadelphia: [T. K. and P. G. Collins, Printers], 1849.

Howard: Trial of Mrs. Margaret Howard, for the Murder of Miss Mary Ellen Smith, Her Husband's Paramour, in Cincinnati, on the 2nd of Feb. Last. Cincinnati, Ohio: n.p., 1850.

Huntington: Gilman, Chandler R. *A Medico-Legal Examination of the Case of Charles B. Huntington, with Remarks on Moral Insanity and on the Legal Test of Insanity.* New York: Baker & Goodwin, 1857.

Trial of Charles B. Huntington for Forgery. Principal Defence: Insanity. Prepared for Publication by the Defendant's Counsel, from Full Stenographic Notes Taken by Messrs. Roberts & Warburton, Law Reporters. New York: John S. Voorhies, Law Bookseller and Publisher, 1857.

Johnson, John: "Trial for Murder,—Mysterious Disclosures," *AJI,* IV (April, 1848), 303–346. (Reprinted from the report of the trial of John Johnson in the *Binghamton Courier.*)

Johnson, Richard: A Correct Copy of the Trial & Conviction of Richard Johnson, for the Murder of Ursula Newman, on the 20th Nov., 1829, by Shooting Her with a Pistol Loaded with Buck Shot or Slugs, Nine of Which Entered Her Body; together with the Charge of the Court, and the Confession of the Prisoner. . . . New York: Christian Brown, n.d.

Joseph: The Trial of Henry Joseph and Amos Otis, for the Murder of James Crosby, Captain of the Brig Juniper, on the High Seas. In the Circuit Court of the United States, District of Massachusetts, Holden at Boston, October Term 1834. Boston: Light and Horton, 1834.

Kellogg: "Homicidal Insanity. Trial of Ashbel Kellogg for the Murder of His Son, at Yorkville, Mich., 6th August 1849," *AJI*, VI (January, 1850), 247–254. (Taken from the *Kalamazoo News*.)

Kleim: "Homicidal Insanity. Court of Oyer and Terminer, City of New York. Before Judge Edmonds and Aldermen Henry and Seaman; M. C. Paterson, Esq., District Attorney. May 21, 1845.—Case of Murder. [Trial of Andrew Kleim for Murder of Catherine Hanlin, December 23, 1844]," *AJI*, II (January, 1846), 245–266.

Kramer: "Trial of a Question of Insanity. Mary Smith vs. Rebecca Kramer, Philadelphia Nisi Prius, February 1853," *AJI*, X (July, 1853), 62–67. (From the *American Law Register*, April, 1853.)

Layman: "Homicide and Insanity; the Case of John W. Layman," *AJI*, XIV (January, 1858), 240–248.

Mitchell: Report of the Trial of Major Mitchell, for Felonious Assault and Maiming, on the Person of David H. Crawford. Before the Supreme Judicial Court of the State of Maine, at the Term for the County of Cumberland, Held at Portland, on the First Tuesday of November, 1834. With the Argument of Counsel. By James F. Otis, Attorney at Law. Portland: Colman & Chisholm, 1834.

Packard: Packard, Elizabeth P. W. Marital Power Exemplified in Mrs. Packard's Trial, and Self-Defence from the Charge of Insanity; or, Three Years' Imprisonment for Religious Belief. . . . Hartford: Case, Lockwood & Company, 1866.

Parish: New York (County) Surrogate's Court. In the Matter of Proving the Last Will of Henry Parish Deceased; Testimony and Exhibits. 3 vols. New York: Wm. C. Bryant & Co., 1857.

The Parish Will Case Before the Surrogate of the City of New York; Medical Opinions upon the Mental Competency of Mr. Parish, by John Watson, M.D., D. T. Brown, M.D., M. H. Ranney, M.D., Sir Henry Holland, Bart., M.D., F.R.S., Pliny Earle, M.D., Luther V. Bell, M.D., LL.D., I. Ray, M.D. New York: John F. Trow, Printer, 1857.

Phelps: "Law Cases Bearing on the Subject of Insanity. Trial of Adeline Phelps, *Alias* Bass, for the Murder of Her Father, Elihu Phelps," *AJI*, XI (July, 1854), 63–83. (From the *Monthly Law Reporter*, May, 1854.)

Pienovi: "Lawrence Pienovi's Case," *New-York City-Hall Recorder*, III (July-August, 1818), 123–127.

Prescott: Report of the Trial of Abraham Prescott, on an Indictment for the Murder of Mrs. Sally Cochran, before the Court of Common Pleas, Holden at Concord in the County of Merrimack, on the First Tuesday of September, A.D. 1834. Concord: M.G. Atwood and Currier & Hall, 1834.

Rabello: The Trial of Agostinho Rabello for the Murder of Ferris Beardsley, at New Preston, Con., April 27, 1835. With Some Particulars in Relation to the Life of Rabello. Litchfield: Printed for Birdsey Gibs, 1835.

"The Trial of Agostinho Rabello, for the Murder of Ferris Beardsley, at New Preston, Conn., April 27, 1835," *AJI*, III (July, 1846), 41–67.

Ransom: Horrid, Brutish, and Bloody Murder; Trial & Sentence of James Ransom, for the Murder of His Wife, Who Was Executed on the 7th of January, 1832. New York: n.p., n.d.

Rogers, Abner: B., H.A. "Medical Jurisprudence of Insanity," *AJI*, I (January, 1845), 258–274. (Review of *Report of the Trial of Abner Rogers, Jr.* . . .)

Report of the Trial of Abner Rogers, Jr., Indicted for the Murder of Charles Lincoln, Jr., Late Warden of the Massachusetts State Prison; before the Supreme Judicial Court of Massachusetts, Holden at Boston, on Tuesday, January 30, 1844. By George Tyler Bigelow and George Bemis, Esqrs., Counsel for the Defendant. Boston: Charles C. Little and James Brown, 1844.

Rogers, James: "Decision of the Court of Appeals of the State of New York, in the Case of James Rogers, Convicted of Murder. Main Plea, Intoxication," *AJI*, XV (January, 1859), 258–271.

Sellick: "Diana Sellick's Case," *New-York City-Hall Recorder*, I (December, 1816), 185–191.

Speirs: "The Case of William Speirs. Arson. Plea of Insanity," *AJI*, XV (October, 1858), 200–225.

Sprague: Nichols, Charles H., "The Case of Charles Sprague," *AJI*, VI (January, 1850), 254–263.

Streeter: *The Life of Milton W. Streeter, the Jealous and Infatuated Murderer, Who Murdered His Young and Beautiful Wife Elvira W. Streeter. . . .* Pawtucket, R. I.: H. F. Tingley, 1850.

Tirrell: *The Trial of Albert J. Tirrell, Charged with the Murder of Mrs. Maria A. Bickford before the Supreme Court in Boston.* Boston: *Daily Mail* Report [1846].

Van Patten: *The Trial and Life and Confessions of John F. Van Patten, Who Was Indicted, Tried, and Convicted of the Murder of Mrs. Maria Schermerhorn, on the 4th of October Last and Sentenced to Be Executed on the 25th February, 1825.* New York: n.p., 1825.

Windsor: G. "Trial of Capt. John Windsor for the Murder of His Wife, before the Court of Oyer and Terminer Held at Georgetown, Delaware, June 25th, 1851, before His Honor, Chief Justice Booth; Harrington and Wootten, Associates," *AJI*, VIII (January, 1852), 227–267. (From notes furnished by Judge Harrington.)

Y——: "An Account of a Murder Committed by Mr. J—— Y——, upon His Family, in December, A.D. 1781," *New-York Weekly Magazine*, II (July 20, 1796), 20; (July 27, 1796), 28.

Books and Pamphlets

Abbott, Edith (ed.) *Some American Pioneers in Social Welfare; Selected Documents with Editorial Notes.* (The University of Chicago Social Service Series.) Chicago: University of Chicago Press, 1937.

Address of the Trustees of the Massachusetts General Hospital, to the Subscribers and to the Public. [n.p.: 1822].

Alexander, Ashton. *An Inaugural Dissertation on the Influence of One Disease in the Cure of Others.* Philadelphia: Printed by Alexander M'Kenzie, 1795.

Alexander, Archibald. *Thoughts on Religious Experience.* Philadelphia: Presbyterian Board of Publications, c1844.

Allen, Matthew. *Essay on the Classification of the Insane.* London: John Taylor, [1838?].

Allen, Nathan. *An Essay on the Connection of Mental Philosophy with Medicine.* Philadelphia: Printed by Adam Waldie, 1841. (Inaugural thesis, Pennsylvania Medical College.)

American Temperance Society. *Permanent Temperance Documents of the American Temperance Society.* Vol. I. Boston: Seth Bliss and Perkins, Marvin, and Co., 1835.

Anderson, Alexander. *An Inaugural Dissertation on Chronic Mania.* New York: Printed by T. and J. Swords, 1796.

An Appeal to the Citizens of Pennsylvania for Means to Provide Additional Accommodations for the Insane. Philadelphia: T. K. and P. G. Collins, Printers, 1854.

An Appeal to the People of Pennsylvania on the Subject of an Asylum for the Insane Poor of the Commonwealth. Philadelphia: Printed for the Committee, 1838.

An Appeal to the Citizens of New Hampshire in Behalf of the Suffering Insane. Portsmouth: C. W. Brewster, Printer, 1838. (Reprinted in the Appendix to *Extracts from Newspapers and Periodicals . . . New Hampshire.*)

Baker, Jacob, Rev. *Human Magnetism: Its Origin, Progress, Philosophy and Curative Qualities, with Instructions for Its Application.* Worcester, Mass.: Jacob Baker and M. D. Phillips [1843].

Barnard, Henry. *Tribute to Gallaudet. A Discourse in Commemoration of the Life, Character, and Services, of the Rev. Thomas H. Gallaudet, LL.D. Delivered before the Citizens of Hartford Jan. 7th, 1852. With an Appendix, Containing History of Deaf-Mute Instruction and Institutions, and other Documents.* Hartford: Published by Brockett & Hutchinson, 1852.

Battie, William. *A Treatise on Madness.* London: Printed for J. Whiston, and B. White, 1758.

Beck, Theodric Romeyn, and Beck, John B. *Elements of Medical Jurisprudence.* 6th ed. 2 vols. Philadelphia: Thomas, Cowperthwait & Co., 1838.

———. *An Inaugural Dissertation on Insanity.* New York: Printed by J. Seymour, 1811.

Beers, Clifford Whittingham. *A Mind That Found Itself; an Autobiography.* 5th ed., rev., reprinted, with additions. Garden City, N. Y.: Doubleday & Company, Inc., 1960.

Bell, Luther V. *Report Made to the Legislature of New Hampshire on the Subject of the Insane.* June Session, 1836. Concord: Cyrus Barton, Printer, 1836.

Bowditch, N. I. *A History of the Massachusetts General Hospital.* Boston: Printed by John Wilson & Son, 1851.

Brigham, Amariah. *An Inquiry Concerning the Diseases and Functions of the Brain, the Spinal Cord, and the Nerves.* New York: George Adlard, 1840.

———. *A Letter from Doctor Brigham to David M. Reese, M.D., Author of Phrenology Known by Its Fruits, Etc.* Hartford, Conn.: n.p., 1835.

———. *Observations on the Influence of Religion upon the Health and Physical Welfare of Mankind.* Boston: Marsh, Capen & Lyon, 1835.

———. *Remarks on the Influence of Mental Cultivation and Mental Excitement upon Health.* 3d ed. Philadelphia: Lea & Blanchard, 1845.

Broussais, F.J.V. *On Irritation and Insanity; a Work Wherein the Relations of the Physical with the Moral Conditions of Man Are Established on the Basis of Physiological Medicine.* Translated by Thomas Cooper. To Which Are Added *Two Tracts on Materialism,* and an *Outline of the Association of Ideas,* by Thomas Cooper. Columbia, S. C.: Printed by S. J. M'Morris, 1831.

Brown, Albert G. *Speech of Albert G. Brown, of Mississippi, on the President's Veto Message, and in Defence of the Bill Making a Grant of Land to the Several States for the Benefit of the Indigent Insane.* Delivered in the Senate of the United States, May 17, 1854. Washington: Printed by John T. and Lem. Towers, 1854.

Brown, Charles Brockden. *Edgar Huntly; or, Memoirs of a Sleep-Walker.* Edited with introduction by David Lee Clark. New York: The Macmillan Company, 1928.

———. *Wieland; or, The Transformation, together with Memoirs of Carwin, the Biloquist, a Fragment.* Edited with an introduction by Fred Lewis Pattee. (American Authors Series.) New York: Hafner Publishing Co., 1958.

Brown, Clark. *Human Life Not Always Desirable.* Sermon Delivered at Richmond, N. H., November 17, 1813 at the Funeral of Mr. Solomon Atherton, AET. 73. Keene: Printed by John Prentiss, 1814.

Buchan, William. *Domestic Medicine; or, The Family Physician . . .* Philadelphia: Printed by John Dunlap, for R. Aitken, 1772.

————. *Domestic Medicine; or, The Family Physician* . . . Edinburgh: Printed by Balfour, Auld, and Smellie, 1769.

Buchanan, Joseph R. *Outlines of Lectures on the Neurological System of Anthropology, as Discovered, Demonstrated and Taught in 1841 and 1842.* Cincinnati: Printed at the Office of *Buchanan's Journal of Man*, 1854.

Bucknill, John Charles, and Tuke, Daniel H. *A Manual of Psychological Medicine: Containing the History, Nosology, Description, Statistics, Diagnosis, Pathology, and Treatment of Insanity.* With an Appendix of Cases. Philadelphia: Blanchard and Lea, 1858.

Capron, E. W. *Modern Spiritualism: Its Facts and Fanaticisms, Its Consistencies and Contradictions.* With an Appendix. Boston: Bela Marsh, 1855.

Cheyne, George. *The English Malady; or, A Treatise of Nervous Diseases of All Kinds, as Spleen, Vapours, Lowness of Spirits, Hypochondrical, and Hysterical Distempers, Etc.* London: Printed, and Dublin: Reprinted by S. Powell for George Risk, George Ewing, and William Smith, 1733.

Clay, C. C., Jr. *President's Veto Message. Speech of Mr. C. C. Clay, Jr., of Alabama, on the President's Veto Message, Rejecting the Indigent Insane Bill, and against Giving Away the Public Lands.* Delivered in the Senate of the United States, June 20, 1854. Washington: Printed by John and Lem. Towers, 1854.

Clayton, John M. *Speech of Hon. John M. Clayton, of Delaware, on the Veto Message of the President, on the Bill for the Benefit of the Indigent Insane.* In the Senate of the United States, June 15, 1854. Washington: Printed at the *Congressional Globe* Office, 1854.

Collins, Stephen. *Report on Pauper Insanity; Presented to the City Council of Baltimore, on March 28th, 1845, by Dr. Stephen Collins, Chairman of the Committee.* Baltimore: Printed by James Lucas, 1845.

Conover, Samuel Forman. *An Inaugural Dissertation on Sleep and Dreams, Their Effects on the Faculties of the Mind; and the Causes of Dreams.* [Philadelphia]: Printed by T. Lang, 1791.

Cook, George. *Remarks on the Care and Treatment of the Chronic Insane Poor.* Canandaigua, N. Y.: Milliken, Printer, *Ontario County Times* Office, 1867.

Cox, Joseph Mason. *Practical Observations on Insanity. . . . To Which Are Subjoined Remarks on Medical Jurisprudence as Connected with Diseased Intellect.* From 2nd corrected and enlarged London ed. Philadelphia: Thomas Dobson, 1811.

Cullen, William. *First Lines of the Practice of Physic.* 2 vols. Philadelphia: Thomas Dobson, 1816.

Curwen, John. *A Manual for Attendants in Hospitals for the Insane.* Philadelphia: William S. Martien, 1851.

Cutbush, Edward. *An Inaugural Dissertation on Insanity.* Philadelphia: Zachariah Poulson, 1794

Denny, Lydia B. *Statement of Mrs. Lydia B. Denny in Regard to Her Alleged Insanity.* [n.p.: 1865?].

Dods, John Bovee. *Spirit Manifestations Examined and Explained, Judge Edmonds Refuted; or, An Exposition of the Involuntary Powers and Instincts of the Human Mind.* New York: DeWitt & Davenport, c1854.

Dunglison, Robley. *Human Physiology.* 5th ed., greatly modified and improved. 2 vols. Philadelphia: Lea and Blanchard, 1844.

Earle, Pliny. *The Curability of Insanity.* Read before the New England Psychological Society, on Retiring from Office as Its President, December 14, 1876; and Published by that Society. Utica, N. Y.: Ellis H. Roberts & Co., 1877.

————. *Memoirs of Pliny Earle, M.D., with Extracts from His Diary and Letters (1830–1892)*

and Selections from His Professional Writings (1839–1891). Edited, with a general introduction by F. B. Sanborn. Boston: Damrell & Upham, 1898.

Elliot, John. *The Medical Pocket-Book for Those Who Are, and for All Who Wish, to Be
Physicians*. . . . Philadelphia: Printed and Sold by Robert Bell, 1784.

Ellis, Sir W. C. *A Treatise on the Nature, Symptoms, Causes, and Treatment of Insanity,
with Practical Observations on Lunatic Asylums, and a Description of the Pauper
Lunatic Asylum for the County of Middlesex, at Hanwell, with a Detailed Account of
Its Management*. London: Samuel Holdsworth, 1838.

*Extracts from Newspapers and Periodicals in Relation to the Condition of the Insane in
New Hampshire, Previous to the Erection of the N. H. Asylum for the Insane*. [Con-
cord, N. H.?]: Asylum Press, 1890.

Ferriar, John. *Medical Histories and Reflections*. 1st American ed. 4 vols. in 1. Philadelphia:
Thomas Dobson, 1816.

Finney, Charles G. *Lectures on Revivals of Religion*. Edited by William G. McLaughlin.
(The John Harvard Library.) Cambridge, Mass.: The Belknap Press of Harvard University Press, 1960.

———. *Memoirs of Rev. Charles G. Finney*. New York: A. S. Barnes & Company, 1876.

Fowler, Orson S. *Hereditary Descent: Its Laws and Facts, Illustrated and Applied to the
Improvement of Mankind*. . . . New York: O. S. & L. W. Fowler, 1843.

———. *Physiology, Animal and Mental: Applied to the Preservation and Restoration of
Health of Body, and Power of Mind*. 6th ed. New York: Fowler and Wells, 1854.

———. *Self-Culture, and Perfection of Character, Including Management of Youth*. New
York: Fowler and Wells, [1847].

Franklin, Benjamin. *Benjamin Franklin's Experiments; a New Edition of Franklin's Experiments and Observations in Electricity*. Edited, with a critical and historical introduction, by I. Bernard Cohen. Cambridge, Mass.: Harvard University Press, 1941.

———. *Some Account of the Pennsylvania Hospital from Its First Rise, to the Beginning of
the Fifth Month, Called May, 1754*. Philadelphia: Printed by B. Franklin and D. Hall,
1754.

Fuller, Robert. *An Account of the Imprisonment and Sufferings of Robert Fuller of Cam-
bridge, Who, While Peaceably and Quietly and Rationally in Possession of His Own
House, Was Seized and Detained in the McLean Asylum for the Insane, at Charlestown,
Mass. 65 Days, from June 24th to August 28th, 1832. Together with Some Remarks on
That Institution*. Boston: Printed for the Author, 1833.

Galt, John M. *Essays on Asylums for Persons of Unsound Mind*. Richmond: H. K. Ellyson's
Power Press, 1850.

———. ———. Second Series. Richmond: Printed by Ritchies & Dunnavant, 1853.

———. *The Treatment of Insanity*. New York: Harper & Brothers, 1846.

Godwin, William. *Fleetwood: or, The New Man of Feeling*. 3 vols. London: Richard Phillips, 1805

Gordon, William R. *A Three-Fold Test of Modern Spiritualism*. New York: Charles Scribner, 1856.

Graham, Sylvester. *Lectures on the Science of Human Life*. New York: Fowler & Wells, 1858.

Gregory, John. *The Works of the Late John Gregory*. 4 vols. Edinburgh: Printed for A.
Strahan and T. Cadell, London; and W. Creech, Edinburgh, 1788.

Harper, Andrew. *A Treatise on the Real Cause and Cure of Insanity; in Which the Nature
and Distinctions of This Disease Are Fully Explained, and the Treatment Established
on New Principles*. London: Printed for C. Stalker and J. Walter, 1789.

Haslam, John. *Considerations on the Moral Management of Insane Persons*. London:
Printed for R. Hunter, 1817.

Hayward, George. *Some Observations on Dr. Rush's Work, on "The Diseases of the Mind."* *With Remarks on the Nature and Treatment of Insanity.* Boston: n.p., 1818. (Extracted from the *New England Journal of Medicine and Surgery*.)

Hill, Robert Gardiner. *Total Abolition of Personal Restraint in the Treatment of the Insane; a Lecture on the Management of Lunatic Asylums and the Treatment of the Insane; Delivered at the Mechanics' Institution, Lincoln, on the 21st of June 1838* London: Simkin, Marshall and Co. [1839?].

Hogg, James. *The Private Memoirs and Confessions of a Justified Sinner.* With an introduction by André Gide. New York: Grove Press, Inc., 1959.

Holmes, Oliver Wendell. *The Benefactors of the Medical School of Harvard University; with a Biographical Sketch of the Late Dr. George Parkman.* An Introductory Lecture, Delivered at the Massachusetts Medical College, November 7, 1850. Boston: Ticknor, Reed, and Fields, 1850.

————. *Currents and Counter-Currents in Medical Science, with Other Addresses and Essays.* Boston: Ticknor and Fields, 1861.

————. *The Psychiatric Novels of Oliver Wendell Holmes.* Abridgement, introduction and psychiatric annotations by Clarence P. Oberndorf. 2d ed., rev. and enl. New York: Columbia University Press, 1946.

Hosack, David. *An Introductory Discourse, to a Course of Lectures on the Theory and Practice of Physic; Containing Observations on the Inductive System of Prosecuting Medical Inquiries; and a Tribute to the Memory of the Late Dr. Benjamin Rush.* Delivered at the College of Physicians and Surgeons, on the Third Day of November, 1813. New York: Printed by C. S. Van Winkle, 1813.

Howard, Horton. *An Improved System of Botanic Medicine. . . .* New ed. Cincinnati: Kost, Bigger & Hart, 1854.

Howe, Samuel Gridley. *An Essay on Separate and Congregate Systems of Prison Discipline; Being a Report Made to the Boston Prison Discipline Society.* Boston: William D. Ticknor and Company, 1846.

————. *Report Made to the Legislature of Massachusetts, upon Idiocy.* Boston: Printed from the State Edition by Coolidge & Wiley, 1848.

Hunt, Isaac H. *Astounding Disclosures! Three Years in a Mad-House, By a Victim, Written by Himself. A True Account of the Barbarous, Inhuman and Cruel Treatment of Isaac H. Hunt, in the Maine Insane Hospital, in the Years 1844, '45, '46, '47, by Drs. Isaac Ray, James Bates, and Their Assistants and Attendants. . . .* 2d ed. [n.p.]: Printed for Isaac H. Hunt, the Author, 1852.

[Jarvis, Edward]. *The Causes and Prevention of Idiocy.* Boston: Coolidge & Wiley, 1848. (Reprinted from the *Massachusetts Quarterly Review*, No. III.)

————. *Tendency of Misdirected Education and the Unbalanced Mind to Produce Insanity.* [Hartford]: n.p., 1858. (From *Barnard's Journal of Education* for March, 1858.)

Jones, Joseph H. *Man, Moral and Physical; or, The Influence of Health and Disease on Religious Experience.* 2d ed. Philadelphia: James S. Claxton, 1865.

Knapp, Samuel Lorenzo. *The Life of Thomas Eddy; Comprising an Extensive Correspondence with Many of the Most Distinguished Philosophers and Philanthropists of This and Other Countries.* New York: Conner & Cooke, 1834.

Lieber, Francis. *A Popular Essay on Subjects of Penal Law, and on Uninterrupted Solitary Confinement at Labor, as Contradistinguished to Solitary Confinement at Night and Joint Labor by Day, in a Letter to John Bacon, Esquire, President of the Philadelphia Society for Alleviating the Miseries of Public Prisons.* Philadelphia: Published by Order of the Society, 1838.

Kost, J. *Domestic Medicine; a Treatise on the Practice of Medicine, Adapted to the Reformed System, Comprising a Materia Medica.* Cincinnati: J. W. Sewell, 1859.

Macbride, David. *A Methodical Introduction to the Theory and Practice of Physic.* London: Printed for W. Strahan [and others], 1772.

Marks, Elias. *Conjectural Inquiry into the Relative Influence of the Mind and Stomach: an Inaugural Dissertation.* New York: Printed by Van Winkle & Wiley, 1815.

Massachusetts. Commission on Lunacy, 1854. *Report on Insanity and Idiocy in Massachusetts,* by the Commission on Lunacy, under Resolve of the Legislature of 1854 ([Massachusetts. General Court, 1855.] House [Doc.] No. 144.) Boston: William White, Printer to the State, 1855.

——. Commissioners to Investigate Insanity. [*Report of the Commissioners Appointed under Chapter 91, Resolves of 1863, to Make Certain Investigations of the Subject of Insanity.*] ([Massachusetts. General Court.] Senate [Doc.], No. 72.) [Boston: n.p., 1864.]

[Maturin, Charles Robert]. *Melmoth the Wanderer; A Tale,* by the author of "Bertram," &c. 4 vols. Edinburgh: Printed for Archibald Constable and Company, 1820.

Mead, Richard. *The Medical Works of Richard Mead, M.D., Physician to His Late Majesty King George II.* A new ed. Edinburgh: Printed for Alexander Donaldson and Charles Elliot, 1775.

Newman, John B. *Fascination; or, The Philosophy of Charming, Illustrating the Principles of Life in Connection with Spirit and Matter.* New York: Fowler and Wells, 1848.

Nichols, Thomas L. *Esoteric Anthropology.* Cincinnati: Valentine Nicholson & Co., 1853.

Otto, John C. *An Inaugural Essay on Epilepsy.* Philadelphia: Printed by Lang & Ustick, 1796.

[Packard, Frederick Adolphus]. *An Inquiry into the Alleged Tendency of the Separation of Convicts, One from the Other, to Produce Disease and Derangement.* By a Citizen of Philadelphia. Philadelphia: E. C. & J. Biddle, 1849.

[——]. *The Relations of Religion to What Are Called "Diseases of the Mind."* Philadelphia: J. W. Moore, 1850. ("The substance of these remarks originally appeared in the *Biblical Repertory* and *Princeton Review* for January 1850.")

Parkman, George. *Management of Lunatics with Illustrations of Insanity.* Boston: Printed by John Elliot, 1817.

——. *Insanity.* Appendix to a Book, Presented in Manuscript to the Trustees of the Gen. Hospital More Than a Year Ago, Entitled, "Management of Lunatics, with Illustrations of Insanity, by Geo. Parkman, M.D." [Boston?]: n.p., 1818.

Parrish, Joseph. *An Inaugural Dissertation on the Influence of the Passions upon the Body, in the Production and Cure of Diseases.* Philadelphia: Printed by Kimber, Conrad, & Co., 1805.

Pennsylvania. Legislature. House of Representatives. *Report in Relation to an Asylum for the Insane Poor.* Mr. Konigmacher, Chairman. Read in the House of Representatives, March 11, 1839. Harrisburg: Boas & Coplan, Printers, 1839.

Perry, William. *Lecture Delivered by Dr. William Perry, of Exeter, June Session, 1834, in the Representatives' Hall, at Concord, N. H., on Insanity, the Condition of the Insane, and the Necessity of an Asylum.* Concord, N. H.: Printed by the Asylum Press, 1890. (Reprinted in the Appendix to *Extracts from Newspapers and Periodicals . . . New Hampshire.*)

Peters, John C. *A Treatise on Nervous Derangements and Mental Disorders Based upon Th. J. Rückert's "Clinical Experience in Homoeopathy."* New York: William Radde, 1854.

Pinel, Philippe. *Traité médico-philosophique sur l'aliénation mentale, ou la manie.* Paris: Richard, Caille, et Ravier, an IX [1801].

———. *A Treatise on Insanity.* . . . Translated from the French, by D. D. Davis. Sheffield: Printed by W. Todd, for Cadell and Davies, London, 1806.

Prichard, James Cowles. *A Treatise on Insanity and Other Disorders Affecting the Mind.* London: Sherwood, Gilbert, and Piper, 1835.

Pulte, J. H. *Homeopathic Domestic Physician, Containing the Treatment of Diseases; Popular Explanations of Anatomy, Physiology, Hygiene and Hydropathy; a Treatise on Domestic Surgery; and an Abridged Materia Medica.* 7th ed., enl. and rev. version. Cincinnati: Moore, Wilstach, Keys & Co., 1859.

Ray, Isaac. *Address Delivered on the Occasion of Laying the Corner Stone of the State Hospital for the Insane, at Danville, Penn'a.* . . . *August 26th, 1869.* Harrisburg: Theo. F. Schaffer, Printer, 1869.

———. *Contributions to Mental Pathology.* Boston: Little, Brown, and Company, 1873.

———. *Mental Hygiene.* Boston: Ticknor and Fields, 1863.

———. *A Treatise on the Medical Jurisprudence of Insanity.* Boston: Charles C. Little and James Brown, 1838.

Reese, David Meredith. *Humbugs of New-York: Being a Remonstrance against Popular Delusion; Whether in Science, Philosophy, or Religion.* New-York: Weeks, Jordan & Co., 1838.

———. *Phrenology Known by Its Fruits.* New York: Howe and Bates, 1836.

Reid, John. *Essays on Hypochondriacal and other Nervous Affections.* Philadelphia: M. Carey & Son, 1817.

Rice, Nathan L. *Modern Spiritualism: What are We to Think of It?* Philadelphia: Presbyterian Board of Publications, n.d.

Robbins, Thomas. *The Design and Tendency of Christianity to Diminish the Miseries and Increase the Happiness of Mankind.* An Address Delivered at the Retreat for the Insane, in Hartford, at the Dedication of that Institution to the Blessing of Almighty God, and to the Purposes for Which It Was Established, April 1, 1824. Hartford: Printed by Goodwin & Co., 1824.

Robinson, Alex. C. *Report of the Lunatic Department of the Baltimore Alms-House; Presented to the Board of Trustees, December, 1840. To Which is Added an Appendix, Containing an Appeal in Behalf of the Insane Poor of Maryland.* Baltimore: Printed by S. Robinson, 1841.

Rose, Henry. *An Inaugural Dissertation on the Effects of the Passions upon the Body.* Philadelphia: Printed by W. W. Woodward, 1794.

Rush, Benjamin. *The Autobiography of Benjamin Rush; His "Travels through Life" together with His Commonplace Book for 1789–1813.* Edited with introduction and notes by George W. Corner. (Memoirs of the American Philosophical Society, Vol. 25.) [Princeton, N.J.]: Published for the American Philosophical Society by Princeton University Press, 1948.

———. *Letters of Benjamin Rush.* Edited by L. H. Butterfield. 2 vols. (Memoirs of the American Philosophical Society, Vol. 30, Pt. 1–2.) [Princeton, N. J.]: Published for the American Philosophical Society by Princeton University Press, 1951.

———. *Medical Inquiries and Observations.* 2d ed., rev. and enl. by the author. 4 vols. Philadelphia: J. Conrad & Co., 1805.

———. *Medical Inquiries and Observations upon the Diseases of the Mind.* With an introduction by Dr. S. Bernard Wortis. (The History of Medicine Series, Issued under the Auspices of the Library of the New York Academy of Medicine, No. 15.) New York: Published under the Auspices of the Library of the New York Academy of Medicine by Hafner Publishing Company, 1962. (Facsimile of the original first edition, published in 1812.)

——. *Medical Inquiries and Observations upon the Diseases of the Mind.* 4th ed. Philadelphia: John Grigg, 1830.

——. *The Selected Writings of Benjamin Rush.* Edited by Dagobert D. Runes. New York: Philosophical Library, c1947.

Sampson, M. B. *Rationale of Crime, and Its Appropriate Treatment; Being a Treatise on Criminal Jurisprudence Considered in Relation to Cerebral Organization.* From the 2nd London ed. with notes and illustrations by E. W. Farnham, Matron of Mount Pleasant State Prison. New York: D. Appleton & Company, 1846.

Sanders, Daniel Clark. *A Discourse, on the Decease of Mrs. Martha Russell, Who Died, at Burlington, January 23d—Interred on the 26th, 1805, after a Mental Derangement during the Seven Preceding Years,—Aged 50—the Consort of David Russell, Esquire.* Bennington: Printed by Haswell & Smead, 1805.

Scattergood, Thomas. *Memoirs of Thomas Scattergood.* . . . Compiled by William Evans and Thomas Evans. London: Charles Gilpin, 1845.

Scott, Sir Walter. *The Bride of Lammermoor.* (The Waverly Novels, Vol. IV.) Abbotsford ed. Philadelphia: J. B. Lippincott & Co., 1856.

Seaman, Valentine. *A Dissertation on the Mineral Waters of Saratoga. Including an Account of the Waters of Ballston,* 2d ed., enl. New-York: Printed and Sold by Collins & Perkins, 1809.

A Second Appeal to the People of Pennsylvania on the Subject of an Asylum for the Insane Poor of the Commonwealth. Philadelphia: Printed for the Insane Poor of the Committee [by] Brown, Becking & Guilbert, 1840.

[Sedgwick, Catharine M.] *Clarence; or, A Tale of Our Times.* 2 vols. Philadelphia: Carey & Lea, 1830.

——. *Life and Letters of Catharine M. Sedgwick.* Edited by Mary E. Dewey. New York: Harper & Brothers, 1871.

Sewall, Samuel E. *Petition, to the Honorable Senate and House of Representatives of the Commonwealth of Massachusetts.* ([Massachusetts. General Court.] House [Doc.], No. 57.) [Boston: n.p., 1862].

Shew, Joel. *The Hydropathic Family Physician; A Ready Prescriber and Hygienic Adviser with Reference to the Nature, Causes, Prevention, and Treatment of Diseases, Accidents, and Casualties of Every Kind.* New York: Fowler and Wells, 1854.

——. *Hydropathy; or, The Water-Cure: Its Principles, Modes of Treatment, &c.* . . . *Compiled Chiefly from the Most Eminent English Authors on the Subject.* New York: Wiley & Putnam, 1844.

——. *Tobacco: Its History, Nature, and Effects on the Body and Mind.* . . . New York: Fowler and Wells, [1849].

Shipman, George E. *The Homoeopathic Family Guide, for the Use of Twenty-Five Principal Remedies in the Treatment of the More Simple Forms of Disease.* 2d ed. Chicago: C. S. Halsey, 1865.

Skinner, Otis Ainsworth. *Letters to Rev. B. Stow, R. H. Neale, and R. W. Cushman, on Modern Revivals.* Boston: Abel Tompkins, 1842.

Smith, Joseph Mather, *A Discourse on the Influence of Disease on the Intellectual and Moral Powers.* Delivered as an Introductory Lecture at the College of Physicians and Surgeons, in the City of New York, October 30th, 1848. New York: Daniel Adee, 1848.

Stone, Elizabeth T. *Exposing the Modern Secret Way of Persecuting Christians in Order to Hush the Voice of Truth. Insane Hospitals Are Inquisition Houses.* . . . Boston: Printed for the Author, 1859.

Stuart, Thomas Middleton. *An Inaugural Essay on Genius and Its Diseases.* New York: Printed by Collins and Co., 1819.

Sweetser, William. *Mental Hygiene; or, An Examination of the Intellect and Passions, Designed to Illustrate Their Influence on Health and the Duration of Life.* New York: J. & H. G. Langley, 1843.

Thomson, Samuel. *The Thomsonian Materia Medica; or, Botanic Family Physician.* . . . 13th ed. Albany: J. Munsell, 1841.

Trotter, Thomas. *A View of the Nervous Temperament; Being a Practical Inquiry into the Increasing Prevalence, Prevention, and Treatment of Those Diseases Commonly Called Nervous, Bilious, Stomach & Liver Complaints; Indigestion; Low Spirits, Gout, &c.* Troy, N. Y.: Wright, Goodenow, & Stockwell, 1808.

Tudor, William, Jun. *A Discourse Delivered before the Humane Society at Their Anniversary, May, 1817.* Published at the Request of the Society. Boston: Printed by John Eliot, 1817.

Tuke, Daniel Hack. *Reform in the Treatment of the Insane. Early History of the Retreat, York; Its Objects and Influence, with a Report of the Celebrations of Its Centenary.* London: J. & A. Churchill, 1892.

Tuke, Samuel. *A Letter on Pauper Lunatic Asylums.* New York: Printed by Samuel Wood & Sons, 1815.

Upham, Thomas C. *Outlines of Imperfect and Disordered Mental Action.* (Family Library, No. 100.) New York: Harper & Brothers, 1840.

Wallis, George. *The Art of Preventing Diseases, and Restoring Health, Founded on Rational Principles and Adapted to Persons of Every Capacity.* New York: Printed by Samuel Campbell, 1794.

Waterston, Robert Cassie. *The Condition of the Insane in Massachusetts.* Boston: James Munroe and Company, 1843.

Welling, Rev. D. S. *Information for the People; or, The Asylums of Ohio, with Miscellaneous Observations on Health, Diet, and Morals and the Causes, Symptoms, and Proper Treatment of Nervous Diseases and Insanity.* Pittsburgh: Printed by Geo. Parkin & Co., 1851.

Wesley, John. *Primitive Physick; or, An Easy and Natural Method of Curing Most Diseases.* 14th ed., corrected and much enl. Philadelphia: Printed by Joseph Crukshank, 1770.

Wharton, Francis. *A Monograph on Mental Unsoundness.* Philadelphia: Kay and Brother, 1855.

——. *A Treatise on Mental Unsoundness, Embracing a General View of Psychological Law.* [3d ed.] 2 vols. Philadelphia: Kay & Brother, 1873.

White, Samuel. *Address on Insanity Delivered before the New York State Medical Society.* February 5th, 1844. Albany: Printed by J. Munsell, 1844.

Whytt, Robert. *Observations on the Nature, Causes, and Cure of Those Disorders Which Have Been Commonly Called Nervous, Hypochondriac, or Hysteric: to Which Are Prefixed Some Remarks on the Sympathy of Nerves.* 2d ed., corrected. Edinburgh: Printed for T. Becket, and P. A. De Hondt, London; and J. Balfour, Edinburgh, 1765.

Willard, Sylvester D. *Report on the Condition of the Insane Poor in the County Poor Houses of New York.* (New York State. [Legislature.] Assembly. [Report], No. 19.) Albany: Chas. Van Benthuysen Printer, 1865.

Winfield, Aaron Burr. *Sermon at the Interment of the Bodies of John G. Van Nest, Mrs. Sarah Van Nest, G. W. Van Nest, Their Son, and Mrs. Phebe Wykoff, Who Were Murdered March Twelfth Inst., by a Colored Man Named William Freeman.* Preached in the R. D. Church, at Sand Beach, Owasco Lake, March Fifteenth. Auburn, N. Y.: Napier Press of J. C. Merrell & Co., 1846.

Wyman, Rufus. *A Discourse on Mental Philosophy as Connected with Mental Disease.*

Delivered before the Massachusetts Medical Society, June 2, 1830. Boston: From the Office of the *Daily Advertiser*, 1830.

Periodicals, Newspapers, etc.

This is a list of titles in which were found relevant items on insanity for the years indicated. Newspapers were consulted only for certain specified items. A list of specific periodical articles which have been cited in the text, plus a few other useful ones, is given in the section following this one.

American Almanac and Repository of Useful Knowledge. 1830–1861.
American Journal of Insanity. 1844–1913.
American Journal of the Medical Sciences. 1829–1860.
American Medical and Philosophical Register. 1810–1814.
American Phrenological Journal. 1838–1861.
American Review. 1845–1852.
Analectic Magazine. 1813–1820.
Atheneum. 1817–1827.
Atkinson's Casket; or, Gems of Literature, Wit, and Sentiment. 1830–1834.
Biblical Repertory and Princeton Review. 1825–1865. (Also called *Biblical Repertory*.)
Boston Medical and Surgical Journal. 1828–1865.
Boston Medical Intelligencer. 1827.
Buchanan's Journal of Man. 1848, 1850, 1853.
Christian Journal and Literary Register. 1817–1830.
Christian Spectator. 1819–1838.
Church Review and Ecclesiastical Register. 1848–1865.
Congressional Globe. 1848–1854.
Connecticut Courant. 1835.
DeBow's Review. 1846–1860.
Eclectic Magazine. 1844–1865.
Friends' Review. 1847–1865.
Harper's New Monthly Magazine. 1850–1865.
Journal of Nervous and Mental Disease. 1876–1902.
Knickerbocker. 1833–1862.
Literary Magazine, and American Register. 1803–1807.
Littell's Living Age. 1844–1865.
Medical Repository. 1797–1824.
Merchants' Magazine. 1839–1865. (Also called *Hunt's Merchants' Magazine*.)
Museum of Foreign Literature, Science, and Art. 1817–1842. (Also called *Museum of Foreign Literature and Science*.)
National Magazine. 1854–55, 1857–58.
National Quarterly Review. 1845–1865.
New England Journal of Medicine and Surgery. 1812–1826.
New-England Magazine. 1831–1835.
New Englander. 1843–1865.
New York Commercial Advertiser. 1818.
[New York] *Evening Post*. 1829, 1846, 1856.
New York Herald. 1845, 1846, 1856.
New-York Medical and Physical Journal. 1822–1830.

New York Times. 1856.
New York Tribune. 1846, 1856.
North American Medical and Surgical Journal. 1826–1831.
North American Review. 1815–1865.
Philadelphia Journal of the Medical and Physical Sciences. 1820–1827.
Philadelphia Medical and Physical Journal. 1805–1808.
[Philadelphia] *Public Ledger.* 1849.
Portland Transcript [Maine]. 1856.
Prison Discipline Society of Boston. *Reports.* 1832–1860.
Southern Quarterly Review. 1850–1857.
United States Magazine and Democratic Review. 1838–1858.
Universalist Union. 1841–1845.
Western Literary Messenger. 1848–1851.
Water-Cure Journal and Herald of Reforms. 1848–1860.

Individual Articles

Allen, John R. "On the Treatment of Insanity," *AJI,* VI (January, 1850), 263–283. (From the *Transylvania Medical Journal.*)
"American Hospitals for the Insane," *North American Review,* LXXIX (July, 1854), 67–90. (By Isaac Ray?)
Annan, S. "Observations on Functional and Organic Diseases," *AJI,* XIII (April, 1857), 305–308.
"Annual Meeting of the Association of Medical Superintendents of American Institutions for the Insane," *AJI,* XX (July, 1863), 60–143.
Beck, Theodric Romeyn. "An Account of Some of the Lunatic Asylums in the United States," *New-York Medical and Physical Journal,* VII (April, May, and June, 1828), 186–206.
[Bell, Luther V.]. "Insanity and Crime," *AJI,* VI (April, 1850), 318–321. (According to the editors of the *AJI,* Bell was the author.)
Benedict, Dr. "Moral Insanity," *Boston Medical and Surgical Journal,* XLIV (May 7, 1851), 285.
"Blackwell's Island Lunatic Asylum," *Harper's New Monthly Magazine,* XXXII (February, 1866), 273–294.
* [Brigham, Amariah]. "Definition of Insanity—Nature of the Disease," *AJI,* I (October, 1844), 97–116.
[———]. "Exemption of the Cherokee Indians and Africans from Insanity," *AJI,* I (January, 1845), 287–288.
[———]. "Insanity and Insane Hospitals," *North American Review,* XLIV (January, 1837), 91–121.
[———]. "Insanity—Illustrated by Histories of Distinguished Men, and by the Writings of Poets and Novelists," *AJI,* I (July, 1844), 9–46.
[———]. "Institutions for the Insane in the United States," *AJI,* V (July, 1848), 53–62.
[———]. "The Medical Treatment of Insanity," *AJI,* III (April, 1847), 353–357.
[———]. "The Moral Treatment of Insanity," *AJI,* IV (July, 1847), 1–15.

* An editorial note in the *AJI* reads: "While on the subject of the Journal, it may be proper to state, that for all the articles without any name or initials attached, Dr. Brigham, the principal Editor, is alone responsible" (*AJI,* I [January, 1845], 288).

[——]. "Number of the Insane and Idiotic, with Brief Notices of the Lunatic Asylums in the United States," *AJI*, I (July, 1844), 78–81.

——. "Religious Services in Lunatic Asylums—Duties of the Chaplain," *AJI*, II (October, 1845), 115–123.

[——]. Review of *Life among Lunatics*. By J. B. Derby, Author of *Scenes in a Mad-House;* etc. AJI, IV (July, 1847), 81–84.

[——]. Review of *Traité complèt de l'hypochondrie*, par J. L. Brachet. *AJI*, I (January, 1845), 278–280.

[——]. "Sleep: Its Importance in Preventing Insanity," *AJI*, I (April, 1845), 319–323.

[——]. "Statistics of Insanity," *AJI*, VI (October, 1849), 141–145.

Brown, G. G. "The Efficacy of Cold in Madness," *Medical Repository*, IV, no. 2 (1801), 209–210.

Brown, Samuel. "An Account of Two Cases of Convulsions, Alternating with Temporary Insanity, Relieved by Violent Pressure over the Stomach," *Medical Repository*, Second hexade, V (August, September, and October, 1807), 145–147.

Bucknill, John Charles. "The Pathology of Insanity," *AJI*, XIV (July, 1857-April, 1858), 29–57, 172–193, 254–289, 348–363; XV (July, 1858), 69–76.

Buttolph, H. A. "Modern Asylums and Their Adaptation to the Treatment of the Insane," *AJI*, III (April, 1847), 364–378.

Chaillé, Stanford. "Insane Asylum of the State of Louisiana, at Jackson," *New Orleans Medical and Surgical Journal*, XV (January, 1858), 103–124.

——. "Report of the Board of Administrators of the Insane Asylum at Jackson, to the Legislature of Louisiana," *New Orleans Medical and Surgical Journal*, XVI (May, 1859), 374–377.

Chipley, W. S. ["Intemperance and Insanity"], in "In Court of Appeals, State of Kentucky, Smith vs. Commonwealth, with Remarks by W. S. Chipley, M.D. . . . ," *AJI*, XXIII (July, 1866), 6–45.

Cook, George. "Mental Hygiene," *AJI*, XV (January-April, 1859), 272–282, 353–365.

D. Review of *Mental Hygiene; or, An Examination of the Intellect and Passions . . .* by William Sweetser, M.D., *Southern Quarterly Review*, XIX, new series, III (January, 1851), 51–73.

"Death of Dr. Brigham," *Western Literary Messenger*, XIII (October, 1849), 62–63. (From the *Utica Gazette*.)

Dickson, Dr. "Dr. Dickson (of South Carolina) on Monomania," *AJI*, IX (January, 1853), 292. (Quotation from "Dr. Dickson's Essays on Life, Sleep and Pain.")

"Dr. Burrows and Others on Insanity," *Museum of Foreign Literature and Science*, XIV (April, 1829), 359–367.

"Dr. Dunglison's Statistics of Insanity in the United States," *AJI*, XVII (July, 1860), 111.

Earle, Pliny, "Bloodletting in Mental Disorders," *AJI*, X (April, 1854), 287–405.

——. "The Curability of Insanity," *AJI*, XLII (October, 1885), 179–209.

——. "Institutions for the Insane in Prussia, Austria and Germany," *AJI*, IX (October, 1852-April, 1853), 106–150, 224–277, 305–364; X (July, 1853), 1–62.

——. "On the Causes of Insanity, as Exhibited by the Records of the Bloomingdale Asylum from June 16th, 1821, to December 31st, 1844," *AJI*, IV (January, 1848), 185–211.

——. "On the Curability of Insanity," *American Journal of the Medical Sciences*, new series, V (April, 1843), 344–363.

——. "The Poetry of Insanity," *AJI*, I (January, 1845), 193–224.

——. "Psychologic Medicine; Its Importance as Part of the Medical Curriculum," *AJI*, XXIV (January, 1868), 257–280.

——. "Researches in Reference to the Causes, Duration, Termination, and Moral Treatment of Insanity," *American Journal of the Medical Sciences*, XXII (August, 1838), 339–356.

Eddy, Thomas. "Proposals for Improving the Care of the Insane, 1815," in Edith Abbott (ed.), *Some American Pioneers in Social Welfare; Selected Documents with Editorial Notes* ("The University of Chicago Social Science Series"; Chicago: University of Chicago Press, 1937), 59–65.

[Edwards, I.] "Insanity—How Far a Legal Defence," *American Review*, VIII (September, 1848), 269–275.

Evans, Charles. "Insanity with Complete Taciturnity for Nearly Three Years—Application of Galvanic Plates—Restoration of Speech," *American Journal of the Medical Sciences*, XXIII (November, 1838), 97–98.

——, and Porter, R. R. "Reports of Cases of Insanity, Treated at the Friends' Asylum, near Frankford," *American Journal of the Medical Sciences*, XX (May, 1837), 61–77.

——, and Porter, R. R. "Reports of Cases of Insanity, Treated at the Friends' Asylum, near Frankford, with Remarks," *American Journal of the Medical Sciences*, XIX (November, 1836), 99–108.

"Extracts from a Lawyer's Port-Folio," *Atheneum*, IV (October 15, 1818), 68–74. (From the *European Magazine.*)

Fowler, Orson S. "Hereditary Descent . . . ," *American Phrenological Journal*, V (November, 1843), 481–538.

Galt, John M. "Fragments on Insanity," *AJI*, I (October, 1844), 122–133.

"German and French Criminal Procedure," *North American Review*, XCIV (January, 1862), 75–108.

[Gray, John P.]. "Bertrand on Suicide," *AJI*, XIV (October, 1857), 207–214. (Unsigned review of *Traité du suicide considéré dans ses rapports avec la philosophie, la théologie, la médecine, et la jurisprudence*, par Louis Bertrand. Paris, 1857.)

——. "The Dependence of Insanity on Physical Disease," *AJI*, XXVII (April, 1871), 377–408.

——. "Homicide in Insanity," *AJI*, XIV (October, 1857), 119–145.

——. "Insanity: Its Frequency: and Some of Its Preventable Causes," *AJI*, XLII (July, 1885), 1–45.

[——]. "Moral Insanity," *AJI*, XIV (April, 1858), 311–322.

H., T. "Is Insanity a Disease of the Mind, or of the Body?" *AJI*, XXIX (July, 1872), 71–91.

Hayden, C. B. "On the Distribution of Insanity," *Southern Literary Messenger*, X (March, 1844), 178–181.

[Howe, Samuel Gridley]. "Insanity in Massachusetts," *North American Review*, LVI (January, 1843), 171–191.

——. "Idiots," *AJI*, XIV (April, 1858), 402–403. (From Howe's *Report of the Mass. School for Idiots and Feeble-Minded Youth.*)

"Hypochondriacs.—Nerves.—Blue Devils," *Atheneum*, IX (September 1–15, 1821), 443–445, 479–482.

"In Court of Appeals, State of Kentucky, Smith vs. Commonwealth, with Remarks by W. S. Chipley, M.D. . . ." *AJI*, XXIII (July, 1866), 1–45.

"Influence of Religion upon the Health," *Christian Spectator*, 3d series, VIII (March, 1836), 51–80. (Review of *Observations on the Influence of Religion upon the Health and Physical Welfare of Mankind*, by Amariah Brigham.)

"The Increase of Crimes against Life," *New Englander*, II (July, 1844), 346–350.

"Influence of Nervous Disorders upon Religious Experience," *Christian Spectator*, new series, I (April, 1827), 177–205.

"The Insane," *Littell's Living Age*, VIII (March 7, 1846), 462.

"The Insane and Their Treatment Past and Present," *National Quarterly Review,* VII (September, 1863), 207–232.

"Insanity in Kentucky," *Boston Medical and Surgical Journal,* XXIV (April 21, 1841), 165–171.

Jarvis, Edward. "Causes of Mental Disease," *North American Review,* LXXXIX (October, 1859), 316–339.

——. "Insanity among the Colored Population of the Free States," *AJI,* VIII (January, 1852), 268–282.

——. "Insanity among the Coloured Population of the Free States," *American Journal of the Medical Sciences,* new series, VII (January, 1844), 71–83.

——. "Insanity among the Coloured Population of the Free States," *Friends' Review,* V (January 31-February 7, 1852), 313–315, 329–331. (From the *AJI.*)

——. "On the Proper Functions of Private Institutions or Homes for the Insane," *AJI,* XVII (July, 1860), 19–31.

——. "On the Supposed Increase of Insanity," *AJI,* VIII (April, 1852), 333–364.

——. "Statistics of Insanity in the United States," *Boston Medical and Surgical Journal,* XXVII (September 21, 1842), 116–121.

——. "Statistics of Insanity in the United States," *Boston Medical and Surgical Journal,* XXVII (November 30, 1842), 281–282.

——, Thornton, J. Wingate, and Brigham, Wm. "The Sixth Census of the United States—a Memorial to the Honorable the Senate and House of Representatives, in Congress Assembled," *Merchants' Magazine,* XII (February, 1845), 125–139.

"The Jurisprudence of Insanity," *North American Review,* LX (January, 1845), 1–37.

"Kentucky Lunatic Asylum," *Boston Medical and Surgical Journal,* XXVI (March 9, 1842), 80–81.

Kirkbride, Thomas S. Review of *Observations on the Admission of Medical Pupils to the Wards of Bethlem Hospital, for the Purpose of Studying Mental Diseases,* by John Webster, M.D., 3d ed., *American Journal of the Medical Sciences,* new series, V (April, 1843), 416–418. (Signed: T.S.K.)

"Lunatic Asylum in Lancashire," *Atheneum,* III (June 15, 1818), 216–219.

Macdonald, James. "Puerperal Insanity," *AJI,* IV (October, 1847), 113–163.

Mayo, Thomas. "On the Moral Phenomena of Insanity and Eccentricity," *Living Age,* LXX (July-September, 1861), 216–221.

"Mental and Physical Characteristics of Pauperism," *AJI,* XIII (April, 1857), 309–320.

"Mental Derangement," *Boston Medical Intelligencer,* V (October 16, 1827), 351–357. (Review of *Des causes morales et physiques des maladies mentales, et des quelques autres affections nerveuses, &c.,* par F. Voisin . . . and *Observations on the Causes, Symptoms, and Treatment of Derangement of the Mind, Founded on an Extensive Moral and Physical Practice in the Treatment of Lunatics,* by Paul Slade Knight. . . . Article is reprinted from *"Med. Chir. Rev."*)

"Mental Exercise as a Cure of Insanity," *Water-Cure Journal and Herald of Reforms,* VII (March, 1849), 72–74. (From *Moral and Intellectual Science.*)

"Modern Spiritualism," *Church Review and Ecclesiastical Register,* VIII (July, 1855), 169–188.

"Moral Insanity," *AJI,* XIV (April, 1858), 311–322.

"Moral Insanity," *AJI,* XXII (July, 1865), 133–137. (Reprint of an article in the *Saturday Review.*)

"Moral Insanity," *Biblical Repertory and Princeton Review,* XXIX (July, 1857), 345–375.

Morris, O.W. "An Inquiry Whether Deaf Mutes Are More Subject to Insanity than the Blind," *AJI,* VIII (July, 1851), 17–35.

Obituary of Hon. Silas Wright, *AJI*, IV (October, 1857), 183–184.

Ordronaux, John. "Moral Insanity," *AJI*, XXIX (January, 1873), 313–340.

[Packard, Frederick A.] "The Relations of Religion to What Are Called Diseases of the Mind," *Biblical Repertory and Princeton Review*, XXII (January, 1850), 1–41.

Panum, Peter Ludwig. "Iagttagelser, anstillede under Maeslinger-Epidemien paa Faeroerne i Aaret 1846 (Observations Made during the Epidemic of Measles on the Faroe Islands in Year 1846)," translated by Mrs. A. S. Hatcher, *Medical Classics*, III (May, 1939) 829–886.

Parigot, J. "Dr. J. Parigot on Moral Insanity in Relation to Criminal Acts," *AJI*, XVIII (January, 1862), 305–312.

Porter, R. R. "Reports of Cases of Insanity, Treated at Friends' Asylum, near Frankford," *American Journal of the Medical Sciences*, XX (August, 1837), 350–369.

"Proceedings of the Association of Medical Superintendents, [23d]," *AJI*, XXVI (October, 1869), 129–203.

"Proceedings of the Eighth Annual Meeting of the Association of Medical Superintendents of American Institutions for the Insane," *AJI*, X (July, 1853), 70–89.

"Proceedings of the Tenth Annual Meeting of the Association of Medical Superintendents of American Institutions for the Insane," *AJI*, XII (July, 1855), 39–101.

"Proceedings of the Twelfth Annual Meeting of the Association of Medical Superintendents of American Institutions for the Insane," *AJI*, XIV (July, 1857), 69–109.

"Proceedings of the Fourteenth Annual Meeting of the Association of Medical Superintendents of American Institutions for the Insane," *AJI*, XVI (July, 1859), 42–96.

"Proceedings of the Fifteenth Annual Meeting of the Association of Medical Superintendents of American Institutions for the Insane," *AJI*, XVII (July, 1860), 32–73.

R., D. M. "Chronic Disease of the Brain," *American Phrenological Journal and Miscellany*, II (July 1, 1840), 456–458. ("From Vol. II, No. 24, of the *Boston Medical and Surgical Journal*.")

Ranney, M. H. "On Insane Foreigners," *AJI*, VII (July, 1850), 53–63.

Ray, Isaac. "An Examination of the Objections to the Doctrine of Moral Insanity," *AJI*, XVIII (October, 1861), 112–138.

——. "Hereditary Insanity," *North American Review*, CIX (July, 1869), 1–29.

——. "Hints to the Medical Witness in Questions of Insanity," *AJI*, VIII (July, 1851), 53–67.

——. "Ideal Characters of the Officers of a Hospital for the Insane," *AJI*, XXX (July, 1873), 64–83.

——. "Moral Aspects of Phrenology," in Perry Miller (ed.), *The Transcendentalists, an Anthology* (Cambridge, Mass.: Harvard University Press, 1950), pp. 75–78.

——. "Observations on the Principal Hospitals for the Insane, in Great Britain, France and Germany," *AJI*, II (April, 1846), 289–390.

——. "The Popular Feeling towards Hospitals for the Insane," *AJI*, IX (July, 1851), 36–65.

——. "The Statistics of Insane Hospitals," *AJI*, VI (July, 1849), 23–52.

[——]. "Statistics of Insanity in Massachusetts," *North American Review*, LXXXII (January, 1856), 78–100.

"Reflections on the Census of 1840," *Southern Literary Messenger*, IX (June, 1843), 340–352.

"Religious Melancholy," *Biblical Repertory and Princeton Review*, XVI (July, 1844), 352–379.

"Religious Insanity," *AJI*, XXXIII (July, 1876), 126–131.

"Retreat for the Insane," *Christian Spectator*, III (June, 1821), 316–318.

"Retreat for the Insane," *Christian Spectator*, VI (April, 1824), 219.

Review of *Address Delivered before the Medical Society of the State of Pennsylvania at Its*

Annual Session, June, 1869, by John Curwen, M.D., President, *AJI,* XX (January, 1870), 369–372.

Review of *Ceremonies on Laying the Corner-Stone of the New York State Inebriate Asylum, at Binghamton, September 24, 1858, North American Review,* XCIV (April, 1862), 387–407.

"A Review of *The Doctrine of Diseases,* Taught at Present by Benjamin Rush, M.D., Professor of the Institutes and Practice of Medicine, &c., in the University of Pennsylvania," *American Medical and Philosophical Register,* I (July, 1810), 49–60; (October, 1810), 160–168.

Review of *Elements of Medical Jurisprudence,* by R. T. Beck, M.D., . . . Second edition, *Museum of Foreign Literature and Science,* VI (June, 1825), 547–549.

Review of *Essays on Hypochondriacal and other Nervous Afflictions,* by John Reid, M.D., *Analectic Magazine,* X (July, 1817), 61–73.

Review of *An Inaugural Dissertation on Insanity* . . . by Theodric Romeyn Beck, *American Medical and Philosophical Register,* II (January, 1812), 349–355.

Review of *Man, Moral and Physical; or, The Influence of Health and Disease on Religious Experience,* by the Rev. Joseph H. Jones, D.D., *Biblical Repertory and Princeton Review,* XXXII (April, 1860), 308–335.

Review of *Medical Inquiries and Observations upon the Diseases of the Mind,* by Benjamin Rush, *Medical Repository,* new series, I, no. 2 (1813), 145–156.

Review of *Mental Cultivation and Excitement upon Health,* by Amariah Brigham, *American Review,* I (March, 1845), 325–326.

Review of *Mental Hygiene; or, An Examination of the Intellect and Passions* . . . by William Sweetser, M.D., *Knickerbocker,* XXIII (June, 1844), 581.

Review of *Mental Hygiene; or, An Examination of the Intellect and Passions* . . . by William Sweetser, M.D., *Southern Quarterly Review,* XIX (January, 1851), 51–73.

Review of *Phrenology Known by Its Fruits* . . . by David Meredith Reese, M.D., *Knickerbocker,* VIII (November, 1836), 615–617.

Review of *The Treatment of Insanity,* by John Galt, M.D., *American Review,* V (May, 1847), 540–541.

Rogers, William C. "The Hartford Retreat for the Insane," *American Phrenological Journal,* XVIII (July, 1853), 43–44.

Sizer, Nelson. "Death of Dr. Brigham," *Water-Cure Journal and Herald of Reforms,* VIII (November, 1849), 154. (From *Phrenological Journal.*)

Spear, J. A. "Insanity and Delirium Tremens," *Water-Cure Journal,* XI (May, 1851), 118–119.

"Startling Facts from the Census (from the *New-York Observer*)," *AJI,* VIII (October, 1851), 153–155.

Stokes, William H. "On a Court of Medical Experts in Cases of Insanity," *AJI,* X (October, 1853), 112–122.

"The Study of Mind," *AJI,* XVII (January, 1861), 233–249.

Theobald, Samuel. "Some Account of the Lunatic Asylum of Kentucky, with Remarks, &c.," *Transylvania Journal of Medicine,* II (November, 1829), 500–511; III (February, 1830), 79–94.

Trall, R. T. "Physiological Development," *Water-Cure Journal,* XV (January, 1853), 3–4.

Utley, Vine. "An Historical Essay on Epileptic Convulsions, Exemplified by a Case, Successfully Treated by Dr. Vine Utley, of New-London, Connecticut," *Medical Repository,* new series, I, no. 4 (1813), 344–350.

Vaughan, John. "Remarkable Cases of Madness; Communicated by Dr. John Vaughan, of

Wilmington (State of Delaware), to Dr. Mitchill," *Medical Repository*, V, no. 4 (1802), 408–412.

"Vermont Asylum for the Insane," *Water-Cure Journal and Herald of Reforms*, VII (January, 1849), 14.

"The Vital Statistics of Negroes in the United States," *DeBow's Review*, XXI (October, 1856), 405–410.

W. "Insane Hospitals in the United States, in Operation in May, 1838," *Boston Medical and Surgical Journal*, XVIII (June 22, 1838), 309–313.

W. "Insanity," *Boston Medical and Surgical Journal*, XII (June 3, 1835), 264–266.

Wilbur, H. B. "Materialism in Its Relations to the Causes, Conditions and Treatment of Insanity," *Journal of Psychological Medicine*, VI (January, 1872), 29–61.

Woodward, Samuel B. "Moral Insanity," *Boston Medical and Surgical Journal*, XVIII (March 28, 1838), 124–126.

———. "Moral Insanity," *Boston Medical and Surgical Journal*, XXX (April 17, 1844), 228.

Workman, Joseph. "Case of Moral Mania?" *AJI*, XIX (April, 1863), 406–416.

———. "Insanity of the Religious-Emotional Type, and Its Occasional Physical Relations," *AJI*, XXVI (July, 1869), 33–48.

———. "Moral Insanity—What Is It?" *AJI*, XXXIX (January, 1883), 334–348.

Worthington, J. H. "On a Form of Insanity for Which the Name of Congestive Mania Has Been Proposed," *AJI*, XVII (October, 1860), 113–126.

———. "On the Construction of Baths, and the Utility of Warm and Cold Bathing in the Treatment of Insanity," *AJI*, VII (January, 1851), 201–213.

Miscellaneous

U. S. Dept. of State. *Errors in the Sixth Census. Letter from the Secretary of State, Relative to Alleged Errors of the Sixth Census.* February 13, 1845. Read, and Referred to the Select Committee on That Subject. 28th Cong., 2d Sess., Executive Documents, III, Doc. No. 116 (House). Serial No. 465.

SECONDARY SOURCES

Books

Aaron, Richard I. *John Locke.* 2d ed. Oxford: At the Clarendon Press, 1955.

Ackerknect, Erwin H. *A Short History of Medicine.* New York: Ronald Press Company, c1955.

———. *A Short History of Psychiatry.* Translated from the German by Sulammith Wolff New York: Hafner Publishing Company, 1959.

Adams, Grace, and Hutter, Edward. *The Mad Forties.* New York: Harper & Brothers, c1942.

Altschule, Mark D., with the Collaboration of Evelyn Russ. *Roots of Modern Psychiatry: Essays in the History of Psychiatry.* New York: Grune & Stratton, 1957.

American Handbook of Psychiatry. Silvano Arieti, ed. 2 vols. New York: Basic Books, Inc., 1959.

American Journal of Psychiatry, 1844–1944. Centennial Anniversary Issue. [n.p.: 1944].

Brett, G. S. *History of Psychology.* Edited and abridged by R. S. Peters. London: George Allen & Unwin, Ltd.; New York: Macmillan Company, 1953.

Birkhead, Edith. *The Tale of Terror, a Study of the Gothic Romance.* London: Constable & Company, Ltd., 1921.

Blau, Joseph L. *Men and Movements in American Philosophy.* (Prentice-Hall Philosophy Series.) New York: Prentice Hall, Inc., c1952.

Boorstin, Daniel J. *The Lost World of Thomas Jefferson.* New York: Henry Holt and Company, c1948.

Boring, Edwin G. *A History of Experimental Psychology.* 2d ed. New York: Appleton-Century-Crofts, Inc., c1950.

Bromberg, Walter. *The Mind of Man; the Story of Man's Conquest of Mental Illness.* New York: Harper & Brothers, 1937.

Brooks, Gladys. *Three Wise Virgins.* New York: E. P. Dutton & Co., Inc., 1957.

Bryson, Gladys. *Man and Society: The Scottish Inquiry of the Eighteenth Century.* Princeton, N. J.: Princeton University Press, 1945.

Canning, Albert S. G. *Sir Walter Scott Studied in Eight Novels.* London: T. Fisher Unwin, 1910.

Centennial Papers, Saint Elizabeths Hospital, 1855–1955. Washington, D.C.: Centennial Commission, Saint Elizabeths Hospital, c1956.

Conrad, Earl. *Mr. Seward for the Defense.* New York: Rinehart & Company, c1956.

Cross, Whitney R. *The Burned-Over District; the Social and Intellectual History of Enthusiastic Religion in Western New York, 1800–1850.* Ithaca, N. Y.: Cornell University Press, 1950.

Curti, Merle. *The Social Ideas of American Educators;* with New Chapter on the Last Twenty-Five Years. Vol. X of *Report of the American Historical Association Commission on the Social Studies.* Paterson, N. J.: Littlefield, Adams & Co., 1959.

Dalziel, Margaret. *Popular Fiction 100 Years Ago; an Unexplored Tract of Literary History.* Philadelphia: Dufour Editions, 1958.

Davies, John D. *Phrenology: Fad and Science; a 19th-Century American Crusade.* (Yale Historical Publications. Miscellany 62.) New Haven: Yale University Press, 1955.

Davis, David Brion. *Homicide in American Fiction, 1798–1860; a Study in Social Values.* Ithaca, N. Y.: Cornell University Press, 1957.

Deutsch, Albert. *The Mentally Ill in America; a History of Their Care and Treatment from Colonial Times.* 2d ed., rev. and enl. New York: Columbia University Press, c1949.

Diller, Theodore. *Franklin's Contribution to Medicine; Being a Collection of Letters Written by Benjamin Franklin Bearing on the Science and Art of Medicine and Exhibiting His Social and Professional Intercourse with Various Physicians of Europe and America.* Brooklyn: A. T. Huntington, 1912.

Dimond, Sydney G. *The Psychology of the Methodist Revival; an Empirical & Descriptive Study.* London: Oxford University Press, 1926.

Draper, J. *Insanity in Vermont, 1835 to 1885.* Montpelier, Vt.: Argus and Patriot Book and Job Printing House, 1886. (From the *Transactions* of the State Medical Society, 1885.)

Eaton, Leonard K. *New England Hospitals, 1790–1833.* Ann Arbor: The University of Michigan Press, c1957.

Fay, Jay Wharton. *American Psychology before William James.* (Rutgers University Studies in Psychology, No. 1.) New Brunswick, N. J.: Rutgers University Press, 1939.

Friends' Asylum for the Insane, Philadelphia, 1813–1913; a Descriptive Account from Its Foundation, List of Managers and Officers from the Beginning, Facts and Events in Its History, with Appendix. Philadelphia: Press of the John C. Winston Company, n.d.

Gibson, James. *Locke's Theory of Knowledge and Its Historical Relations.* Cambridge: At the University Press, 1960.

Gillispie, Charles Coulston. *Genesis and Geology; a Study in the Relations of Scientific Thought, Natural Theology, and Social Opinion in Great Britain, 1790–1850.* New York: Harper & Brothers, 1959, c1951.

Goldhamer, Herbert, and Marshall, Andrew W. *Psychosis and Civilization: Two Studies in the Frequency of Mental Disease.* Glencoe, Ill.: Free Press, c1953.

Goodman, Nathan G. *Benjamin Rush, Physician and Citizen, 1746–1813.* Philadelphia: University of Pennsylvania Press, 1934.

Godwin, George. *The Great Revivalists.* Boston: Beacon Press, 1950.

Grave, S. A. *The Scottish Philosophy of Common Sense.* Oxford: At the Clarendon Press, 1960.

Greenblatt, Milton, York, Richard H., and Brown, Esther Lucille. *From Custodial to Therapeutic Patient Care in Mental Hospitals.* New York: Russell Sage Foundation, 1955.

Greene, John C. *The Death of Adam; Evolution and Its Impact on Western Thought.* Ames, Iowa: Iowa State University Press, c1959.

Hill, A. Wesley. *John Wesley among the Physicians; a Study of Eighteenth-Century Medicine.* London: The Epworth Press, 1958.

Hindle, Brooke. *The Pursuit of Science in Revolutionary America, 1735–1789.* Chapel Hill: Published for the Institute of Early American History and Culture, Williamsburg, Virginia, by the University of North Carolina Press, c1956.

Hollingshead, August B., and Redlich, Frederick C. *Social Class and Mental Illness: A Community Study.* New York: John Wiley and Sons, Inc., c1958.

Humphrey, Heman. *The Life and Labors of the Rev. T. H. Gallaudet, LL.D.* New York: Robert Carter & Brothers, 1857.

Hurd, Henry M. (ed.). *The Institutional Care of the Insane in the United States and Canada,* by Henry M. Hurd, *et al.* 4 vols. Baltimore: The Johns Hopkins Press, 1916.

Joint Commission on Mental Illness and Health. *Action for Mental Health. Final Report of the Joint Commission on Mental Illness and Health.* New York: Basic Books, Inc., 1961.

Jones, Kathleen. *Lunacy, Law, and Conscience, 1744–1845; the Social History of the Care of the Insane.* London: Routledge & Kegan Paul Limited, 1955.

King, Lester S. *The Medical World of the Eighteenth Century.* Chicago: The University of Chicago Press, 1958.

Kraepelin, Emil. *One Hundred Years of Psychiatry.* Translated by Wade Baskin from the German. New York: The Citadel Press, 1962.

Lawrence, Charles. *History of the Philadelphia Almshouses and Hospitals from the Beginning of the Eighteenth to the Ending of the Nineteenth Centuries. . . .* Philadelphia: The Author, 1905.

Long, Esmond Ray. *A History of American Pathology.* Springfield, Ill.: Charles C. Thomas, c1962.

——. *A History of Pathology.* Baltimore: Williams & Wilkins Company, 1928.

Lovejoy, Arthur O. *Reflections on Human Nature.* Baltimore: The Johns Hopkins Press, c1961.

——. *The Revolt against Dualism; an Inquiry Concerning the Existence of Ideas.* (The Paul Carus Lectures, Series 2.) Published by the Foundation Established in Memory of Paul Carus. La Salle, Ill.: The Open Court Publishing Company, 1960.

McLoughlin, William G., Jr. *Modern Revivalism; Charles Grandison Finney to Billy Graham.* New York: Ronald Press Company, c1959.

McNeill, John T. *A History of the Cure of Souls.* New York: Harper & Brothers, c1951.

Mann, Mary Peabody. *Life of Horace Mann.* Centennial ed. in facsimile. Washington, D. C.: National Education Association of the United States, 1937.

Marshall, Helen E. *Dorothea Dix, Forgotten Samaritan.* Chapel Hill: University of North Carolina Press, 1937.

Miller, Perry. *The New England Mind: The Seventeenth Century.* Cambridge, Mass.: Harvard University Press, 1954.

———. *The New England Mind: From Colony to Province.* Cambridge, Mass.: Harvard University Press, 1953.

——— (ed.). *The Transcendentalists, an Anthology.* Cambridge, Mass.: Harvard University Press, 1950.

Morris, Charles W. *Six Theories of Mind.* Chicago: University of Chicago Press, c1932.

Morton, Thomas G., Assisted by Frank Woodbury. *The History of the Pennsylvania Hospital, 1751–1895.* Rev. ed. Philadelphia: Times Printing House, 1897.

Norwood, William Frederick. *Medical Education in the United States before the Civil War.* Philadelphia: University of Pennsylvania Press, 1944.

Nunnally, Jum C., Jr. *Popular Conceptions of Mental Health, Their Development and Change.* New York: Holt, Rinehart and Winston, c1961.

Oberndorf, Clarence P. *A History of Psychoanalysis in America.* New York: Grune & Stratton, 1953.

One Hundred Years of American Psychiatry. New York: Published for the American Psychiatric Association by the Columbia University Press, c1944.

Packard, Francis R. *History of Medicine in the United States.* 2 vols. New York: Paul B. Hoeber, Inc., 1931.

Pastore, Nicholas. *The Nature-Nurture Controversy.* With a foreword by Goodwin Watson. New York: King's Crown Press, Columbia University, 1949.

Pepper, William. *The Medical Side of Benjamin Franklin.* Philadelphia: William J. Campbell, 1911.

Persons, Stow. *American Minds; a History of Ideas.* New York: Henry Holt and Company, c1958.

Pickard, Madge E., and Buley, R. Carlyle. *The Midwest Pioneer; His Ills, Cures & Doctors.* New York: Henry Schuman, 1946.

Pillsbury, W. B. *The History of Psychology.* New York: W. W. Norton & Company, Inc., c1929.

Riley, I. Woodbridge. *American Philosophy, the Early Schools.* New York: Dodd, Mead & Company, 1907.

Russell, William Logie. *The New York Hospital; a History of the Psychiatric Service, 1771–1936.* New York: Columbia University Press, 1945.

Ryle, Gilbert. *The Concept of Mind.* New York: Barnes and Noble, Inc., [1959], c1949.

Sanborn, F. B. *Dr. S. G. Howe, the Philanthropist.* New York: Funk & Wagnalls, 1891.

Schneider, Herbert W. *A History of American Philosophy.* (Columbia Studies in American Culture, No. 18.) New York: Columbia University Press, c1946.

Schwartz, Harold. *Samuel Gridley Howe, Social Reformer, 1801–1876.* (Harvard Historical Studies, Vol. LXVII.) Cambridge: Harvard University Press, 1956.

Shafer, Henry Burnell. *The American Medical Profession, 1783 to 1850.* New York: Columbia University Press, 1936.

Shryock, Richard H. *American Medical Research, Past and Present.* (The New York Academy of Medicine Committee on Medicine and the Changing Order. *Monograph Studies.*) New York: The Commonwealth Fund, 1947.

———. *The Development of Modern Medicine; an Interpretation of the Social and Scientific Factors Involved.* Philadelphia: University of Pennsylvania Press, 1936.

———. *Medicine and Society in America, 1660–1820.* (Anson G. Phelps Lectureships on Early American History.) [New York]: New York University Press, 1960.

Smith, Hilrie Shelton. *Changing Conceptions of Original Sin; a Study in American Theology since 1750.* New York: Scribner's Sons, 1955.

Smith, Timothy L. *Revivalism and Social Reform in Mid-Nineteenth-Century America.* New York: Abingdon Press, c1957.

Smith, Wilson. *Professors & Public Ethics; Studies of Northern Moral Philosophers before the Civil War.* Ithaca, N. Y.: Published for the American Historical Association [by] Cornell University Press, c1956.

Spiller, Robert E., *et al. Literary History of the United States.* 3 vols. New York: The Macmillan Company, 1948.

Stanton, William. *The Leopard's Spots; Scientific Attitudes toward Race in America, 1815–59.* Chicago: University of Chicago Press, 1960.

Struik, Dirk J. *Yankee Science in the Making.* Boston: Little, Brown and Company, 1948.

Tiffany, Francis. *Life of Dorothea Lynde Dix.* Boston: Houghton, Mifflin and Company, 1892.

Tolles, Frederick B. *Meeting House and Counting House; the Quaker Merchants of Colonial Philadelphia, 1682–1763.* Chapel Hill: Published for the Institute of Early American History and Culture at Williamsburg, Virginia, by the University of North Carolina Press, 1948.

Tyler, Alice Felt. *Freedom's Ferment; Phases of American Social History to 1860.* Minneapolis: University of Minnesota Press, 1944.

Warfel, Harry R. *Charles Brockden Brown, American Gothic Novelist.* Gainesville: University of Florida Press, 1949.

Whyte, Lancelot Law. *The Unconscious before Freud.* New York: Basic Books, Inc., c1960.

Wiley, Lulu Rumsey. *The Sources and Influence of the Novels of Charles Brockden Brown.* New York: Vantage Press, Inc., c1950.

Wood, Robert Williams. *Memorial of Edward Jarvis, M. D.* Boston: T. R. Marvin & Son, Printers, 1885. (For the American Statistical Association.)

Wyman, Morrill, Jr. *A Brief Record of the Lives and Writings of Dr. Rufus Wyman (1778–1842) and His Son, Dr. Morrill Wyman (1812–1903).* Cambridge: Privately Printed, 1913.

Zilboorg, Gregory, in Collaboration with George W. Henry. *A History of Medical Psychology.* New York: W. W. Norton & Company, Inc., c1941.

Articles

Bockoven, J. Sanbourne. "Moral Treatment in American Psychiatry," *Journal of Nervous and Mental Disease,* CXXIV (August-September, 1956), 167–194, 292–321.

Brill, A. A. "An American Precursor of Freud," *Bulletin of the New York Academy of Medicine,* 2d series, XVI (October, 1940), 631–641.

Carlson, Eric T. "Amariah Brigham: I. Life and Works," *American Journal of Psychiatry,* CXII (April, 1956), 831–836.

———. "Amariah Brigham: II. Psychiatric Thought and Practice," *American Journal of Psychiatry,* CXIII (April, 1957), 911–916.

———. "The Influence of Phrenology on Early American Psychiatric Thought," *American Journal of Psychiatry,* CXV (December, 1958), 535–538.

———, and Chale, May F. "Dr. Rufus Wyman of the McLean Asylum," *American Journal of Psychiatry,* CXVI (May, 1960), 1034–1037.

———, and Dain, Norman. "The Meaning of Moral Insanity." *Bulletin of the History of Medicine,* XXXVI (March-April, 1962), 130–140.

———, and Dain, Norman. "The Psychotherapy That Was Moral Treatment," *American Journal of Psychiatry,* CXVII (December, 1960), 519–524.

Curti, Merle. "Human Nature in American Thought: Retreat from Reason in the Age of Science," *Political Science Quarterly*, LXVIII (December, 1953), 492–510.

——. "Human Nature in American Thought; The Age of Reason and Morality, 1750–1860," *Political Science Quarterly*, LXVIII (September, 1953), 354–375.

Dain, Norman, and Carlson, Eric T. "Milieu Therapy in the Nineteenth Century; Patient Care at the Friends' Asylum, Frankford, Pennsylvania, 1817–1861," *Journal of Nervous and Mental Disease*, CXXXI (October, 1960), 277–290.

——, and Carlson, Eric T. "Social Class and Psychological Medicine in the United States, 1789–1824," *Bulletin of the History of Medicine*, XXXIII (September-October, 1959), 454–465.

Deutsch, Albert. "The First U. S. Census of the Insane (1840), and Its Use as Pro-Slavery Propaganda," *Bulletin of the History of Medicine*, XV (May, 1944), 469–482.

Eaton, Leonard K. "Eli Todd and the Hartford Retreat," *New England Quarterly*, XXVI (December, 1953), 435–453.

Ebert, Myrl. "The Rise and Development of the American Medical Periodical, 1797–1850," *Bulletin of the Medical Library Association*, XL (July, 1952), 243–276.

Gibson, James E. "Benjamin Rush's Apprenticed Students," *Transactions and Studies of the College of Physicians of Philadelphia*, 4th series, XIV (December, 1946), 127–132.

Grange, Kathleen M. "Pinel and Eighteenth-Century Psychiatry," *Bulletin of the History of Medicine*, XXXV (September-October, 1961), 442–453.

Greeley, Hugh P. "Early Wisconsin Medical History," *Wisconsin Medical Journal*, XX (April, 1922), 558–569.

Grob, Gerald N. "Samuel B. Woodward and the Practice of Psychiatry in Early Nineteenth-Century America," *Bulletin of the History of Medicine*, XXXVI (September-October, 1962), 420–443.

Hurd, Henry M. "The Religious Delusions of the Insane," *AJI*, XLIV (April, 1888), 471–487.

Lloyd, James Hendrie. "Benjamin Rush and His Critics," *Annals of Medical History*, new series, II (September, 1930), 470–475.

Meyer, Adolf. "Revaluation of Benjamin Rush," *American Journal of Psychiatry*, CI (January, 1945), 433–442.

Michael, Stanley T. "Social Attitudes, Socio-Economic Status and Psychiatric Symptoms," *Acta Psychiatrica et Neurologica Scandinavica*, XXXV, fasc. 4 (1960), 509–516.

Mills, Charles K. "Benjamin Rush and American Psychiatry," *Medico-Legal Journal*, IV (1886), 238–273.

Mora, George. "Vincenzo Chiarugi (1759–1820)—His Contribution to Psychiatry," *Bulletin of the Isaac Ray Medical Library*, II (April, 1954), 51–104.

Overholser, Winfred. "Cox and Trotter—Two Psychiatric Precursors of Benjamin Rush," *American Journal of Psychiatry*, CX (May, 1954), 825–830.

Page, Charles Whitney. "Dr. Eli Todd and the Hartford Retreat," *AJI*, LXIX (April, 1913), 761–785.

Powell, O. T. "A Sketch of Psychiatry in Southern States," *AJI*, LIV (July, 1897), 21–36.

Rosen, George. "The Philosophy of Ideology and the Emergence of Modern Medicine in France," *Bulletin of the History of Medicine*, XX (July, 1946), 328–339.

——. "Political Order and Human Health in Jeffersonian Thought," *Bulletin of the History of Medicine*, XXVI (January-February, 1952), 32–44.

——. "Social Stress and Mental Disease from the Eighteenth Century to the Present: Some Origins of Social Psychiatry," *Milbank Memorial Fund Quarterly*, XXXVII (January, 1959), 5–32.

Rosenberg, Charles E. "The Cholera Epidemic of 1832 in New York City," *Bulletin of the History of Medicine*, XXXIII (January-February, 1959), 37–49.

Shryock, Richard H. "The Psychiatry of Benjamin Rush," *American Journal of Psychiatry*, CI (January, 1945), 429–432.

Temkin, Owsei. "Basic Science, Medicine, and the Romantic Era," *Bulletin of the History of Medicine*, XXXVII (March-April, 1963), 97–129.

Terris, Milton. "An Early System of Compulsory Health Insurance in the United States, 1798–1884," *Bulletin of the History of Medicine*, XV (May, 1944), 433–444.

Wittels, Fritz. "The Contribution of Benjamin Rush to Psychiatry," *Bulletin of the History of Medicine*, XX (July, 1946), 157–166.

Woods, Evelyn A., and Carlson, Eric T. "The Psychiatry of Philippe Pinel," *Bulletin of the History of Medicine*, XXXV (January-February 1961), 14–25.

Unpublished Material

Carlson, Eric T. "The Medical Psychology of Benjamin Rush." Unpublished paper, New York, 1962. (Typescript.)

Greenawalt, Jack Curry. "Public Institutional Care for the Mentally Ill in Allegheny County, Pennsylvania, 1850 to 1890." Unpublished Ph.D. dissertation, University of Pittsburgh, 1956. (Microfilm copy.)

Perlman, Lawrence V. "Samuel Bayard Woodward, M.D. (1787–1850); New England Physician and Reformer." Unpublished Master's thesis, Yale University, 1957. (Typescript.)

Stewart, Charles Ashley. "A Study of Opinions Regarding Mental Illnesses and Facilities for their Care as Related to Social Class Membership." Unpublished Ph.D. dissertation, Florida State University, 1958. (Microfilm copy.)

Stolley, Paul. "Psychiatry in New York State (1770–1820)." Unpublished paper written under the supervision of Dr. Eric T. Carlson at Payne Whitney Psychiatric Clinic, New York Hospital (Dept. of Psychiatry, Cornell University Medical College), Summer, 1959. (Typescript.)

[Woodward, Samuel B.] (grandson of the early psychiatrist Samuel B. Woodward). "The American Branch of the Woodwards of Lancashire, England, 1635–1934." (Typescript volume, American Antiquarian Society.)

entele, 194, 235n*24*, 243n*33;* conditions of insane, 21, 214n*34*, 216n*60;* decline of moral treatment, 138; establishment, 29, 30, 167, 213n*24;* exhibition of insane, 51; fees, 244n*35;* Irish in, 103; medical therapy, 15, 218n*78;* B. Rush's work at, xiii, 5, 15, 21, 37, 214n*34*, 214n*35;* 221n*21;* John Rush at, 33

Pepperell, Mass., 103

Perfectibility of man, 11–12, 31, 167

Periodicals: general, 35, 166, 197; medical. *See* Medical literature

Personality, 7, 49; pre-psychotic, in fiction, 42; psychopathic, 74

Pessimism, xiii, 4, 11–12, 24, 25, 28–29, 39, 50, 58, 83, 112, 113, 125–139, 203, 209. *See also* Curability; Optimism

Peters, John C., 162

Philadelphia, establishment of mental hospital, 22

Philadelphia, Friends Hospital. *See* Friends' Asylum

Philadelphia, Pennsylvania Hospital. *See* Pennsylvania Hospital

Philadelphia Journal of the Medical Sciences, 104

Philadelphia prison system, 181–182

Philadelphia *Public Ledger,* 196–197

Philosophers, moral, 184, 185–186

Phrenology, 61–63, 70, 76–77, 80, 87, 96, 167, 173; popular, 160, 161, 162–163

Physical exercise, as therapy, 5, 39, 117, 135

Physicians: general, 4, 5–11, 21–27, 147–154, 225n*3;* sectarian, 161–164; testimony at trials, 155–159. *See also* Psychiatrists

Pierce, Franklin, 176

Pinel, Philippe, 3, 4, 14, 29, 34, 68, 162, 186, 205, 216n*63*, 228n*37;* compared with B. Rush, 21, 23; criteria for insanity, 48–49; influence, 4, 14, 15, 21, 22, 23, 25, 26–27, 30, 149, 159, 206; on moral insanity, 26, 48–49, 73, 74; and moral treatment, 4–5, 12, 13, 220n*15;* on pathology of insanity, 13, 67, 69; his *Treatise on Insanity,* 37–38

Placebos, 118

Poetry and insanity, 93

Politicians and reform movement, 165, 175–177

Popular opinion: concepts of insanity, xii, xiii, 4, 7–8, 28–29, 37–52, 66, 177, 194–195, 197–202 *passim,* 208, 209–210; on curability, 39, 121, 195, 202–203, 208; difficulty of determining, 37; on mental hospitals, 28–29, 39, 51, 121, 151–152, 194–197, 202–203; toward mentally ill, xi–xii, 4, 20, 37–52 *passim,* 198–199, 202, 208, 209–210; role of clergy, 183; on treatment of mentally ill, 4, 20, 28–29, 43, 152, 154, 194–195, 202–203

Porter, Noah, 186

Porter, R. R., 154

Possession, Demoniac. *See* Demoniac possession

Poverty and insanity, 91, 98

Precipitating causes, 7–8, 19, 85, 108, 110, 112

Predisposing causes, 7–8, 85, 109, 110, 161

Pre-psychotic personality, in fiction, 42

Presbyterians, 183

Prevention. *See* Insanity—Prevention

Prichard, James C., 73, 74, 75, 186; his *Treatise on Insanity . . . ,* 73, 74

Priestley, Joseph, 33

Primitive peoples, insanity among, 89

Primitive Physic (Wesley), 40

Prison discipline reform, 11, 59, 180–182

Prisons, insane in, 3, 4, 126, 127, 129, 174, 177, 244n*48*

Private Memoirs and Confessions of a Justified Sinner (Hogg), 41

Private mental hospitals. *See* Mental hospitals —Proprietary

Prognosis. *See* Insanity—Prognosis

Progress and insanity, 88–91, 93. *See also* Civilization and insanity

Proprietary mental hospitals. *See* Mental hospitals—Proprietary

Protestant clergymen. *See* Clergymen, Protestant

Providence, R.I., Butler Hospital *See* Butler Hospital

Psychiatric education, 23, 25, 149, 150, 151

Psychiatric literature, 25, 71, 132, 166

Psychiatric research, 137, 139–144

Psychiatrists, 55–59, 119; attitudes toward D. Dix, 172; attitudes toward Irish, 99–104; attitudes toward lower classes, 97–104, 111–112, 124, 126; attitudes toward science, 142–144; attitudes toward theory, 63, 141, 142–144; cited by D. Dix, 251n*12;* cited by moral philosophers, 186; class origin and outlook, 57–58, 126, 207–208; contact with leaders of society, 140, 178; instructions to general practitioners, 159; legal testimony, 46, 75, 155 ff., 198; number in U.S., 56; and phrenology, 61–63; and politics, 226n*10;* pragmatism of, 59, 63, 71, 132, 138, 141–142, 143; recognition by medical profession, 147–148, 159; research, 139–144; and Scottish common sense philosophy, 60–61, 80–81; statistical work, 133, 139–140; as teachers, 149; training, 22–23, 57, 149; use of term, 55. *See also* names of individual psychiatrists

Psychiatry: as a specialty, 55–57, 133, 138, 204; use of term, 55

Psychological medicine, use of term, 5n. *See also* Moral treatment; Therapy, psychological

Psychological therapy. *See* Therapy, psychological

Psychology: modern, 85; theories of, 59–63. *See also* Faculty psychology

Psychopathic personality, 74

Psychosis, recent statistical study, 246n*80.* *See also* Insanity

Psychosomatic disease, concept of, 69, 86

Psychosomatic medicine, 229n*46*

Public opinion. *See* Popular opinion

Puerperal insanity, 249n*39*

Punishment, 4, 13, 59, 117, 119. *See also* Restraint

Scott, Sir Walter, 190, 223n61; his *Bride of Lammermoor*, 41, 42
Scottish common sense philosophy, 16, 60–62, 63, 80–81, 185–186
Sects, medical. *See* Medical cults
Sedatives, 60, 120
Sedgwick, Catharine, 179–180
Self-control and mental illness, 85, 86, 96
Self-denial and mental illness, 86
Senile dementia. *See* Dementia
Sensationism, 36, 59–61, 62, 226n13
Seward, William H., 199
Sexual life and mental illness, 7, 91–92. *See also* Masturbation
Shakespeare, William, 63
Shew, Joel, 160–161
Shipman, George E., *Homoeopathic Family Guide*, 162
Shock therapy, 11, 13, 15, 18. *See also* Electric shock therapy
Sin. *See* Immorality
Skinner, Otis A., 190
Slavery and insanity, 105–107. *See also* Negroes
Smith, James M'Cune, 107
Smith, Joseph Mather, 232n74
Smith, S. V. C., 150
Social classes. *See* Classes, social
Society of Friends. *See* Quakers
Socio-economic factors, as causes of insanity, 7, 87 ff., 212n9. *See also* Environment
Solidism, 9, 10
Somatic therapy. *See* Therapy, somatic
Somaticism, 65–66, 70, 77, 83, 86–87, 118, 133, 136, 137, 206. *See also* Insanity: as a somatic disease; mind-body relationship
Soul, immortal, xii, 10, 26, 44–45, 64–65, 67, 71
Southern Literary Messenger, 105, 107
Southern states: appeals of D. Dix, 177; insanity in, 90–91; mental institutions in, 128, 225n2, 242n17; reform of care of insane, 217n63
Spiritualism, 189–190, 236n40, 257n34
Spurzheim, J. G., 61
State legislators, 127, 167, 170, 176–177, 253n49
State Lunatic Hospital at Taunton, Mass., 77, 93, 100, 130, 237n66, 238n71
State Lunatic Hospital at Worcester, Mass., 43, 59, 109, 128, 243n34; conditions at, 126, 128–130, 172–173; fees, 129, 244n48; and S. G. Howe, 129, 173; Irish in, 99–100, 101; and H. Mann, 129, 172–173
State mental hospitals. *See* Mental hospitals—Publicly supported
Statistics of insanity, 89, 90, 101–102, 104–107, 108, 139–140, 239n91. *See also* Recovery rates
Staunton, Va., Western Lunatic Asylum of Virginia. *See* Western Lunatic Asylum of Virginia
Stearns, H. P., 134
Stewart, Dugald, 60–61, 62, 63, 80, 186
Stribling, Francis T., 128, 239n103, 247n14
Suicide, 232–233n90
Sumner, Charles, 178, 181–182

Sumner, George, 243n34
Sumner, Increase, 98
Superintendents of mental hospitals. *See* Psychiatrists
Suppression, Brigham's theory of, 229n46
Sweetser, Seth, 179
Sydenham, Thomas, 40
Symptoms. *See* Insanity—Symptoms
Syphilis, 134

Tardieu, Auguste A., 63
Taunton, Mass., State Lunatic Hospital. *See* State Lunatic Hospital at Taunton
Temperance movement, 11, 59, 180
Temporary insanity, 48
Terror as therapy, 4, 15, 19
Therapeutic community, 13, 209
Therapeutic environment, 13
Therapeutic nihilism, 160, 164
Therapy: baths and showers, 13, 117, 118; of 18th cent. physicians, 4, 10–11; 38–40; of 19th cent. general practitioners, 152–154; painful, 4, 11, 20; psychological, 5, 10–11, 20–21, 38, 39, 68–69, 70–71, 86, 87, 118, 133–136 ff., 142, 248n18; recreational, 5, 11, 39, 117, 118–119, 135, 242n11; religious, 31, 185, 188–189; somatic, 4, 10–11, 26–27, 31–32, 86, 118, 119–120, 135–136, 138, 152–154, 206. *See also* Depletion as therapy; Electric shock therapy; Milieu therapy; Moral treatment
Thomson, Samuel, 161; his "Recipe to Cure a Crazy Man," 153–154
Thomsonianism, 161, 164
Tiffany, Francis, 168, 223–224n69
Todd, Eli, 22–23, 26, 27, 29, 134, 149, 174–175, 179, 217n65, 252n35
Tolles, Frederick B., 30
Total push therapy, 209
Tranquilizer chair, 19
Tranquilizing drugs, 209
Transcendentalism, 83, 236n40
Treatise on Insanity, A (Pinel), 37–38
Treatise on Insanity . . . (Prichard), 73, 74
Treatise on the Medical Jurisprudence of Insanity, A (Ray), 75, 150, 178
Treatment of insane. *See* Insane; Therapy
Treatment, moral. *See* Moral treatment
Trials involving insanity, 45–49, 155–159, 198–202
Tudor, William, Jr., 35
Tuke, Daniel H., 159; and Bucknill, John C., *Manual of Psychological Medicine*, 150
Tuke, William, 4–5, 12, 14, 32, 37, 48–49; influence in U.S., 14, 22, 25, 26, 30, 31, 37–38, 205
Tyler, John E., 79, 123, 231n66, 241n132

Unconscious, theories of, 20
Unitarians, 187
United States Congress: and bill for mental hospitals, 175–176; and Census of 1840, 104, 107
United States Government, and mentally ill seamen, 221n21